REWINDING SMALL MOTORS

OTHER BOOKS

By

DANIEL H. BRAYMER

and

A. C. ROE

BRAYMER'S
  Armature Winding and Motor Repair

BRAYMER AND ROE'S
  Repair Shop Diagrams and Connecting Tables

  Rewinding Small Motors

  Rewinding and Connecting Alternating-current Motors

TAYLOR AND BRAYMER'S
  American Hydroelectric Practice

ANNETT AND ROE'S
  Connecting and Testing Direct-current Machines

VAN BRUNT AND ROE'S
  Rewinding Data for Direct-current Armatures

Frontispiece.— This rack shows the variety of small armatures to which the winding procedure discussed in this book applies.

REWINDING SMALL MOTORS

*Practical Details of Repair Shop Practice with Step-by-step
Procedure for Rewinding All Types and Designs of
Fractional Horsepower Direct and Alternating
Current Motors*

BY

DANIEL H. BRAYMER

*Consulting Engineer; Member American Institute of Electrical Engineers;
Member American Society of Mechanical Engineers; Formerly
Editoral Director, "Industrial Engineer"; Author
of "Armature Winding and
Motor Repair"*

AND

A. C. ROE

*Industrial and Insulation Engineer, Renewal Parts Engineering Department, Westinghouse
Electric and Mfg. Company, Formerly with New York Service Department and
Repair Superintendent, Detroit Service Department of Same Company*

SECOND EDITION
TENTH IMPRESSION

McGRAW-HILL BOOK COMPANY, Inc.

NEW YORK AND LONDON

1932

THE MAPLE PRESS COMPANY, YORK, PA.

PREFACE TO THE SECOND EDITION

During recent years there has been a marked increase in the use of small motors for special services, including the following: Fractional horsepower motors to operate devices in the home, such as refrigerators, oil burners, washing machines and vacuum cleaners; somewhat larger ratings of small motors required in garages, filling stations, meat markets, ice-cream parlors, etc., where only single-phase service is available; and those devices requiring two and three speeds from single-phase motors, such as propeller fans used on steam and gas unit heaters and comfort coolers. Because of these special requirements, the motor manufacturers have developed a new type of single-phase motor known as the condenser or capacitor type, which has definite advantages over either the split-phase or the repulsion-induction type.

This development has made it advisable to include in this edition an appendix giving details of the operating characteristics and the construction of this new motor. Included in this appendix are details on the elimination of radio interference due to the use of small motors and other data on some special motors not discussed in the first edition of this book.

It will also be noted that many of the suggestions received from readers have been incorporated in other chapters and that the complete text has been brought up-to-date.

DANIEL H. BRAYMER.

A. C. ROE.

OMAHA, NEB.
June, 1932.

PREFACE TO THE FIRST EDITION

Armature winding calls for a combination of skill, care and common sense together with a practical knowledge of motor construction and operation that usually grows out of years of winding and repair experience. But even the experienced man cannot always acquire the same degree of skill in rewinding all varieties of motors. However, when experience is supplemented by practical information in usable form, any good winder can quickly pick up the essential details that make a good winding job.

In view of the fact that there has been little practical information published on winding procedure for fractional horsepower, direct and alternating-current motors, the authors have attempted to compile in this volume such details for all the common types of windings used for portable drills, grinders, automobile starting motors, sewing machine motors, desk and ceiling fans, vacuum cleaner and washing machine motors, and other similar applications of small direct and alternating current motors. This information has been presented in step-by-step details from the start to the finish of a winding job so as to make it easy for the experienced winder to understand the procedure and give him a grasp of the essential requirements of the windings that are used by the manufacturers of small motors and to enable him to rewind or change them as conditions require, even though he may not have had much experience in rewinding small motors.

Small motor rewinding jobs are, for the most part, simple, hand-winding operations but they call for the same good judgment and care as when rewinding larger motors. In the commercial repair shop to rewind small motors at a profit in view of the low cost of the motor when new, a low labor cost is essential and this calls for speed and a thorough knowledge of the kinds of windings used so that no errors will be found when the completed winding is tested out. There are some short cuts to be learned as well as steps in performing the work that will produce the quickest and most satisfactory job from a workmanship standpoint. These factors have been taken into consideration in writing this book so that the practical side of the winding operations have been dealt with in detail, giving as little technical information as required to understand the reasons for the winding procedure that is presented.

This is then a practical man's handbook on the winding of small direct and alternating current motors rather than a textbook on the subject.

However, it will be found a useful reference book for those trade and manual training schools that conduct practical courses in motor winding.

The information presented in many of the chapters of this book has been based on articles that have appeared in Industrial Engineer. To E. H. Hubert, formerly associate editor of Industrial Engineer, acknowledgment is made for assistance in arranging a part of the original material and preparing some of the sketches. The authors also extend their thanks to electrical manufacturers who have liberally furnished photographs and winding information.

In compiling a book of practical information giving details and examples of practice, certain errors may creep into data and diagrams. While the authors have checked all information carefully they will be grateful to those who discover errors and report them for correction.

DANIEL H. BRAYMER.

A. C. ROE.

CHICAGO, ILL.
June, 1925.

CONTENTS

PAGE

PREFACE TO THE SECOND EDITION. vii

PREFACE TO THE FIRST EDITION. ix

PART I

REWINDING PROCEDURE FOR SMALL DIRECT-CURRENT MOTORS

CHAPTER I

THINGS TO DO BEFORE A JOB IS SENT TO THE REPAIR BENCH

Information on Receiving Tag 2
Work Order or Job Ticket 3
Material and Time Tickets. 4
Complete Cost and Billing Information 4
Inspection Tests 5
Checking Up Field Coils. 5
Outfits for Making Accurate Tests 6
Checks for Bearings and Shaft 9

CHAPTER II

RECORDING WINDING DATA AND STRIPPING A DIRECT-CURRENT ARMATURE

Winding Data That Should Be Recorded. 10
How to Mark Slots and Bars to Agree with Information Recorded 12
Examples Showing Proper Marking of Slots and Bars and Recording of Connec-
    tions. 16
Recording Coil and Commutator Throws When Complete Coils of Winding are
    Made Up of Two or More Single Coils. 17
Winding Information for Automobile Starting and Lighting Armatures. . . . 20
Recording Data for Coils. 21
Stripping the Armature 21

CHAPTER III

INSULATING THE ARMATURE CORE

Cleaning Slots and Truing Up Laminations. 24
Building Up New Cores 25
Insulating Ends of Old Core 26
Insulating the Shaft. 27
Insulating the Slots 27
Continuous Strip Insulation for Slots 28
Kind of Wire and Its Insulation for Small Motors. 31

CHAPTER IV

THE LOOP WINDING

Advantages and Disadvantages of a Loop Winding 35
Starting a Loop Winding. 35

	PAGE
Left-hand and Right-hand Loop Windings	36
Loop Winding with More Than One Coil Per Slot	39
Loop Winding with More Than One Wire in Hand	39
Testing Straight Loop Winding for Grounds	40

CHAPTER V

SPECIAL CHORDED SPLIT-PITCH LOOP WINDING

Example Showing Advantage of This Winding	41
Armature Wound with One Wire in Hand	42
Colored Sleeves Used to Mark Commutator Loops	43
Method of Connecting Loops to Commutator	45

CHAPTER VI

CHORDED SPLIT-LOOP WINDING

Advantages of the Chorded Split-loop Winding	47
Steps When Winding a Chorded Split-loop Winding	47
Method of Putting on Chorded Split Winding When Number of Slots is not Divisible by Four	51
Using a Winding Machine for Chorded Split Winding	54
Easy Method for Winding a Split Winding	54
Shove Through Coils for Closed-slot Armatures	57

CHAPTER VII

THE SPLIT V-LOOP WINDING (I)

Advantages and Disadvantages of Split V-loop Winding	59
Split V-loop Winding Used on Automobile Generator Armatures	60
Steps When Putting Winding on Armature	60
Precautions When Inserting Sleeves on Coil Leads	61

DIAMETRICALLY-SPLIT WINDING (II)

Steps When Winding a Diametrically-split Winding	62

PROGRESSIVE-SPLIT-HAND WINDING THAT SAVES TIME IN REWINDING ARMATURES (III)

Winding in Coils of a Progressive-split Winding	66

CHAPTER VIII

WINDING AUTOMOBILE STARTER AND GENERATOR ARMATURES

Cleaning Automobile Armatures	69
Insulation Required	69
Taking Data from Automobile Armatures	70
Size of Wire for Coils	72
Varnishing and Baking	72
Winding 32-volt Armatures	72
Layer Winding for Automobile Armatures	72
Steps When Winding a Layer Winding	74
Making Ends of Coils Wind in Layers	74
Connecting Coil Leads to Commutator	75

CHAPTER IX

How to Determine the Position of Commutator on the Shaft

Commutator Position for Full-pitch Winding. 76
Commutator Position for Chorded-pitch Winding. 76
Checking Position of Commutator with Armature in the Motor. 78
Distance Commutator Should Be Pressed on Shaft 78
Lining Up Armature Slots or Teeth with Commutator Mica or Bars. 78

CHAPTER X

Connecting Up Hand-wound Armatures

How to Use Sleeves for Marking Coil Leads of Loop Windings 81
Marking Coil Leads When Wound with More than One Wire in Hand. . . . 81
Location of Brushes for Full and Chorded Pitch Windings 81
Filling Hollow between Coil Ends and Commutator. 82
Connecting Leads of First Coil to Commutator Bars. 82
Connecting Leads of First Coil When There are Several Leads in One Sleeve . . 83
Connecting Leads of First Coil When There are Two or More Coils per Slot . . 84
Test to Locate Top Leads before Connecting Them to Commutator. 85
Connecting Leads of First Coil for Split V-loop Winding. 85
Checks to Make After Connecting Up Commutator. 88
Soldering Leads to Commutator. 89

CHAPTER XI

Testing Armatures While and After Winding

Points During Winding When Tests Should Be Made 90
Testing Commutator for Grounds. 91
Testing Commutator for Shorts. 91
Testing Winding for Grounds before Connecting to Commutator 92
Test for Locating Grounds after Leads Are Connected to Commutator. . . . 93
Checking Coil Connections for Reversed or Crossed Leads 94
Checking for Reversed Coil Leads Due to Use of Wrong Colors of Sleeves . . . 95
Tests for Locating Short Circuits 96
Use of a Growler for Locating Shorted Coils 97
Reasons for Variations in Readings with Bar-to-bar Test. 102
Strip and Rewind When Troubles Cannot Be Located. 103

PART II

Rewinding Procedure for Small Alternating-current Motors

CHAPTER XII

Testing and Locating Faults in Small Alternating-current Motors When Received for Repairs

How to Locate Troubles When Motor Will Not Start 107
How to Locate Troubles When Motor Starts but Will Not Pull Load 108
Troubles with Starting Circuit Switch. 108
Causes for Repulsion Motor Failing to Start 108
Locating Troubles in Universal Type of Motor 109
Split-phase Motors 110
Repulsion-starting Motors 110

Page

Shading-coil Motors. 111
Series Motors of the Commutator Type 111

CHAPTER XIII

INFORMATION TO RECORD FOR SMALL ALTERNATING-CURRENT MOTORS BEFORE STRIPPING THEM

How to Get Winding and Connecting Information from an Old Motor. 112
Information Needed for Hand and Skein Windings 115
Six Points to Note before Stripping a Stator 116

CHAPTER XIV

INSULATING THE CORE AND THE WINDING

Insulating Slots with Fish-paper Only 117
Insulating Slots with Fish-paper and Treated Cloth. 117
Varnishing and Baking Winding 119
Tying Ends of Coils with Cord 120
End Rings to Protect Overhanging Coils. 120

CHAPTER XV

HOW TO MAKE UP A SKEIN AND WIND IT IN SMALL ALTERNATING-CURRENT STATORS

Winding a Skein on the Stator 121
How to Start Winding in Proper Place on a Stator 122
Easy Method for Winding a Skein. 125
When a Split-skein Can be Used 126
How to Bring Out Stator Leads. 128
How to Calculate the Length of Skein to Use. 128

CHAPTER XVI

HOW A HAND WINDING IS PUT ON A STATOR

Starting Hand-wound Coils. 131
How to Keep Wires from Climbing above Core. 132
Winding Coils without Cutting the Wire between Coils 133
How Starting and Running Windings Are Distributed in Slots 135
Mould and Hand Windings. 138
Main Features of Single-phase Motors. 138

CHAPTER XVII

CONNECTING A SKEIN-WOUND OR A HAND-WOUND STATOR

Connecting Up Coils of Hand-wound and Skein-wound Stator 140
How to Determine Direction of Rotation. 141
Connecting Various Types of Single-phase Motors. 144
Changing Single-phase Motor for Operation at Two Speeds. 146

CHAPTER XVIII

REWINDING SMALL UNIVERSAL MOTORS

The Straight Series Type of Universal Motors 148
Straight Series Universal Motor with Distributed Field and Shifted Brushes . . 149
The Compensated-series Universal Motor with Two Independent Windings . . 149
Points to Remember When Stripping a Universal Motor. 151
Kinds of Windings Used on Universal Motors. 151

PAGE

Compensating Windings for Universal Motors 153
Two Unusual Features of Universal Motors 156
Insulating Slots and Inserting Coils 157
Possible Trouble When Slot Containing Main Coils Are Not Marked 157

CHAPTER XIX

REWINDING A COMPENSATED-SERIES MOTOR

Winding Compensating Coils on Stator 160
Winding Main Coils on Stator 160

CHAPTER XX

SINGLE-PHASE FAN MOTOR WINDINGS

Commutator-type Series Fan Motors 164
Induction-type Fan Motor 165
Distributed Pole Fan Windings 166
Starting Windings 168
Controlling the Speed of a Fan Motor 168
Speed Change by Taps on an Auxiliary Winding 170
Windings for Ceiling Fans 170
Construction of Fan Motor for Use on Direct or Alternating-current 170
Induction Fan Motor Winding with High Starting Torque 171
Effect of Changing Number of Blades on Fan Motor 174

CHAPTER XXI

REWINDING SMALL TWO- AND THREE-PHASE MOTORS

The Basket Winding 178
Insulating the Slots and Core 180
Inserting Coils in a Basket Winding 180
Two-layer Winding with One Coil Side per Slot 181
Checking Pitch of a Two-layer Winding 182
Two-layer Windings with Flat Diamond Mush Coils 183
Three Steps in Inserting Diamond Mush Coils 183
Extra Insulation between Phase Coils 185
Two-layer Winding with Diamond Mush Pulled Coils 187
Threaded-in Strap-copper Coils 187

CHAPTER XXII

CHANGING SINGLE-PHASE WINDINGS FOR TWO AND THREE PHASE OPERATION

Estimating the Two and Three-phase Rating of a Single-phase Motor Frame . . 189
How to Use Tables for Finding Hp. Rating of Single-phase Frame for 2- or 3-phase
Change 189
How to Determine Turns, Size of Wire and Coil Pitch When Changing Single-
phase Winding 190

CHAPTER XXIII

TESTING SINGLE-PHASE MOTORS WHILE AND AFTER WINDING

Checking Polarity of Windings 197
Balancing the Rotor 198
Testing Rotor for Poor Bar Contact 199
Testing Centrifugal Switch 199

PAGE

Testing for Brush Position. 199
Checking for Wrong Connections 199
Locating Troubles in Single-phase Repulsion Motors. 199
Failure to Start. 199
Failure to Release Brushes on Full Load. 200
Failure to Release Brushes on No Load 202
Brushes Return to Commutator after Being Released 203
Hot Bearings. 203
Motor Heats on Light Loads 203
Motor Heats When Loaded. 204
Spring Barrel Assembly 204
Motor Assembly 205

CHAPTER XXIV

REPAIR SHOP TOOLS

A Convenient Work Bench. 210
Armature Centers and Stator Holders 213
Special Chuck for Winding Small Coils. 216
Holders for Wire and Tape Reels 218
Tension Block for Magnet Wire. 218
Slot Insulation Cutter and Former 220
Testing Equipment 223
Transformer for High-voltage Tests. 223
Low-voltage High-current Capacity Transformers. 227
Telephone Head Set Testing Outfit 228
Winder's Hand Tools 230
Slot Wedge Driver 233
Tools Made from Old Hacksaw Blades. 233
Arbor Press and Tool for Removing Fields from Single-phase Motor Housings . 233
Dipping Armatures Wound with Single Cotton and Enamel Insulation. . . . 235
Baking Armatures and Stators 237
Points on Soldering 238

Appendix 241

INDEX. 257

REWINDING SMALL MOTORS

CHAPTER I

THINGS TO DO BEFORE A JOB IS SENT TO THE REPAIR BENCH

In both small and large repair shops mistakes and misunderstandings can be prevented during repair operations and at the time the work is being billed to the customer, when a simple but complete record system is kept that will show the condition of the job as received and full details of the work to be done. Such information can be provided on a work order or job ticket bearing a job number to which all time and material can be charged. A simple record system that can be used for a wide variety of repair work should include the following forms:

1. A receiving tag bearing the job number.
2. A work order or job ticket bearing the job number.
3. A material ticket for use when drawing material out of stock.
4. A time ticket for recording the time of each man required on the job.

Before a job is assigned to a repair man all the necessary information relating to the work to be done should be recorded on these forms. The time it takes to do this will be decidedly worth while in making sure that the details of the order are complete in one place so that every one having to handle any part of the work will refer to the same source of information. This will go far in avoiding misunderstandings and preventing expensive changes when the customer is hard to satisfy and checks the work carefully when it is received.

Repair records and forms differ in almost every shop. There is a tendency to start with a simple system and then add to it until it becomes expensive to maintain and adds unnecessary cost to each complete job. The following details are given for forms that are easy to fill out and provide sufficient information to answer all the essential questions about a job while work is being done on it and also at the time the customer is billed for the cost. They also provide information that will be of value when estimates are required in a hurry. The keeping of such a record is just as important as striving for high quality of work done, and the proper filling out of the following forms as described and illustrated is the first step in a repair operation and should be so considered rather than a clerical detail assigned to a clerk with little accurate knowledge of repair details.

Unless the original record of repair instructions and customer's requirements are clear, specific and accurate, the finished job is likely to show the same indifference in the way it looks when completed or shows up on test. Many good shops that have the equipment and experience to do good work have unknowingly gained the reputation of being sloppy and inaccurate in following instructions, when the real fault is not lack of ability to follow instructions accurately but failure to force the customer to furnish full details of his requirements and reduce this to writing on such forms as have been found essential to provide complete

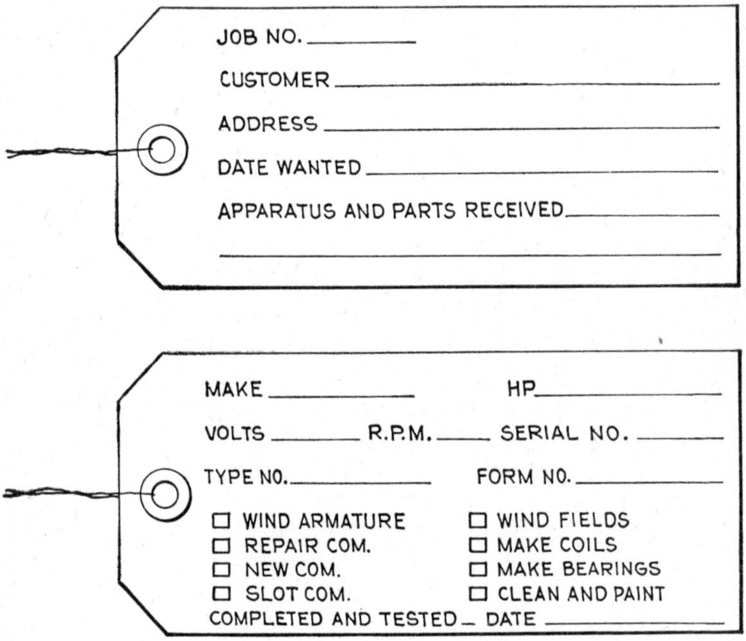

FIG. 1.—A convenient form of receiving tag that furnishes information for identifying the job and indicating the nature of repair work to be done.

repair information. Such information and suitable forms for recording it are shown in the accompanying illustrations and described in the following paragraphs.

Information on Receiving Tag.—A receiving tag should be attached to the motor or other apparatus to be repaired before it is assigned to the repairman for the work to be done. It should never be removed until the time when the completed job is to be shipped and given its final check for completeness of work ordered and the number of parts or auxiliary devices received with it. A suitable form of tag for use in a small repair shop is shown in Fig. 1. This receiving tag should show the job number and the parts received for repairs. Columns should also be provided so that the work order of job ticket can be checked against the receiving tag to make sure that all the work has been done that was called for and that all the parts received have been assembled for shipment. It is a good plan to make a notation on this receiving slip covering extra parts, such as pulleys, bed plates, rails, starting boxes, etc., and then check

---

WORK ORDER OR JOB TICKET

Job No. _____   Customer _____

                        Address _____

Date Job was Received_____

Date Promised _____

Ship by Express _____ Parcel Post _____

Will Call _____ C. O. D. Yes or No _____.

APPARATUS RECEIVED

Make _____ Hp. _____ Volts _____

R. P. M. _____ Serial No. _____ Type No._____

Form No. _____

WORK TO BE DONE, CHECK, ITEMS

Wind Armature _____ Wind Fields _____

Make Coils _____

Insulate Commutator _____ New Commutator _____

Make Bearings _____ Crating _____

Remarks covering other work _____

Date Completed _____

Material used $ _____

Labor $ _____

Crating $ _____

    Total Cost $

FIG. 2.—A simple form of work order or job ticket for a small repair shop.

the outgoing shipments for these extras. Little items of this nature promote satisfaction on the part of the customer for a missing gear or pulley makes the returned apparatus useless.

Work Order or Job Ticket.—The job ticket should be held by the shop foreman and should provide spaces for the following information: (1) Details of the job as received, including make, type and other identifying numbers; (2) Promised or scheduled date of completion; (3) Details of work to be done; (4) Details of special work not called for in the original repair order, but authorized as a part of the work to be done; (5) Details of packing and how shipment should be marked.

A form of job ticket that embodies this information and has been found useful in arriving at an accurate cost of the work done is shown in Fig. 2. This ticket can be made up on cardboard 6 by 8 in. about as heavy as the regulation post card and filed in a vertical positon in a foreman's desk rack.

Material and Time Tickets.—These forms should be made out to show the kinds of materials used, the amounts and the actual hours of

MATERIAL	REEL NO.	AMOUNT			UNIT PRICE	VALUE
		OUT	IN	USED		
Wire						
Slot Insulation						
Mica						
Commutator Bars						
Varnish						
Paint						
Gas for Baking						
Misc						

JOB NO.　DATE　CONSUMER'S NAME
WORKMAN'S NAME　APPARATUS REPAIRED

Fig. 3.—A material-used form on which materials used in repair and finishing operations can be recorded for a particular job.

time put in by each man working on the job. They should also provide a space for the value of the material used and the wage rate and value of time spent in doing the job. Figure 3 shows a material form for repair operations and for finishing operations such as varnishing and baking. Figure 4 shows a convenient form of time ticket.

Complete Cost and Billing Information.—The information provided on the forms shown as Figs. 2, 3 and 4 make it possible to make up accurate costs for a job and the total price to be billed. Details of the final cost and also instructions for the return shipment are shown on the form in Fig. 2. This particular form can be made as an envelope in which all the records on the job including correspondence and forms shown as Figs. 2, 3 and 4 can be enclosed and filed for future reference on a similar job or for use in estimating new work of a similar character.

Inspection Tests.—After the receiving record forms have been properly filled out, the next step in handling a repair job is an inspection to determine the extent and nature of repairs that are required. Except in those cases where a motor has been through a fire or is so badly damaged otherwise that it is clearly evident that a complete dismantling and rewinding job must be done, some inspection tests are usually necessary. In the case of small motors with ratings of $\frac{1}{6}$, $\frac{1}{8}$ and $\frac{1}{4}$ horsepower, the cost of a new motor is so small that a repair shop must be equipped with facilities and men experienced in handling small work or the repair costs will be excessive. However when careful attention is paid to the rewind-

```
JOB NO. _____        DATE _____

WINDERS NAME_____

OPERATION _____

REGULAR TIME ON_____ HRS. _____ MIN. _____

OVERTIME ON _____   HRS._____ MIN._____

TOTAL HOURS ON JOB_____

RATE _____ TOTAL $_____
```

FIG. 4.—A convenient form of time ticket that can be used by each winder working on a particular job.

ing of small armatures and making other repairs, with an aim to speed up operations and hold waste of material to the minimum, small motor repair work provides a profitable source of revenue for a private repair shop. This is particularly true of automobile starting motors and lighting generators, fan motors, washing machine and vacuum cleaner motors, small drill motors and the like.

When these types of motors are received for repairs, a burned out armature or field coil can either be seen or the motor will have a burned smell. Tapping the armatures with a screw driver will cause the insulation to drop off if the armature is roasted, and the solder where the armature leads are attached to the commutator will, in some cases, have melted so that the leads are loose or held so that they are easily pried out with a screw driver.

Before attempting to start a motor on test, look the commutator over for open circuits and shorts. An open circuit in the armature will cause a blackening of the bars between which the opening exists. A short circuit will also cause a burned appearance but the mica between the bars will be burned deeper.

Checking Up Field Coils.—When testing field coils put the complete set of coils in series across the line voltage, on which the motor is to be used, as shown in Fig. 5, and measure the voltage drop across each coil. A low reading for any coil indicates a short circuit in that coil. Shunt field coils can be tested for shorts by connecting them across the proper line voltage for about a minute. If the coil is shorted, a burned smell will be noticed. These are rough and quick tests that will indicate correct results nine times out of ten when performed by an experienced repairman. For more accurate tests when the trouble seems to be difficult to locate, the following equipment and methods should be used.

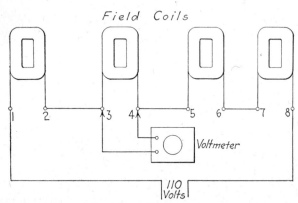

Fig. 5.—Equal readings of the voltmeter between points 1-2, 3-4, 5-6, and 7-8 indicates that coil insulation has not been broken down. A low reading for any coil indicates a short circuit in that coil.

Outfits for Making Accurate Tests.—For locating troubles in small direct-current armatures the testing transformer shown in Fig. 6 can be used and will give quick and accurate results.

For use on a 110-volt, 60-cycle circuit this transformer is wound with 150 turns of No. 10 B. & S. gage square double-cotton-covered magnet wire. For 220 volts, 60 cycles, 300 turns of No. 13 is used and for 110 volts, 25 cycles, 356 turns of No. 14. The core is of H-shaped laminations measuring 5 by 6 in. over all. These are built up to a depth of $3\frac{1}{2}$ in. and are held together by $\frac{1}{4}$-in. bolts which are insulated from the laminations by paper or tape bushings and washers. In making the core, blank laminations 5 by 6 in. may be bolted together after the holes are drilled and the whole core may be milled to shape in one operation. After milling, all burrs should be removed with a file.

In winding the coil a fiber or bakelite sleeve should be put around the core. After each layer is wound it is painted with bakelite and baked. When the winding is completed the coil is bound with friction tape or a band of $\frac{1}{8}$-in. cord. A snap-or-push switch in the connecting cord facilitates shifting the transformer when testing large motors.

For testing small direct-current armatures about 2 to 4 in. in diameter, the transformer is placed on a bench and the armature is place das shown at the left in Fig. 6. Short circuits may be located with the feeler placed on the top of the motor directly above its center. If the feeler vibrates when bridging a certain slot, then one of the coils in that slot is short-circuited.

For locating reversed leads and open coils as well as short circuits, a bar-to-bar test is made, revolving the motor between the poles. For this test a telephone receiver or a flashlamp is used connected to two points of a testing fork which spans one commutator mica segment. This fork is always kept within two or three bars of the top of the commutator while the armature is revolved a step at a time. Any change in the tone of the telephone or in brightness of the lamp indicates that a coil is defective. It is good practice to make the feeler test also before soldering the commutator leads when the armature is being rewound.

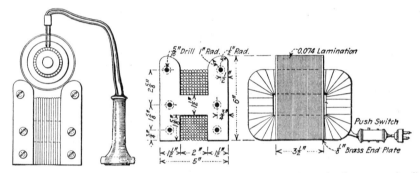

Fig. 6.—Construction and use of a small growler for locating short circuits, reversed coils and open circuits in small direct current armatures.

To determine whether a short circuit is in a coil or between bars, take the blade of a knife and bridge the two bars and then break contact with one bar. If a spark is noticed when the contact is broken there is a short in the coil. If no spark is noticed then the bars are shorted. This method is quicker than the milli-voltmeter bar-to-bar test and in most cases is just as accurate.

A wrong throw of leads on the armature will cause it to run hot and speed up. Also a short-circuited shunt field coil will cause the motor to run above its rated speed.

A convenient test board for use on a repair bench can be wired as shown in Figs. 7 and 8 and used on both direct-current and alternating-current circuits. This board is 24 in. long and 14 in. high. In Fig. 8A only the direct-current wiring is shown. The alternating-current wiring is an exact duplicate.

In wiring the board a three-wire, 110 to 220-volt direct-current line is connected to the three-pole, single-throw fused switch E. A, B and C are the three binding posts to which test leads are attached, but only two test leads should be used, one permanently attached to C and the other shifted from A to B for 220 volts and for 110 volts respectively. For 110-volt tests with lamps in series, switch D is thrown to the left and the

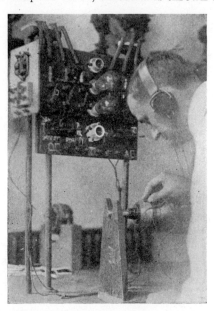

FIG. 7.—Repair-shop test board for which a wiring diagram is shown in Fig. 8.

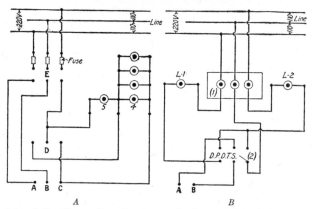

FIGS. 8A and B.—Connections for the repair-shop test board shown in Fig. 7.

In Fig. 8A, for direct-current 110-volt tests, attach test leads to BC, close switch E and throw switch D to left. For direct-current 220-volt tests, attach test leads to AC, close switch E and leave switch D open. For using 110-volt direct-current direct—that is, for running motors, etc. without any lamps in series—attach test leads to BC, close switch E and throw switch D to the right. For 220-volt tests, attach test leads to AC, close E and throw D to right.

In Fig. 8B, for 110-volt tests, throw switch 2 to the right, test leads attached to AB. For 220-volt tests, throw switch 2 to the left and attach test leads to AB.

current may be regulated by the four lamps. For 220-volt tests the leads are connected to A and C and switch D is left open. If D is closed and a heavy current is drawn by the tested apparatus, the lamp (4) may burn out. For direct connection to the line, the switch D is thrown to the right.

Another convenient board, shown in Fig. 8B, gives 110 or 220 volts through a lamp resistance. The line comes into the board through the fuse block (1), the outside wires each leading to a lamp and the neutral to the double-pole, double-throw switch (2). On the posts A and B 110 volts or 220 volts may be obtained by throwing the switch respectively to the right or the left.

Checks for Bearings and Shaft.—Bearings on small motors should be replaced when they show wear of more then 0.008 of an inch or when there is a noticeable movement of the shaft when it is wiggled with the fingers in its bearing. Except in special cases avoid making a special bearing for a turned-down shaft. It is cheaper to install new bearings and a new shaft.

CHAPTER II

RECORDING WINDING DATA AND STRIPPING A DIRECT-CURRENT ARMATURE

When rewinding small direct-current armatures, there are a number of points that should be noted before the armature is stripped in order to provide information and data needed when the armature is being rewound. An experienced repairman will require less information than a man who is not familiar with small motors but knows more about the larger types. It is a good plan, therefore, to take too much information from the winding and core as received than too little, for this information may be useful on other jobs, particularly on those that come into the shop with the core stripped of its old winding.

Winding Data That Should Be Recorded.—It is advisable to adopt a standard information form in the shape of a card that will fit a standard file box that can be purchased at a stationary store. These cards measure 3 by 5 in.; 4 by 6 in.; and 6 by 8 in. and are the most convenient sizes to use. Then make up a rubber stamp that can be used to print on these cards the information and coil diagram as shown in Fig. 9.

In connection with these card forms, it is always advisable to use a sketch of one or more coils showing their connections to the commutator so that there will be no chance for making a mistake in using the data that is recorded on the card form in the spaces provided on it. A simple and widely used form of coil diagram is shown on the bottom part of Fig. 9. The way it is used is illustrated in the diagrams of Figs. 10 to 20. When a more detailed sketch is necessary, in those cases where a complete coil is made up of two or more single coils, the coil diagram can be drawn as shown in Fig. 21. Other handy forms of coil diagrams that are more detailed than Fig. 9 are shown on page 77 of Chap. XI, in Fig. 62. These will be found convenient at times when it is necessary to record details of special windings. The upper diagrams of Fig. 62 show an armature connected on the half while the lower diagrams of Fig. 62 show an armature wound on the half but connected straight out.

For most small armatures the coil diagram shown at the bottom of the card form in Fig. 9 will be the one most used and particular reference is made to that in the following paragraphs. It can be used for all types of wave or lap windings with one or more coils per slot, windings having a dead (idle) coil or half idle bar or with any brush position.

10

When filling out the card form in Fig. 9, on the lines following the tob number and the customers name write in the name plate information on the motor. Then fill in the kind of winding, that is, loop, split-loop, etc.; amount of end room as indicated at (*a*) on the coil diagram of Fig. 9; turns per coil; coil pitch; number of slots; number of commutator bars;

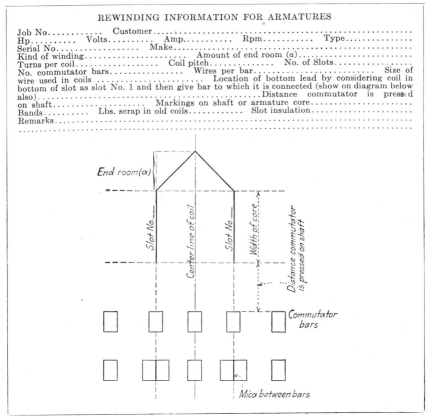

REWINDING INFORMATION FOR ARMATURES

Job No............ Customer..
Hp.......... Volts.......... Amp........... Rpm........... Type.............
Serial No................. Make...
Kind of winding.................... Amount of end room (*a*).................
Turns per coil................... Coil pitch............. No. of Slots...........
No. commutator bars............... Wires per bar.......................... Size of
wire used in coils .... Location of bottom lead by considering coil in
bottom of slot as slot No. 1 and then give bar to which it is connected (show on diagram below
also)...Distance commutator is pressed
on shaft.................... Markings on shaft or armature core...................
Bands.......... Lbs. scrap in old coils............ Slot insulation....................
Remarks..
....

End room (a)

Slot No.

Center line of coil

Slot No.

Width of core

Distance commutator is pressed on shaft

Commutator bars

Mica between bars

Fɪɢ. 9.—This form should be filled in by the winder before the armature is stripped and the bars and slots center punched to agree with the information recorded. The diagram provides a means for indicating the position of the commutator and how to connect the bottom lead of the first coil to be put on when the armature is rewound.

wires per bar; size of wire used for the coils; location of the bottom coil lead by considering the coil in the bottom of the slot as slot No. 1 and then give the number of the bar to which it is connected as shown in the sketch; the distance the commutator is pressed on the shaft as indicated in the sketch; all markings stamped on the armature core or shaft; details of the banding as to turns and size of wire; pounds of scrap wire in the old coils which will indicate the amount of wire required for new coils, and layers, thickness and kind of slot insulation.

The term "Wires per Bar" on this form refers to the number of leads attached to each commutator bar and does not include dummies nor fillers. This will serve as a check on the number of wires in hand while winding the coils. That is, when there are two wires per bar, the coils are wound with one wire in hand and there will be the same number of bars as there are slots. When there are twice the number of bars as slots, the coils will be wound with two wires in hand. When there are four wires per bar, with the same number of bars as slots, the coils are wound with two wires in hand. When there are twice as many bars as slots and four wires per bar, the coils are wound with four wires in hand.

After the word "Bands" in the form in Fig. 9 write in the number of bands, size of wire, kind of wire, and width of bands in number of turns. This is important since on some armatures the core bands project into the air gap. That is, there are no band grooves so that when a heavy wire and clips are used the air gap is decreased and in some cases the bands are liable to rub on the pole pieces. Under "Remarks" in the form, write in any special features of the winding and comments on changes that might improve it.

The back of the form in Fig. 9 can be used to record the time taken by the winder for each operation for the purpose of computing the cost of the job. This information can then be transferred to the job record system described in Chap. I. The information the winder should keep on time required will call for the following operations and these should be written on the back of the card form with the time taken for each item.

1. Stripping and cleaning the armature.
2. Testing and repairing the commutator.
3. Making coils.
4. Cutting and forming insulation.
5. Winding and connecting armature.
6. Putting on band wires.
7. Soldering leads to commutator.
8. Dipping and baking armature.
9. Turning the commutator.
10. Final inspection and testing.

How to Mark Slots and Bars to Agree with Information Recorded.— At the time the winding data and information is recorded on the form in Fig. 9, the armature should be marked so that after it is stripped, it will be easy for any winder to follow the recorded data that may be taken by another winder. The following instructions cover these markings:

1. Mark the tooth each side of the slot that contains the top half of the coil with two crosses (XX), then put one cross (X) on the tooth each side of the slot that contains the bottom half of the coil.

2. Mark each commutator bar on the end, with a center punch (one dot) that contains a lead from the coil in the slots located by the cross marks.

3. Next line out from the center of the slot between the two teeth marked (XX) to the commutator. If this line falls on the mica, mark one bar either side of the mica, with three center-punch dots. If the line falls on a bar, mark this one bar with three dots.

4. Mark the commutator bars on the center line of the slot between the teeth marked with one X in the same manner, except use two dots.

5. When the commutator is to be removed for repairs, do not mark it.

6. Always fill out data cards as per Fig. 9 on each job and mark the armature as above.

7. If the armature has a dead coil or idle bar, use it for the locating marks, etc.

The reason that two crosses are placed on the teeth each side of the slot in which the top half of the coil lies, and only one cross to mark the bottom, as in Figs. 10 and 11, is to eliminate the possibilities of a right-hand coil being made instead of a left or vice versa. This also preserves the correct coil pitch.

The markings indicated in paragraphs 1, 2, 3 and 4 above will be found particularly useful when a coil is made up and being fitted to the core so as to be used as a sample for making up others. In this case there is no. time lost in looking up the winding record card to find the pitch since this is marked on the core. The markings also show in which slots to put the top and bottom halves of the coils. Another saving in time, that is important in cutting down the cost of winding small armatures, is that the winder does not need to spend time laying out the winding. That has already been done for him and he can start right in on the winding operation. In mills and factories where a repair shop is maintained the marking of the core eliminates the necessity of recording the winding data for the same or a like job when it comes in for the second rewind. Such an armature can be stripped by a less experienced man than a winder.

The reason for using dots when marking the bars on the center lines of the slots containing the first coil as shown in Figs. 10 and 11, is to eliminate the chances of connecting the armature up wrong. On most four-pole wave-wound armatures there are two possible connections: long and short pitch or progressive and retrogressive. Figure 19 shows a possible error in connecting the winding when the bars for the top and bottom leads only are marked. The coil marked *A* in Fig. 19 has a commutator pitch of 1 and 12 or short pitch (retrogressive) which will be assumed as the correct winding. If the winder did not mark the slots nor the bars in front of the slots in which coil *A* was placed on the old winding, then when the new coils were to be wound in, there would

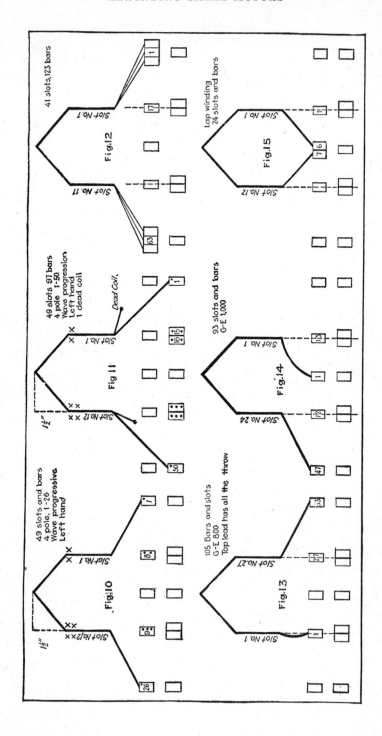

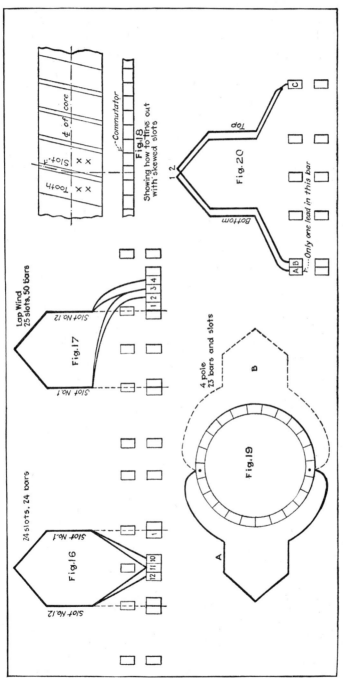

FIGS. 10 to 20.—Eleven examples showing how the coil diagram of Fig. 9 can be used to indicate lead connections to the commutator and how the bars and slots should be punch marked.

be no way of telling which was the correct commutator pitch. The pitch of coil *B* in Fig. 19 which is 1 and 13 or long pitch (progressive) or the pitch of coil *A* which is 1 and 12 or short pitch (retrogressive) might be used. If the pitch of coil *B* is used the direction of rotation would be reversed in the motor or the polarity of the brushes would be reversed in a generator from that resulting when the pitch of coil *A* is used. However, this particular mistake could only happen on a four-pole machine since the four-pole winding is the only one on which either a long or a short pitch coil can be used.

Examples Showing Proper Marking of Slots and Bars and Recording of Connections.—The form for recording winding data shown in Fig. 9 is made up so that a rubber stamp can be used for the tabulation at the top and another rubber stamp for making the diagram of sides and one end of a coil and the squares to indicate the commutator bars. Such a stamp can be used for all types of windings, wave and lap with one or more coils per slot or for windings having a dead (idle) coil or half idle bar or with any brush position. The dotted line connecting the end of the coil to the slot is used to indicate the distance that the winding projects beyond the core. The two rows of squares represent the commutator bars. The top row is used when the center line of the slots lines up on a bar. The bottom row is used when the center line of the slots line up on the mica. When necessary, extra bars can be drawn in and lines drawn from the slot to the bars to show the number of coils per slot. In all cases, slot and bar No. 1 should be used to indicate the bottom half of the coil and bottom lead to the commutator.

In Figs. 10 to 20 eleven different markings and connections are indicated to show how to use the form in Fig. 9 for recording winding data and how the diagram of connections should look after it is completed. The diagram in Fig. 10 is for a wave winding with brushes on the center line of the poles. The bars marked 1 and 26 would have one dot on each while bar 8 would have two. Likewise bar 19 on a line with slot 12 would have three dots. (See instructions for marking slots and bars, paragraphs 3 and 4, page 13.)

The diagram marked Fig. 11 is for an armature with 97 bars and shows how a dead coil is indicated. Figure 12 is for an armature having three times as many bars as slots. When the number of coils per slot is even (2, 4, 6, etc.) use the lead of the coil at the right-hand side of the slot for showing the pitch and connections to the commutator. When the number is odd use the lead of the middle coil as shown in Fig. 12 with the connection to the commutator marked on bars 1 and 63. Figure 13 is a diagram for a winding with all the throw in the top lead and right hand. Figure 14 shows winding data for a General Electric 1,000 armature. Note how the bottom lead is brought over to the center line of the coil and the manner in which this lead is located. Figures 15, 16 and

17 are for lap-wound armatures and show how the diagram on the card form of Fig. 9 can be used for small hand-wound types. When taking data on armatures having skewed slots, line out with a string from the center of the core as shown in Fig. 18 and not from the commutator end of the slot.

A diagram for indicating the connection of an armature with a half idle bar is shown in Fig. 20. This armature has 49 slots and 98 bars. Instead of there being a dead coil, bars A and B are made one by forming a long jumper of the coil. The top leads of the coils 1 and 2 are soldered together and connected to bar C. Then the bottom lead of coil 1 is put in bar A according to the proper connecting data. The bottom lead of coil 2 is put in bar B. The slot in the neck of bar A should be filled with dummies after putting down the bottom lead of coil 1. This is the only lead connected to this bar thus making the equivalent of a 97-bar commutator.

Recording Coil and Commutator Throws When Complete Coils of Winding Are Made Up of Two or More Single Coils.—In those cases where an old winding is wound with coils made up with say, three single-coils or when a dead single coil is used, it is sometimes more convenient to use a coil diagram like that in Fig. 21 instead of the one in Fig. 9. In what follows details are given for using such a diagram with references made to the accompanying diagrams in Figs. 22 and 23.

Before removing all the coil terminals from the commutator necks, test out one coil to locate the slots in which the coil sides lie. The coil side in the bottom of the slot at the right will be called No. 1. The other side of the complete coil (in a double-layer winding) will be in the top of a slot, a distance which is called the coil throw. Count this coil throw in slots. In Fig. 22 a diagram is shown for a lap winding in which a complete coil is made up of three single coils. The bottom coil side of the complete coil is in slot No. 1 and the top coil side is in slot No. 12, so that the coil throw is slots 1 and 12 or 11 slots. Next draw in the center line of the coil and show whether it falls in a slot or on a tooth and also show on the diagram whether this center line of the coil at the commutator falls on a bar or on a mica between bars. If the total number of commutator bars is an even number, the center line of the coil will fall on a bar but if it is an uneven number, the center line will fall on a mica.

In the case of a lap winding shown in Fig. 22, commutator bar No. 1 is assumed to be directly under slot No. 1. Then the number of bars is counted between bar No. 1 and the bar to which the terminal of the coil side in slot No. 1 is connected. This number is marked on the diagram. In Fig. 22 it is bar No. 4.

With the diagram marked in this manner, the slots and bars can be punch marked as explained on page 12 and the coils and commutator

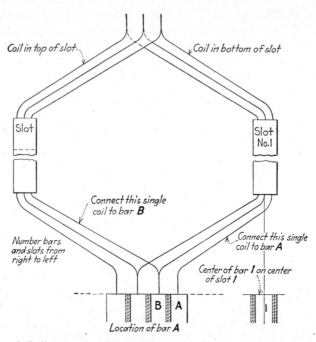

FIG. 21.—Coil diagram showing position of commutator and connection of bottom leads of first coil to be put on and connected to commutator when the complete coil is made up of two or more single coils. To locate bar A use the following formula: Bar $A = \dfrac{B \times (C-1)}{2} + 1$ where B is the number of single coils per coil and C is the coil pitch in slots. When A comes out a whole number and a fraction use the whole number and drop the fraction.

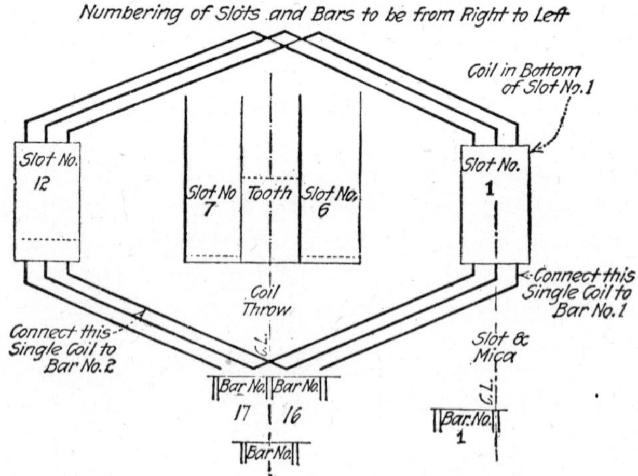

FIG. 22.—This form of diagram can be used for a lap winding when a complete coil is made up of three or more single coils as indicated to show how the bottom leads of the first coil are connected and how to locate the commutator on the shaft when it is replaced. To locate bar A (No. 16 in the diagram) use the formula given under Fig. 21.

removed from the armature. When it is rewound and the commutator replaced the commutator can be lined up as it was originally placed, by referring to the punch marks and checking with the diagram. From the diagram the winder can also tell the type of coil needed and can easily locate the commutator bar to which the bottom lead of the first coil must be connected as the coils are placed in the slots. This is of importance when the winder who stripped the armature does not happen to be the one who rewinds and reconnects it.

In Fig. 23 the use of this diagram is illustrated for recording data for a wave winding. This particular diagram shows how it can be drawn and used for a continuous wave winding or one with a dead coil. The same procedure is followed as in the case of a lap winding except that bar

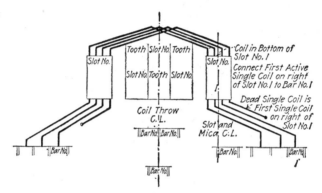

Fig. 23.—This form of diagram can be used for a wave winding that is continuous or one with a dead coil when the complete coil used is made up of two or more single coils to show how the bottom leads of the first coil are connected to the commutator and how to locate the commutator on the shaft.

No. 1 is taken as the one to which the bottom coil side of the complete coil is connected. Then count from bar No. 1 toward the left to the center line of the coil. This count gives the coil throw and is marked on the diagram with the commutator bar drawn in so as to indicate whether the center line of the coil falls on a mica or on a bar. In case the center line falls on a mica the same bar numbers are marked on the bars on each side of this mica. When the center line falls on a commutator bar, the proper number of bar from the coil throw is marked on the bar, always counting to the left from bar No. 1. It should also be noted whether the center line of the coil falls on a slot or on a tooth and the number of slots marked in the same manner as the bars were numbered. The bars and slots should be punch marked before the winding is stripped and the position of the commutator and connections for the new winding checked with the diagram at the time that connections are made to avoid possible errors.

Winding Information for Automobile Starting and Lighting Armatures.—The winding sketch and data card shown in Fig. 24 is used by a large company that rewinds about 2,000 small armatures a month, including a large number of the same type. These drawings are mounted on tough cardboard 5 by 8 in. and covered with celluloid to keep them clean. A binding of black leatherette is sewed around all four sides. One of these drawings is made up for each standard armature that comes in for rewinding and shows the style of winding, the size of wire used, number of turns per coil, the type of winding, the commutator connections and all the limiting dimensions. It also shows the core and shaft diameters and

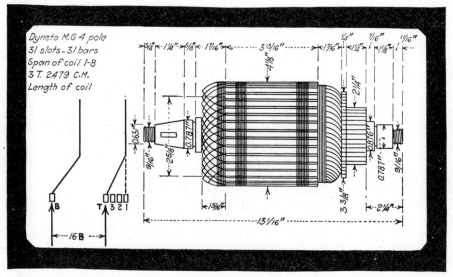

Fig. 24.—Winding diagram that gives winding data and dimensions for a particular type of armature.

In case a new style is received for which no drawing is on file, one can be made up before the armature is stripped. The drawing is mounted on tough cardboard and covered with celluloid. A binding of black leatherette is sewed around all four sides.

other dimensions so that a check can be made to see that everything is correct before the armature is turned over to the customer. This is necessary because many armatures are received by express for rewinding and they cannot be tried out in the motor and therefore must be accurate in dimensions before being shipped.

These drawings are filed according to the style of winding in a wooden card file on the foreman's desk. New drawings are made up as new jobs arrive at the shop for which drawings have not been already made. When an armature comes in for rewinding, it is identified as to style of winding used and a check made to see if a winding card is on file. If there is one this winding card is given to the winder with the armature. If there is no winding card in the file a new one is made up and given to the winder with the armature. This system, therefore, automatically grows and meets the majority of the winders' needs at a decided saving in time and checking cost. In connection with this winding-card system, stock units of wire, insulation and other material needed for a particular job are made up and held in stock. For details of this procedure see Chap. VIII, page 72.

Recording Data for Coils.—After making out the winding card (Fig. 9) before the armature is stripped, remove one complete coil and unwind it and count the number of turns. This can be done by lifting all the leads until the front of the coil is exposed and then cutting open the top of the slot insulation and locating the top lead. Then unwind the coil and count the number of turns.

When the winding is not too old and brittle, a quicker way of finding the turns per coil is as follows: Find a top coil, that is a coil which is exposed across the rear end of the armature from slot to slot and cut it open at the rear end. Be sure to cut open only one complete coil. Then count the total number of wires in this bundle cut through and divide this by *a number* which is found as follows: Divide the total number of bars by the total number of slots and then multiply this by the number of wires in parallel per single coil. When the number of wires cut through is divided by the number thus found, it will give the number of turns per coil. This is a quicker method than unwinding a coil and when once understood can be applied to any winding.

To determine the turns per single coil, first count the number of slots and bars. The number of single coils per slot will be equal to the total number of bars divided by the total number of slots. Then, to find the number of wires in parallel per single coil, lift all the wires to one commutator bar and count them. Do not count wires used as fillers or dummies. One-half the total number of active wires per bar will be the number of wires in parallel per single coil.

Also measure the size of wire and take a note of the kind of insulation, whether the wire is enameled, single cotton-covered, double-cotton-covered, etc. When coils must be purchased or made outside the repair shop, one complete coil should be saved and sent as a sample with the instructions for making the required number of new coils needed.

Stripping the Armature.—The next step is to strip the old winding from the core. For small motors there are several methods that are used, some faster than others which is the main reason for adopting them. First, drive out the wedges with an old hack-saw blade and a hammer. The teeth will dig into the wedge and force it out. When paper wedges are used, the first turn of wire (top leads) can be pulled through the top of the slot from front to back with a pair of pliers and thus cut the paper wedge through the center. After removing the wedges cut the coils off at the rear end of the commutator with a heavy pair of shears or saw them off with a hack saw close up to the ends of the slots of the iron core. The sides of the coils left in the slots can then be pulled through with a pair of pliers from the other end. When they stick and hang, a torch played around the iron of the slots will loosen them and make the pulling easier and quicker.

In one large shop making a specialty of the rewinding of small motors, the coils are removed in the same way they are put on by a special power driven spindle with a slot in the end for winding up the wire. This device is shown in Fig. 25.

Fig. 25.—This is a quick way to unwind a coil of many turns from the slots of an armature.

The end of the coil, cut free from the commutator, is drawn into a slot in the end of the unwinding spindle. This spindle is driven by a belt and controlled by a foot-operated clutch. With the wire drawn into the slot, the clutch is closed and the spindle rotates and unwinds the coil. The armature vibrates between the centers as the coil comes off.

Fig. 26.—The operator is shown using a lathe to cut the connections back of the commutator.

The tool used has a sharp V-shaped point. In case the coils are impregnated and baked hard, two additional cuts, one at each end of the core are made while the armature is in this lathe. When the two ends of the coils are cut off in this manner the remaining portions are driven out of the slots. Otherwise the coils are unwound by the special tool shown in Fig. 25.

In Fig. 26 another method is shown which consists of putting the armatures in a small speed lathe and cutting off the leads just back of the commutator using a cut-off tool with a V-shaped point. If the winding has been impregnated, two other cuts are made one at each end of the core. This removes all the end windings and just leaves the wires in the slots. These wires are then driven out by the use of a drift and hammer as shown in Fig. 27.

When an armature has been insulated or dipped in a compound, such as liquid Bakelite, that makes the ends of the coils a solid mass, the whole armature can be immersed in a boiling solution of caustic soda and allowed to soak until the varnish and compound softens. The commutator, if it can be saved, should be removed from the armature before it is put into the solution. The fiber end rings will be destroyed but these can be easily replaced. No harm will be done to the laminations if the armature is allowed to dry or is baked in an oven before being rewound. The armature should be stripped while it is hot.

Fig. 27.—Driving out sections of impregnated coils from core slots.

The coils are previously cut off at each end of the core. Drifts of suitable size are used to drive out the portion of the coils within the slots. The armature is mounted between centers for convenience.

After the armature has been stripped of its coils, the old insulation and paint can be removed by applying a gas flame or torch. The slots should then be thoroughly cleaned with a file and all burrs removed from the edges of the iron. Finally, blow out each slot with a blast of compressed air. It may be necessary in some cases to brush the slots with a boiling solution of caustic soda to remove insulation that has baked on. Before the armature is rewound make sure that it is thoroughly dry if a cleaning solution has been used on it.

CHAPTER III

INSULATING THE ARMATURE CORE

The process of insulating a small armature core preparatory to rewinding it, is one of the most important steps in rewinding procedure. Particular attention should be paid to the truing up of the core laminations, the selection of the proper insulating material and the method of applying this material. When a little care is given to these three points a second rewinding job can often be prevented.

Cleaning Slots and Truing Up Laminations.—After the old winding has been removed from the armature, the slots, ends of core and shaft must be thoroughly cleaned of all old insulation and varnish. A solution composed of 25 per cent alcohol and 75 per cent benzol will loosen the varnish and old insulation so that it can be scraped from the slots easily. This will produce no bad effects on the laminations or on the winding when the armature is rewound. A hot solution of caustic soda can also be used to loosen old insulation but when caustic soda is used it is liable to creep between laminations and the alkali will damage the insulation of the new winding in spots. When caustic soda is used, therefore, the slots should be washed out and the armature baked in an oven. For methods of removing varnish and paint from an armature core, see Chap. I, page 23.

For scraping the slots, a tool made from bar steel 1 by $\frac{1}{16}$ in., of suitable length and drawn down to a long thin point like a chisel, will be found useful in removing old insulation after it has been softened. Such a tool will also give good results without the use of any chemicals. After removing the insulation in this way, draw a file through the slots to remove small pieces of insulation and smooth off all roughness. The edges of the slots should be filed to remove sharp edges and burrs that would injure the insulation of the new winding when it is being placed in the slots. The entire core should finally be thoroughly cleaned with a blast of compressed air.

The slots should be carefully inspected for rough or irregular spots due to the lamination teeth being bent, broken or burned. These defects can usually be remedied by the use of a steel drift and hammer. Then file the rough places with an ordinary file and make sure there are no sharp edges in the slots or at the ends of the core. When the laminations have flared or separated so that they cannot be driven together with a mallet, the core should be put in a hand press and forced together.

24

The grooves for wedges and band wires must also be trued up so that the wedges can be driven in properly and there will be no difficulty in putting on the proper number of turns of banding wire. It is important that the band grooves should not be filed any deeper than on the original core unless the slots are filed an equal amount, for the winding would raise the banding wire at the slot opening in such cases so much that when the winding is thoroughly dried, the banding may come loose and slip out of the holding grooves.

Building Up New Cores.—Many small armatures have skewed slots. The slot is skewed the width of one tooth in order to reduce the magnetic hum. The conductors on the armature with this construction do not enter the magnetic field with a jump but one tip of the slot wedges into the field and the voltage in the coil tends to build up gradually instead of with a rush.

Fig. 28.—This jig and the block with a skewed key shown in Fig. 29 will give the proper skew when building up laminations for a core with skewed slots.

When assembling new cores proceed as follows: After the shaft is turned to its proper size put on a fiber sleeve or tube about 1 in. long and hold it in place with a cotterpin. This will serve as a stop for the laminations when they are slipped on the shaft, and will also serve to insulate the end winding from the shaft. To obtain uniform skewing as the laminations are slipped on the shaft a device in the form of a jig, such as shown in Fig. 28, is needed. The jig shown has a concave block fitted with a key as illustrated in Fig. 29, which trues up the laminations as they are slipped on the shaft and gives the proper skew to the slot. As the core is built up, force the laminations into close contact by striking a couple of hard blows on a short piece of pipe slipped over the shaft.

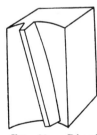

Fig. 29.—Block with skewed key for use with the jig shown in Fig. 28 for building up laminations with skewed slots.

For the first and last laminations use fiber or fullerboard punched to conform to the shape of the laminations. This serves as a protection for the windings that cross the ends of the core. When the laminations have been built up to the required height so as to provide slots of the proper length, slip a second fiber sleeve or tube over the shaft the same length as the first one put on. Then place the inverted U-shaped piece on the jig, as shown in Fig. 28, and press down the top sleeve by means of the screw at the top of the U-shaped piece until the laminations are pressed tightly

together and a cotterpin can be inserted through a hole on the shaft
This will hold the sleeve and laminations in their proper positions on
the shaft.   Finally file the slots smooth and the core will then be ready
for its winding

FIG. 30.—Method of building up laminations of small armatures that have slots parallel
to the shaft.

The core laminations are put on in bundles of a fixed weight, then pressed and clamped.   The jig
shown is set up on a set of scales and enough laminations are slipped over the dummy shaft to balance
the weight on the scale.   These bundles are then tied up as shown.   When ordering laminations it is a
good plan to give the weight of old laminations in addition to the nameplate data on the motor.

Insulating Ends of Old Core.—The next step is to insulate the ends
or heads of the old core.   This insulation is in the form of fiber washers
slipped over the shaft and fitted up against
the ends of the core laminations.   These washers should be of such a size that they will rest
against the bottom of the slot insulation.
This will then take considerable strain off
the corners and ends of the slot insulation
and prevent the wires tearing through it and
causing a ground.   When the first layers of
a coil wound in the slots by hand are drawn
too tight or the entire coil is pounded with a
mallet too hard over the end of the slot,
troubles with grounds are started at this point
by the wires cutting through the slot insulation when this insulation is

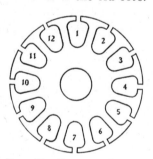

FIG. 31.—Common shapes of
slots used in small motor cores.

not properly supported by a closely fitted end washer. End washers should be made from fiber about $\frac{1}{16}$ in. thick. The proper method of holding the end washers up against the ends of the core, is described under "Building Up New Cores" on page 25.

Insulating the Shaft.—For shaft insulation some material that will allow the wires resting on it to slide easily, such as fish paper or treated cloth (about 10 mils thick) should be used. Use about four layers of this insulation and hold it together with shellac. The usual method of insulating shafts is to put on half-lapped layers of $\frac{3}{4}$ in. treated cloth tape and one layer of friction tape on top of the treated cloth. When friction tape is used it should be well paraffined after being wound on to allow the wires of the coils to slide over it while winding the coils in the slots. Liquid glue should never be used in this connection. Dry or pot glue is sometimes used but it is not recommended. Shellac is much better.

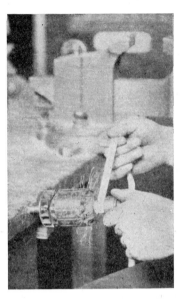

The shaft at both ends of the core should be insulated as described. After the winding is completed and the commutator is pressed on, fill the hollow between the end connections of the armature and the commutator with layers of friction tape up to the level of the bottom of the commutator bars. This will protect the end connections and form a bed for the armature leads so that when they are soldered to the commutator and bound down with twine there will be little chance of vibration breaking them off at the points where they are connected to the commutator.

Fig. 31*A*.—Cotton tape is wound around the armature shaft to fill the space between the commutator and winding and give a firm support for the fine commutator leads. After the leads have been soldered in place they are bound down with string.

Insulating the Slots.—Some form of tough, fibrous paper, commonly called fish paper or Leatheroid, can be used for insulating the slots. However, a better material is that known as combination insulation, which is made up with a 0.004-, 0.007-, 0.010-, or 0.015-in. piece of fish paper as a base and a layer of 0.008- or 0.009-in. piece of tan treated cloth shellaced to the fish paper. This makes a flexible and tough slot insulation with good mechanical and electrical strength. The total thickness is about 0.012-, 0.015-, 0.020-, or 0.023-in. The 0.012- and 0.015-in. thicknesses are used for small 110- to 220-volt armatures and the 0.023-in. for those using a large size of wire.

When using this material the fish paper should be used against the iron of the slot (Fig. 36) so as to take advantage of its good mechanical strength and use the full dielectric strength of the treated cloth next to the wires of the coil in the slot.   The laminations in sides and bottom of the slot are never perfectly smooth as one lamination may project beyond the next only slightly.   When the treated cloth is used next to the iron of the slot, and the wires are pounded down to get the wedges in, the side pressure of the wires against the slot insulation will force the treated cloth against the roughness of laminations.   In some cases this pressure will be sufficient to cut through the cloth and thus weaken its dielectric strength.   The fish paper is mechanically stronger and will resist this cutting action of the laminations and protect the treated cloth so that the full dielectric strength is used in addition to that of the fish paper.

For 110-volt armatures with round slots not over $\frac{3}{8}$ in. in diameter with wire for coils not larger than No. 28 B. & S. gage, 0.007- or 0.010-in. slot insulation is ample.   For 220-volt armatures use 0.010-in. slot insulation or thicker.   For slots larger than $\frac{3}{8}$ in. in diameter and wire as large or larger than No. 18, use slot insulation at least 0.016 in. thick and if possible 0.023 in. thick.   It is better not to use two layers of slot insulation to increase the thickness but use a thicker paper.   Thin paper tears more easily especially in large slots.

Continuous Strip Insulation for Slots.—If the fibre heads or end washers have not been lost from the ends of the armature or damaged, the continuous-strip method of insulating the armature slots may be used, as shown in Fig. 32.   If the head, however, has been lost or damaged, certain precautions must be taken which will be explained later. When using the continuous-strip method, one long strip of insulating material is passed entirely around the outside of the armature slots and looped into each slot.   After the wire has been wound in the slots, this insulation is cut between the slots and the free edges of the insulation tucked over the coil into the opposite sides of the slot in order to hold the coil in place.   When the insulation is tucked over in this manner, the use of armature wedges over the tops of the coils is not necessary when the armature is to be dipped.   But if the slots are full or the armature runs over 900 r.p.m., fibre or wood wedges should be used.

An explanation of this method of insulating the slots is given in an instruction book of the P. E. Chapman Electrical Works, St. Louis, Missouri.   The authors recommend that the insulation should be cut lengthwise of the grain from 0.010-in. fish paper.   The strip of insulation should be $\frac{1}{8}$ in. wider than the length of the slot including the fibre end washers.   This means that the insulation should project $\frac{1}{8}$ in. beyond the fibre end washers on each end of the armature.   It should be long enough to pass entirely around the armature and loop into every slot.

When starting to insulate the first slot, a loop of the fish paper is pushed down into it, leaving about ½ in. of the shorter end sticking out of the slot. In order to hold the insulation tight while inserting it in the next slot, a pin is slipped into the end of the first slot just filling the slot and holding the insulation against the slot on all sides. When the pin is in place, pull the paper tight and loop the paper at the corners where it emerges from both sides of the slot with the drift stick, in order to crease it slightly along the edges of the slot.

Allow a little slack over the tooth between the first and second slots. Then press the insulation into the second slot with a drift tool, the edges of which are rounded to prevent damaging the insulation. Before pressing the insulation to the bottom of the slot, hold the long end of the strip against the back of the tool and press downward and angularly toward

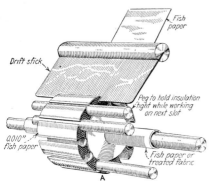

FIG. 32.—Continuous strip method of insulating slots using 0.010-in. fish paper.

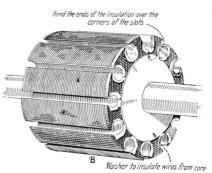

FIG. 33.—After the strip of insulation has been put into all the slots the insulation is bent over the ends of the slots as shown. This armature is shown with the fiber end washer in place.

the slot that has just been insulated, so as to crease the insulation over the edge of the second slot. After forming this crease, release the long end of the insulation and press it down into the slot, when it will be found to curl around and fit the slot. The drift tool is then removed and the second pin is inserted in this slot. Before creasing the insulation over the edge of the slot, twist the pin at the same time pulling on the long end of the paper so as to take the slack out of the paper over the previous teeth. Leave the first pin in place until the second slot has been insulated, then it may be removed and put in the second slot while the third is being insulated. Only two pins are required although three are sometimes used.

When use is made of the kind of insulating material mentioned in following these directions, it is not necessary to cement the insulation in the slots as in the case when treated fabric is used. It is, however, desirable to stick the first and last ends together with thick shellac or some other sticking compound.   Never use liquid glue.   Most liquid glues contain a small portion of acid which will in the course of time corrode the wire after the glue comes in contact with it.   Dry or "pot" glue may be used as a rule but it is not recommended as it does not stick to the fish paper well.

While electrically 0.005- to 0.007-in. thickness is sufficient slot insulation, for mechanical reasons it is not advisable to use less than 0.008- to 0.010-in. thickness to insure against grounds to the core.   In some repair shops a layer of 0.009-in. treated cloth and a layer of 0.004-in. fish paper is used.   Both layers are put in the slot at the same time. The fish paper is placed inside against the coil and the treated cloth outside against the iron.   The reason for placing the fish paper inside instead of against the iron is that when winding the wire will slide more easily over fish paper than it will over sticky treated cloth.   Where maximum dielectric strength is desired, however, the fish paper should be placed next to the iron for the reasons given on page 28.   Where it is desired to use additional insulation between coils in the same slot, a strip of 0.010-in. fish paper may be cut to match the width of the slot and driven down on the top of each coil in a manner to compress the coil into the slot.

Armatures from which the fiber heads or end washers have been lost, either wholly or in part, may be rewound without making a new head if the right method is followed.   An insulating washer must be put on in place of the head as already described.   After putting on this head insulation, if the slot openings are not too narrow, the previous method of insulating the slots by means of a long strip may be followed by using two thicknesses of insulating material (or one piece of double thickness). If the slot openings are very narrow, the following method can be used: Use a thick insulation (see Fig. 35) of 0.016-in. fish paper or common vulcanized fibre $\frac{1}{64}$ in. thick and cut two strips $\frac{1}{8}$ in. longer than the slot including the end insulation and just wide enough to entirely fill the slot.   In order to determine what this width must be, one piece of insulation should be inserted in the slot around the pin or mandrel and marked along the edges of the slot with a knife.   Then take out the strip and cut the sides.   This can be used as a sample to cut other strips. Strips should be cut so that the grain of the paper runs around the slots, or the grain runs parallel to the width of the slot wrapper.   This is done in order to resist tearing.   When a strip is put into a slot the ends should be flared open against the end of the slot to form a round shoulder for the wires to rest upon.   It is sometimes necessary to stick the insulation in the slots, but often the slots are of such shape that this is unnecessary. In winding an armature when the head has been reinsulated in this manner, too much tension must not be put upon the wire while winding or it will cut through the insulation and cause grounds to the core. When using insulation of this kind, it is necessary to close the slots with wedges.

Slot Wedges.—These wedges can be made from $\frac{1}{32}$- or $\frac{1}{16}$-in. fiber or wood, or 0.015- to 0.023-in. fish paper. When the slots are well filled and the wedges cannot be driven in from the ends, a 0.023-in. fish paper wedge cut just a trifle wider than the slot opening can be used and pressed in the slot from the top. To do this put one edge of the wedge under one overhanging edge of the slot and drive the other side of the wedge down under the opposite edge of the slot with a narrow width steel drift and hammer. An old hacksaw blade with teeth ground off can be used for this purpose. This also applies to open slot armatures. The wedge makes a driving fit and after the armature has been dipped in varnish, these wedges will hold as well as one driven in from the end.

Kind of Wire and Its Insulation for Small Motors.—Single-cotton and enamel-covered or double-cotton covered wires are the best for winding small armatures, especially when the size of wire is small, say No. 28 or 30 and finer. This wire will stand a reasonable amount of heat and give good service. Wires with a single insulation of silk or cotton over a bare wire are suitable only for magnet and field coils, and even then the insulation is not enough when the wire is No. 12 and coarser. Silk-covered wire is delicate and stands the least heat, burns out quickest by slow roasting and is most expensive. However, silk covered wire is very useful when a large number of turns are required of fine sizes, and when cotton will make an excessive volume in the slot. A good grade of enamel wire is preferable to single and double silk-covered wire in the finer sizes. Either silk or silk-enamel insulation should by all means be used for armature work on wire sizes coarser than above No. 27 or 28 B. & S. gage. Above this size this kind of insulation must be carefully insulated between coils and sometimes between layers, and if the armature is small such wire will frequently take up more room in the slots than cotton enamel or even double-cotton covered wire when the latter is wound on a good winding machine.

Enameled wire, in general, may be considered as equivalent in over-all size to single-cotton covered wire. Good enameled wire takes the least room, stands a reasonable amount of handling, a good deal of heat (about 280°F.) continuously, and 80 degrees more for a short time. It is useful in small sizes and fills the other places where single covered wires cannot be used. Enameled wires must not be soluble in any of the ordinary solvents such as turpentine, naphtha, gasoline, benzine, linseed oil or its substitutes, machine oils or alcohol. Especially must this be true when using it on armatures. Enameled wire must be of such a grade that it will stand bending without cracking, be tough and hard to scrape off. *It should seldom be used for armature windings without another covering,* either of silk or cotton. The dependable grades are, however, sometimes used in winding small armatures for vacuum cleaners, fans, and small universal motors, without extra covering.

Good grades of asbestos covered wire stand the most heat. Some manufacturers claim a very high heat even to redness. Although the

FIG. 34.—This is the way an armature core looks when strip insulation is used and inserted into the slots.

    This type of insulation is applied in a long strip about ¼ in. wider than the core   The strip is pushed down into each slot and creased over the tops of the teeth.   After the coils are all in place the insulation is cut along the top of the teeth and folded down over the coils.   Slot sticks or wedges are then inserted over the folded-down insulation.

insulation is slightly thicker, it can be used where a double-cotton covered wire can be used. Asbestos wire will not stand much handling, such as pounding or rubbing, and when used should be wound in layers, if possible, with the least tension and pounding possible.

FIG. 35.—For slots with small openings separate pieces of insulation are used in each slot.

    Slot insulation of this type is cut about ¼ in. longer than the armature slot and wide enough to allow the two edges to extend from ½ to ¾ in. out of the slot.   As a rule the insulating material is put into the slots as the coils are started.   Thus there would be only two slots insulated when the first coil is being wound, and the last slot would not be insulated until just before a coil is started in it.

Armatures that are subjected to high heat, such as head light generators on locomotives or motors near ovens, etc., can be wound with asbestos wire. The slots can be milled out if extra room is required. This additional expense is justified by the longer life of the armature when a high heat job is put out. A hard (tin) solder should be used to fasten the leads into the commutator necks. This precaution is necessary as the ordinary half-and-half solder will run and cause a poor contact at the commutator or allow the wires to fly up out of the necks. This is also true in automobile lighting generators which also at times operate at high heat.

When milling out the commutator necks, use a cutter about 0.002 to 0.004 in. thinner than the wire. This will insure a good contact and a

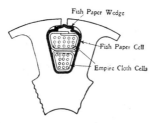

Fig. 36.—Slot insulated with fishpaper so shaped as to cover all the iron inside the slot but leaving the slot opening unobstructed. Inside this is placed another cell of waxed empire cloth, the edges of which project beyond the edge of the slot and serve to guide and protect the wires during winding.

driving fit and often prevent trouble when there is a tendency for the wires to fly out under high heat for a short time only.

The following table shows the average run of coverings used on wire in winding small armatures.

INSULATION THAT SHOULD BE USED ON DIFFERENT SIZES OF WIRES

Size of wire B. & S. gage No.	No. of coverings	Kind of covering
28 and finer..............	Double-covered	Enamel—two coats
28 to 12..................	Double-covered	Double cotton or single cotton and enamel as space permits
12 and coarser............	Double-covered	Single cotton and enamel or double cotton and enamel as space permits

In Fig. 34 the use of strip insulation is shown. Note the insulation around the shaft and the fiber washer or head. When an armature is insulated, as shown in Fig. 35, the projecting part of the cell should be flared open by running the finger between the two sides of the cell and pressing against each side of the slot. This keeps the cell open and allows the wire to run in. It is a good plan to cut away one corner of the slot

insulation at the entering end of the slot.   Then when the wire is brought
around, it can be pressed against the uncut side which will open the cell.

Figure 36 shows a good method of slot insulation.   For 220-volt
armatures or those larger than ¼-hp., a 0.015-in. combination slot insulation should be used fitted to the curvature of the slot and each side of
the slot opening.   A treated cloth slider can be used for each half of the
coil in the slot so that no "willie" or separator is necessary.   A fish-

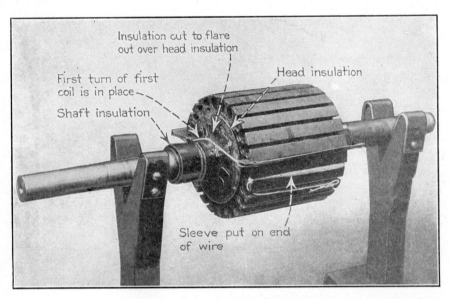

Fig. 37.—The start when winding on the first coils.   The shaft insulation is shown in place
and also the end or head insulation.

paper wedge can be driven or forced in.   Figure 37 shows an armature
insulated with combination slot insulation with the treated cloth slider
in place.

On armatures where the wire fills the slot and makes it hard to drive
in wedges, a thin fish-paper can be forced in and each slot well painted
with liquid Bakelite, which when baked will make a hard retaining wall
that will prevent the wires from coming out of the slots.

CHAPTER IV

THE LOOP WINDING

A type of hand winding for small armatures that is much used is known as the loop winding. It is mostly used on fans, vacuum cleaner armatures, and armatures of small drills and grinders. This winding is distinguished from others by the fact that only one complete coil end is visible on either end of the shaft when the armature is completely wound. This coil is the last one put on as shown in Fig. 38.

Advantages and Disadvantages of a Loop Winding.—The advantages of this type of winding are that it is quickly applied and connected when

Entire end of last coil put on is visible in a loop winding

Fig. 38.—Armature wound with a straight loop winding. The commutator is on the other end. Details for this winding are shown in Fig. 40.

correctly wound and is the best type of winding to use with an armature winding machine, such as shown in Fig. 39. It has also disadvantages in that all the coils are not alike. That is, the first coil is smaller than the last and where there is more than one coil per slot, the resistance of the last coil is greater than that of the first coil, hence the resistance of each coil is different. Also when the turns per coil are great in number or the size of wire is large, the coil ends pile up so that it is hard and sometimes impossible to wind the coils in properly. A loop winding is not equally balanced, therefore, due to the unequal sizes of coils.

Starting a Loop Winding.—Figure 40 shows how the coils are wound in place for a loop winding. The wire is started in slot No. 1 and is run

35

through slot No. 6, (the pitch being 1 and 6) until the required number of turns is put on; then the wire is brought around to the starting point, and a loop made in the wire at F^1S^2 (Fig. 40). This loop is left long enough to reach the commutator and fit in the commutator slot. The wire is not cut but is continued into slots two and seven, etc., in the same manner until the end of the last coil is reached. Then the wire is cut and the free end of the start of coil No. 1 is twisted together with the finish of coil 12 or the last coil put on.

Fig. 39.—Motor operated armature winding machine suitable for winding armatures having coils with a large number of turns.

An assortment of holding clamps to fit various sizes of armatures adapts this machine to a large variety of work. The machine is particularly suitable for armatures having coils with a large number of turns. In this illustration the operator has stopped the machine with a coil half wound. The turn-counting device may be seen just above the operator's left hand. The driving motor is controlled by the foot lever. The hand wheel serves as a brake and is useful in making the last one or two turns.

Left-hand and Right-hand Loop Windings.—In Fig. 40B and D, the difference is shown between winding left hand or right hand. A right-hand winding is shown in D, Fig. 40. With the commutator towards the winder, the leads are on the right-hand side and the coil is wound inside the shaft. The next coils are wound in the adjacent slots counterclockwise. For the left-hand winding B in Fig. 40, with the commutator end towards the winder, the leads are on the left-hand side and the coil is wound outside the shaft in a backward direction from the way a man

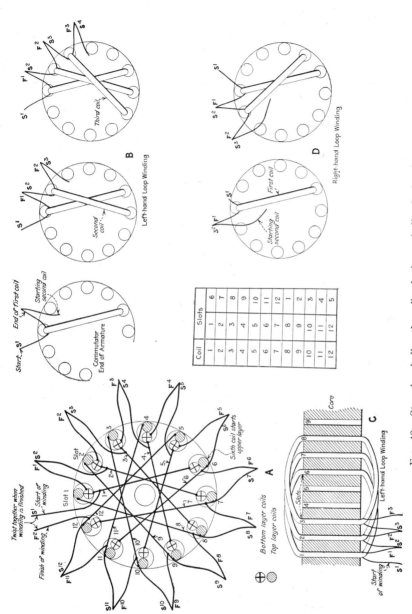

Coil	Slots
1	1 — 6
2	2 — 7
3	3 — 8
4	4 — 9
5	5 — 10
6	6 — 11
7	7 — 12
8	8 — 1
9	9 — 2
10	10 — 3
11	11 — 4
12	12 — 5

Fig. 40.—Steps in winding the coils of a loop winding by hand.

A—Shows a two-pole lap, hand-wound, left-hand chorded loop winding, for 12 slots, 12 bars and a pitch of 1 and 6. The leads can be put down in one layer, and without cutting the loops. S_1 is the starting lead of coil 1. S_2 is the starting lead of coil 2, etc. This is the same motor as shown in Fig. 38. B and C are steps in winding the armature shown at A. D is a right-hand loop winding of same kind as A, B and C.

would naturally wind with his right hand; that is, toward the winder on the top. The next coil is wound in the adjacent slot clockwise.

A lap-wound armature can be wound right or left hand or on either side of the shaft without affecting the direction of rotation of the motor or changing the brush polarity in a generator. The term "chorded" means that the coils are not full pitch, which would be 1 and 7 for the armature shown. The term "loop" is used to denote that the wire is

A loop has been made--->
and covered with sleeving
before starting the second
coil

Wire starting in
<--- second slot

First coil is
in place

Fig. 41.—This illustration shows the first coil of a loop winding wound in its slots and the start of the second coil with a loop formed at the end of the first coil and the start of the second one.

not cut at the start and finish of each coil. The winding in Fig. 38 is a left-hand, chorded-loop winding.

Figure 41 shows the start of the first two coils of a loop winding. The start of the first coil is bent out of the way into the adjacent slot to the left of the starting slot. The loop is shown at the finish of the first coil and the start of the second. In the photo, the third turn of the second coil is ready to be put in, but the starting wire can be seen leaving the bottom of the sleeving to the slot at the right.

Loop Winding with More than One Coil per Slot.—The winding shown in *A* (Fig. 40) has as many bars as slots, but such a winding can be used for any number of bars.   For instance, assume a 12-slot armature with 36 commutator bars and coils having 20 turns per coil.   This armature would be wound by starting in slot No. 1, as per *A* (Fig. 40), winding on 20 turns, making a loop and continuing in the same slot. After 20 turns more are put on, a second loop is made and the next 20 turns put in the same slot.   After a third loop the wire is passed to slot No. 2 and the process repeated.   In this way every slot would

Fig. 42.—Winder's bench showing convenient mounting of wire reels and rotating holder in which armature is centered.

A 110-volt testing circuit with a lamp in series is provided at this winding bench.   When the winder frequently tests his work for grounds he has some assurance that the job is in good condition when completed.   Each armature should be given a final test by an inspector who passes on the quality of the work.

have three loops projecting.   When this type of winding is used, colored sleeving should be put on the loops; that is, white on first loop, blue on second, and red or none at all on the third.   If this is not done there is likely to be trouble when connecting the winding to the commutator.

Loop Winding with More than One Wire in Hand.—The above method uses only one reel of wire when winding, or one wire in hand and is suitable for winding machines, but where there are two, three or more times as many commutator bars as slots and the armature is wound by hand at a bench, as in Fig. 42, three or more reels of wire are used and mounted as shown.   The coils are wound in place as shown in Fig. 40 except that more than one wire is used at one time depending upon the number of times the commutator bars exceed the number of slots.   In this case, the wire is cut at the end of each coil and brought around to the starting lead of the same coil.   With this style of loop winding a different colored sleeving should be put on the starting and finishing leads to distinguish the start from the finish, but all the starting or all the finishing leads of each coil can have the same color of sleeve.

In any loop winding, each slot should have a starting and finishing lead and the winder should be able to distinguish one from the other.

When starting to wind the last two coils in place, a piece of twine should be put under the next to the last coil on the rear end.   Then, when the last turn of the finish coil is in place, this string should be tied to prevent the turns of the last or top coil from flaring out.

Testing Straight Loop Winding for Grounds.—With the straight loop (one wire in hand) winding, one lead of a test light can be connected to the starting coil lead and the other lead of the test light to the armature shaft in such a manner that both leads can revolve with the armature while being wound.   This will show a ground as soon as it occurs, and eliminate the necessity of unwinding to remove a ground.

CHAPTER V

SPECIAL CHORDED SPLIT-PITCH LOOP WINDING

Many small, two-poled motors having an armature with a large number of slots and small end room are wound with a special chorded, split-pitch winding. This winding can be used with any number of slots where there are two or four times as many bars as slots. A feature of this winding is that two coils are wound in three slots on the same side of the shaft, the two coils each having a different pitch as shown in Fig. 43.

Fig. 43.—End of chorded split-pitch loop winding showing two coils wound in three slots which is the feature of this winding.

Example Showing Advantage of This Winding.—The advantages of the special chorded, split-pitch loop winding can be illustrated in the case of a 5-hp., 1,100-r.p.m., two-pole motor having an armature 10 in. in diameter with 24 slots and 48 commutator bars. If this armature is wound full pitch, 1 and 13, the winding would pile up on the ends of the armature and take up too much space. This would be caused by the end turns having to cross the maximum number of coils and also bend around the shaft, since slots 1 and 13 are on diametrically opposite sides of the shaft.

By the use of the special chorded, split-pitch loop winding, the coil pitch is reduced to 80 per cent of the full pitch which eliminates some of the coil crossings and prevents the coil ends from bending around the shaft. On this armature, the full pitch equals 12. Then 80 per cent of the full pitch would be 0.80 × 12 or 9.6. This is equivalent to using slots 1 and 10.6. But since 0.6 of a slot cannot be obtained, the split-pitch winding makes it possible to wind one coil with a pitch of 10, in slots 1 and 11 and to wind the next coil with a pitch 9, in slots 1 and 10, and so on. This gives an average pitch of 9.5 which approximates the desired pitch of 9.6. This particular winding has odd turns; that is, one coil has seven turns and the second has eight turns. The long pitch (1 and 11) coil has eight turns while the short pitch one (1 and 10) has seven turns.

Armature Wound with One Wire in Hand.—This type of winding must be wound with one wire in hand, regardless of the number of times

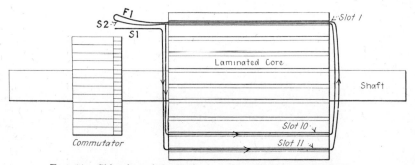

Fig. 44.—Side view of the beginning of a split-pitch, loop winding.

S_1 is the start and F_1 is the finish of the first coil. This coil consists of eight turns wound in slots 1 and 11, as indicated by the arrows. At the finish of the first coil a loop is made long enough to reach the proper commutator bar and at the end of this loop, the second coil is started at S_2 in slot 10. The second coil is wound in slots 1 and 10 as indicated by the arrows. An end view of the first four coils is shown in Fig. 45.

the number of commutator bars exceeds the number of slots. In winding the armature, it should be placed with the commutator on the left-hand side of the winder, as shown in Fig. 44. In this diagram the start of the winding is shown at S_1.

The winding can be started from any slot and the slot from which it is started is called slot 1. The S_1 lead is left long enough to reach to the proper commutator bar, and a white sleeve is put around the lead. The wire is bent down from the front or commutator end of slot 1 and carried across to slot 11, through slot 11 and up the back of the armature to slot 1, and through slot 1 as shown by the arrows in Fig. 44. Eight turns are wound in slots 1 and 11. F_1 is the finishing end of the first coil. A loop is then made of the finishing end, F_1, of the first coil and the starting end, S_2, of the second coil. This loop should be long enough to reach to the proper commutator segment and a red sleeve put on it. The starting end, S_2, of the second coil is carried down the front of the armature to slot 10, through slot 10, up the back of the armature to

slot 1, and through slot 1, as indicated by the arrows in Fig. 44.   Seven
turns are wound in the second coil.   Figure 45 shows the front end of the
armature with the first four coils wound in.   In this figure S_1, F_1, etc.,
refer to the starting and finishing ends of the respective coils, the same
as in Fig. 44.   The small circles in the slots represent the different coils
and the number in the circles indicates the coil number and the order
in which the coil is wound.   The commutator loops made up of the starting and finishing coil ends, F_1, S_2, S_3, etc., are also shown in the diagram.

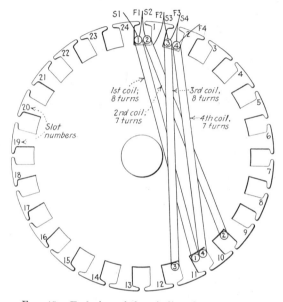

Fig. 45.—End view of the winding shown in Fig. 44.

The coil starts at S_1 and consists of eight turns wound in slots 1 and 11, as shown by the bunch of
wires marked 1 in the two slots.   A loop is made of the finish of the first coil, F_1, and the start of the
second, S_2, which is to be connected to the proper commutator bar.   A red sleeve is put over this loop.
Beginning with S_2 and ending with F_2, the second coil is wound with seven turns in slots 1 and 10.   At
F_1 a loop is made long enough to reach to the proper commutator segment and the third coil is begun
at S_3.   A white sleeve is put over the loop made by F_2 and S_3.   The third coil consists of eight turns
wound in slots 2 and 12.

At this stage of the winding, slot 1 will contain two halves of a coil,
slot 10 one-half, and slot 11 the other half.   With the end F_2 of coil 2 and
the start S_3, of coil 3, a loop is made on which is put a white sleeve.   Coil
3 is wound by running the wire from the loop across the front of the
armature to slot 12, through slot 12 and up the back of the armature to
slot 2 and through slot 2.   Eight turns are wound in this coil through
slots 2 and 12.   At the finish F_3 of coil 3 a loop is made and a red sleeve
is put on it.   The fourth coil is wound with seven turns in a manner
similar to the previous coils, in slots 2 and 11.   There are now four coils
in five slots, as is shown in Fig. 45.

Colored Sleeves Used to Mark Commutator Loops.—The above
procedure is followed through until the forty-eight coils are in place,

remembering to use eight and seven turns alternately and putting white and red sleeves on alternate loops. Figure 46 shows the first twenty-four coils in place. Notice that coil 20 starts the upper layer of coils in slot 10. In Fig. 46 the numbering system is the same as in preceding diagrams. Figure 47 shows all the coils laid in the slots and also shows

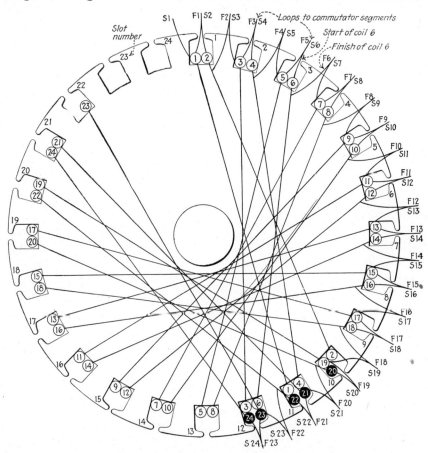

Fig. 46.—This diagram shows the armature with the first half of the coils in place.

Note that the top layer of coils begins in slot 10 with coil 20. The upper layer coils in each slot are indicated by black circles with white letters. The letters S and F indicate the starting and finishing leads of each coil. The numbers in the circles indicate the coil number and the order in which the coil is wound on.

all the loops to the commutator; R and W, indicating red and white sleeves, are marked beside the first few loops to indicate the sequence of the sleeves. The last two coils are drawn complete so as to show how they are wound in. The end, F_{48} of coil 48 is connected to the start S_1 of coil 1 to make the final loop. In this and the preceding diagram, the black circles with white numbers indicate the coils wound in the upper layer of the slots.

Method of Connecting Loops to Commutator.—In *A* of Fig. 48 is shown the commutator connections. The brushes are on the center line of the neutral region as shown in diagram *B* of Fig. 48. Hence the leads are given a forward lead to compensate for the chorded pitch. As will be seen from diagram *A*, the loop made up of S_2 and F_1, is con-

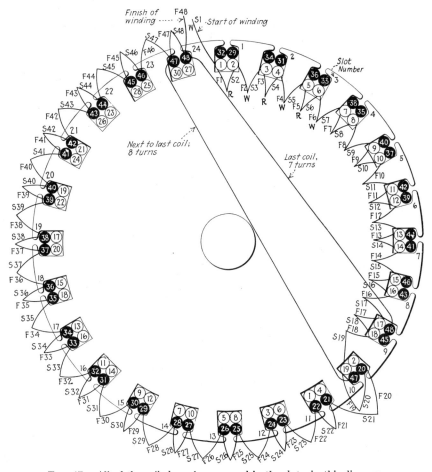

Fig. 47.—All of the coils have been wound in the slots, in this diagram.

The last two coils have been drawn in to show how the winding ends. F_{48} and S_1 are joined together and treated as a loop to be connected to the last commutator bar. The letters *R* and *W* indicate the color of sleeving used for each loop.

nected three bars ahead of the bar in line with slot 1 in which are the top halves of coils 1 and 2. The other loops are connected in a corresponding manner. When connecting the loops to the commutator, first connect a white sleeve, followed by a red sleeve, and follow alternately with a white and a red sleeve until all are connected. Or the loops can be connected in two layers. First connect all the white sleeved loops leaving a bar between each loop. Then put a band of tape over these loops, after which the red-sleeved loops may be connected in order to the remaining bars.

The most important precaution when connecting this type of winding is to get the lead throw correct, as connecting it one or two bars off

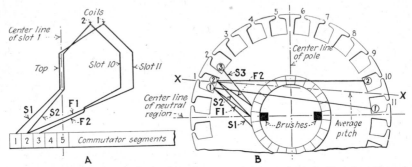

Fig. 48.—The connections of the loops to the commutator are shown in these two diagrams

In *A*, it will be seen that the loop connections to the commutator are given a forward lead. This is to compensate for the chorded pitch. In *B*, coil 2 is shown in position for commutation. The line XX indicates the average pitch.

will considerably shorten the life of the winding. This is due to the fact that when the leads do not have the right throw, one part of the coil will be in an active field, which will generate a current opposing commutation. This will cause the coils to heat and in time roast the winding.

CHAPTER VI

CHORDED SPLIT-LOOP WINDING

A chorded split-loop winding is distinguished by the fact that the last coils wound on the armature are visible on each side of the shaft and are parallel to each other as shown in Fig. 49. The bottom illustration shows a complete winding with the insulation under the ends of each of the coils.

Advantages of the Chorded Split-loop Winding.—Some of the good points of this winding are that it distributes the winding across the ends more evenly which gives a better balance, than in the straight loop winding. The coils are wound parallel across the end, one on each side of the shaft, and both are practically the same length. This tends to give a better mechanical balance. The resistance of the coils is more uniform as there are only six different sizes of coils for the armature which is described, while the loop winding would have twelve coils for the same number of slots and bars. The chorded split winding takes up less end room than a straight loop winding, especially with large sizes of wire and numerous turns. When there is more than one bar to each slot, this type of winding will save time as the coils can all be wound at once by using as many wires in hand as there are coils per slot cell.

The chorded split winding, however, has its disadvantages, among which are the twist of the armature back and forth, when starting new coils, the constant testing to insure against mistakes and having to cut the wire at the end of each coil. This winding is also a little harder to connect than the straight loop winding.

Steps When Winding a Chorded Split-loop Winding.—In the illustrations A to G of Fig. 50, the different steps that are taken in putting on this type of winding are shown, while in H of Fig. 50 the diagram for the complete winding is shown. Diagram H (Fig. 50) shows the slot each coil is started and finished in for an armature that has 12 slots and is wound with a pitch of 1 and 6. The first coil is started as shown in A of Fig. 50, by passing the wire through slot 1 then around the back of the armature and through slot 6 then back to slot 1. After the required number of turns has been put on, the wire is cut off on the commutator side of the armature, and a red sleeve is put on the finishing lead while a white sleeve is put on the starting lead. These sleeves can be put on the winding before winding the coils. A red sleeve is put on first then a white one, then a red, then a white, etc. Enough sleeves for about four

47

or five coils are usually put on a winding. The leads of course are left long enough to reach the commutator easily. It will be noticed that the wire is cut after each coil and that loops are not made as with the loop windings.

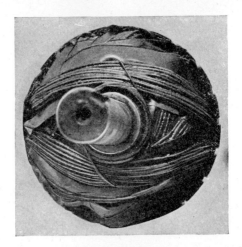

Fɪɢ. 49.—This is the way a chorded-split winding appears at three different stages while winding it in place.

The top illustration at the left, shows how a strip of insulation is put under each coil. The top illustration at the right, shows the method of putting on the shaft and slot insulation. The bottom illustration shows the finished winding with the last two coils visible on each side of the shaft.

After the first coil is in place the armature is turned 180 deg. before starting the second coil, as shown in *B* of Fig. 50. Then after slot 7 has been placed at the top of the armature, the second coil is starting in this slot, as shown at *C* of Fig. 50, and this coil is wound through slots 7 and 12 in the same manner as the first coil. The finishing lead comes out of

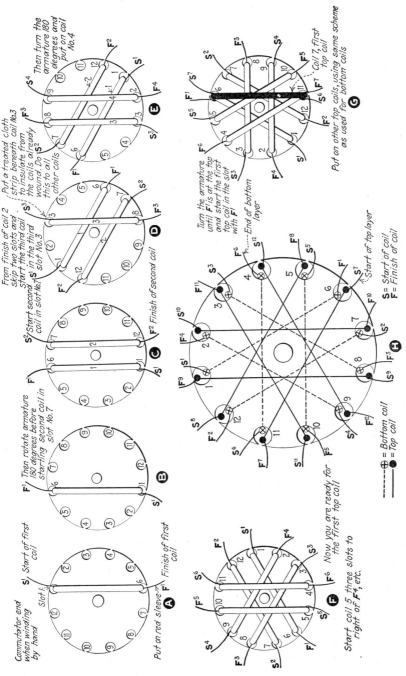

Fig. 50.—Step by step operations when putting on a chorded-split-winding.

If the number of slots can be divided by four, follow this scheme all the way through. If the number of slots is not divisible by four, Fig. 51 must be studied before starting on the coils in the top layer. In any case the number of coils must be even (divisible by two). At *H* is a diagram showing the completed winding. It also shows the slots where each coil was started and stopped. This armature has twelve slots and the pitch is 1 and 6. Figure 49 shows photographs of this winding.

slot 12, after which the wire is cut off and a red sleeve is put on it with a white sleeve on the starting lead.

WINDING CHART FOR CHORDED SPLIT-LOOP WINDING WITH 10, 14, 18, 22, 26, 30, AND 34 SLOTS

Coil No.	10 slots Start in slot No.	Fin-ish in slot No.	14 slots Start in slot No.	Fin-ish in slot No.	18 slots Start in slot No.	Fin-ish in slot No.	22 slots Start in slot No.	Fin-ish in slot No.	26 slots Start in slot No.	Fin-ish in slot No.	30 slots Start in slot No.	Fin-ish in slot No.	34 slots Start in slot No.	Fin-ish in slot No.	Coil No.
* 1	1	& 5	1	& 7	1	& 9	1	& 11	1	& 13	1	& 15	1	& 17	1
2	6	10	8	14	10	18	12	22	14	26	16	30	18	34	2
3	3	7	3	9	3	11	3	13	3	15	3	17	3	19	3
4	8	2	10	2	12	2	14	2	16	2	18	2	20	2	4
5	5	9	5	11	5	13	5	15	5	17	5	19	5	21	5
6	10	4	12	4	14	4	16	4	18	4	20	4	22	4	6
7	7	1	7	13	7	15	7	17	7	19	7	21	7	23	7
8	2	6	14	6	16	6	18	6	20	6	22	6	24	6	8
9	9	3	9	1	9	17	9	19	9	21	9	23	9	25	9
10	4	8	2	8	18	8	20	8	22	8	24	8	26	8	10
11			11	3	11	1	11	21	11	23	11	25	11	27	11
12			4	10	2	10	22	22	24	10	26	10	28	10	12
13			13	5	13	3	13	23	13	25	13	27	13	29	13
14			6	12	4	12	2	12	26	12	28	12	30	12	14
15					15	5	15	3	15	1	15	29	15	31	15
16					6	14	4	14	2	14	30	14	32	14	16
17					17	7	17	5	17	3	17	1	17	33	17
18					8	16	6	16	4	16	2	16	34	16	18
19							19	7	19	5	19	3	19	1	19
20							8	18	6	18	4	18	2	18	20
21							21	9	21	7	21	5	21	3	21
22							10	20	8	20	6	20	4	20	22
23									23	9	23	7	23	5	23
24									10	22	8	22	6	22	24
25									25	11	25	9	25	7	25
26									12	24	10	24	8	24	26
27											27	11	27	9	27
28											12	26	10	26	28
29											29	13	29	11	29
30											14	28	12	28	30
31													31	13	31
32													14	30	32
33													33	15	33
34													16	32	34

↔ Indicates that half of winding ends are on one side of shaft.
* Top line gives the coil pitch with 1 and 4 count throughout.

Special care must be taken to start coil 3 in the correct slot. To find this slot start at the finishing lead of coil 2, moving toward the right, as shown in *D* of Fig. 50. Skip two slots and start the third coil in the third slot which is slot 3. In other words, counting the slot where the finishing lead of coils 2 comes out as the first slot or number one, count over toward the right three slots and the start of coil 3 will be in slot 4 or 1 and 4 to the right.

When putting on the first turn of this coil place a strip of treated cloth insulation both at the back and at the front of the armature beneath the turn covering the other coils. This insulation is always necessary with 110- or 220-volt motors and should be used even with 30-volt motors where there is room enough. After starting the third coil in this manner, wind it as you did the other coils. The finishing leads will come out of slot 8. Then rotate the armature 180 deg. again and start coil 4 in slot 9, passing through slot 2, out of which the finishing lead will come. Put insulation under this coil as you did under coil 3, and do likewise under all other coils which are put on. The next coil, or number 5, is then started in the third slot to the right from the finishing lead of slot 4, as was done in the proceeding case. This slot, as you will see, is slot 5. The coil passes through this slot and slot 10 out of which its finishing lead extends, as seen in *F* of Fig. 50. Then the armature is rotated 180 deg., as was done before, and coil 6 is started in slot 11 shown in *F* of Fig. 50. This completes the bottom layer of coils.

It will be noticed, that taking the leads in rotation around the armature, the first one is the starting lead, the second one the finishing lead, the next a starting lead, etc., in regular order. It is a rule of all hand windings that each slot should contain a starting and finishing lead therefore, the armature shown in Fig. 50 has half a coil in each slot and one lead from each slot.

In *G* of Fig. 50 is shown the first coil of the top layer in place. To find the slot in which this coil should be started begin with the finishing lead of the last coil in the bottom layer, skip one slot to the right, and in the second slot start the coil. This will mean that the first coil in the top layer will start in the same slot which holds the finishing lead of the first coil in the bottom layer or slot number 6. You will notice that in this case, instead of skipping two slots to the right only one slot is skipped. After the first coil of the top layer is in place the next is easy, as the same scheme is followed that you used with the bottom layers. The diagram in *H* of Fig. 50 shows all the layers in place. It also shows just how the layers were put on, and where they were started and finished.

The last two coils put on should be tied together by means of a stout cord as in Fig. 49 (bottom) in order to keep the wires from flying outward when the motor is running. This cord is laid on the ends of the coils already wound, before the last two coils are started.

Method of Putting on Chorded Split Winding When Number of Slots is Not Divisible by Four.—If the number of slots is not divisible by four, the method of starting the top layer of a split winding is slightly different from that already described. Taking a 14-slot armature, as shown in Fig. 51 at *A*, after six coils have been put in place, there will be one empty slot on each side of the armature. To start the seventh coil, skip two slots clockwise and start in slot 7. In other words, the 1 and 4 count is followed throughout the entire winding process. This is different from the method used when the total number of slots was divisible by four, as in such a case, instead of skipping two coils to the right, only one slot

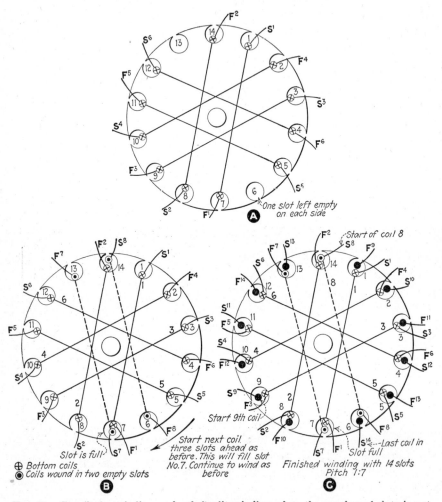

Fig. 51.—Details for winding a chorded-split winding when the number of slots is not divisible by four.

When the number of slots is not divisible by four, there will be one slot left on each side of the armature, as slots 6 and 13 shown at *A*, after all the bottom layer coils are in place. Then the next coil is put on as shown at *B*, skipping two slots to the right from the finish of the last bottom coil, F^5. This puts the start of the next coil, S^7, in slot 7 on top of coil 1, while the finish of coil 7 is an empty slot, No. 13. After starting this coil the rest is easy, as the other coils are put on in the same order as the bottom-layer coils. A chorded-split winding cannot be used if the number of slots is odd.

would have been skipped. The dotted lines in *B* of Fig. 51 show the next two coils in place. It will be noticed that the starting lead of each coil, is put in a slot which already contains one coil, thus filling the slot.

In *C* of Fig. 51 are shown the starting and finishing leads of all coils in place. These coils are put on in the same order as the coils in the bottom layer.

WINDING CHART FOR CHORDED SPLIT-LOOP WINDING WITH 12, 16, 20, 24, 28, 32 AND 36 SLOTS

Coil No.	12 slots		16 slots		20 slots		24 slots		28 slots		32 slots		36 slots	
	Start in slot No.	Finish in slot No.	Start in slot No.	Finish in slot No.	Start in slot No.	Finish in slot No.	Start in slot No.	Finish in slot No.	Start in slot No.	Finish in slot No.	Start in slot No.	Finish in slot No.	Start in slot No.	Finish in slot No.
*1	1	& 6	1	& 8	1	& 10	1	& 12	1	& 14	1	& 16	1	& 18
2	7	12	9	16	11	20	13	24	15	28	17	32	19	36
3	3	8	3	10	3	12	3	14	3	16	3	18	3	20
4	9	2	11	2	13	2	15	2	17	2	19	2	21	2
5	5	10	5	12	5	14	5	16	5	18	5	20	5	22
6	11	4	13	4	15	4	17	4	19	4	21	4	23	4
7	6	11	7	14	7	16	7	18	7	20	7	22	7	24
8	12	5	15	6	17	6	19	6	21	6	23	6	25	6
9	8	1	8	15	9	18	9	20	9	22	9	24	9	26
10	2	7	16	7	19	8	21	8	23	8	25	8	27	8
11	10	3	10	1	10	19	11	22	11	24	11	26	11	28
12	4	9	2	9	20	9	23	10	25	10	27	10	29	10
13			12	3	12	1	12	23	13	26	13	28	13	30
14			4	11	2	11	24	11	27	12	29	12	31	12
15			14	5	14	3	14	1	14	27	15	30	15	32
16			6	13	4	13	2	15	28	13	31	14	33	14
17					16	5	16	3	16	1	16	31	17	34
18					6	15	4	15	2	15	32	15	35	16
19					18	7	18	5	18	3	18	1	18	35
20					8	17	6	17	4	15	2	17	36	17
21							20	7	20	5	20	3	20	1
22							8	19	6	19	4	19	2	19
23							22	9	22	7	22	5	22	3
24							10	21	8	21	6	21	4	21
25									24	9	24	7	24	5
26									10	23	8	23	6	23
27									26	11	26	9	26	7
28									12	25	10	25	8	25
29											28	11	28	9
30											12	27	10	27
31											30	13	30	11
32											14	29	12	29
33													32	13
34													14	31
35													34	15
36													16	33

↔ indicates where the short count (1 and 3) is made to locate the start of the first coil in the top layer. The brackets enclose the coils that split across the shaft. * The top line gives the coil pitch with 1 and 3 count between top and bottom layers.

The method of connecting this winding to the commutator is explained in Chap. X in the details for connecting hand-wound armatures.

Figure 52 shows another type of winding diagram for a split winding and the accompanying table gives the method of putting in the coils.

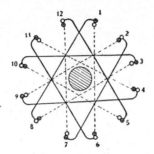

Fig. 52.—Winding diagram for a split winding in which, starting at the commutator end of slot 1 on a 12 slot core, the wire passes over the back of the core and enters slot 6, the slots being numbered consecutively. It is then guided forward across the commutator end of the core and back into slot 1.

The coil is completed with from 40 to 60 turns at the commutator end of slot 6. Then a band of tape should be wrapped around the wires to distinguish the leads at the end of the coil from those at the beginning. The last layer should be tied with string to the previous layer to hold it in position.

WINDING TABLE FOR FIG. 52.—THE COIL NUMBERS REFER TO THE ORDER OF WINDING. THE BRACKETS ENCLOSE THE COILS HAVING PARALLEL END CONNECTIONS

Lower layer			Upper layer		
Coil No.	Slot No.		Coil No.	Slot No.	
	Start	End		Start	End
{ 1	1	6	{ 7	2	7
{ 2	7	12	{ 8	8	1
{ 3	11	4	{ 9	12	5
{ 4	5	10	{ 10	6	11
{ 5	9	2	{ 11	10	3
{ 6	3	8	{ 12	4	9

Using a Winding Machine for Chorded Split Winding.—The information in this chapter describes the method of winding by hand across the right-hand side of the shaft. When a winding machine is used the same method can be employed except that the armature must be turned away from the operator at the top instead of the wire being wound away from the operator. When using a machine the coils may be wound on the left-hand side of the shaft next to the machine if this is desirable.

Easy Method for Winding a Split Winding.—The diagrams of Fig. 52A and 52B and the accompanying tables give information for an easy way of winding chorded split armatures that has the advantage of being easy to remember. It will be noticed that after the first two coils are put on, the slots are filled up as the winding progresses and that most of the top leads are brought out on top of the coil. This makes it easy to put them down and make a nice looking job when finished.

Figure 52A-I shows the first two parallel pair of coils in place on the armature and also indicates where coil 3 should start, indicated by

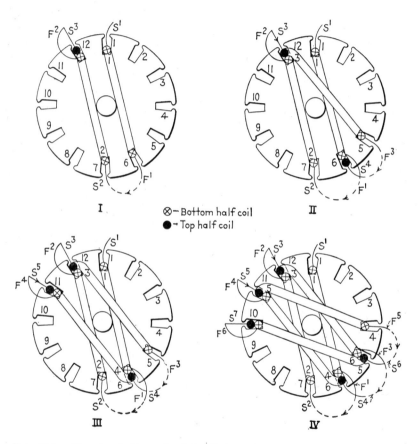

Fig. 52A.—Steps in winding a chorded split-loop winding. At I is shown the first parallel pair of coils placed in the armature slots. The location of the third coil is shown in II. III shows the fourth coil wound in. The third and fourth coils constitute the second parallel pair of coils. In IV the fifth and sixth coils have been wound in.

the black dot in slot 12. Figure 52A-II shows the third coil in position. The dotted line connecting the black dot in slot 6 with the finish of coil 3 denotes where coil 4 should start. Figure 52A-III and 52A-IV show coils 4, 5 and 6 in place, while Fig. 52B shows the completed winding. The last two coils are shown drawn in heavy lines in slots 7, 8, 1 and 2.

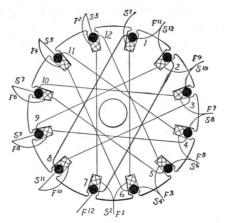

F_{IG}. 52B.—Complete winding diagram for chorded split-loop winding. In this diagram the top half coils are represented by black dots, while the circles with crosses in them indicate the location of the bottom half coils. $S1$ is the start of the first coil, $F1$ is the finish of the first coil, $S2$ is the start of the second coil and so on through the winding.

C_{HART} S_{HOWING} E_{ASY} M_{ETHOD} _{OF} W_{INDING} C_{HORDED} S_{PLIT-LOOP} W_{INDING}

Coil No.	10 slots		12 slots		14 slots		16 slots		18 slots		20 slots		22 slots		Coil No.
	Start in slot No.	Finish in slot No.	Start in slot No.	Finish in slot No.	Start in slot No.	Finish in slot No.	Start in slot No.	Finish in slot No.	Start in slot No.	Finish in slot No.	Start in slot No.	Finish in slot No.	Start in slot No.	Finish in slot No.	
1	1	5	1	6	1	7	1	8	1	9	1	10	1	11	1
2	6	10	7	12	8	14	9	16	10	18	11	20	12	22	2
3	10	4	12	5	14	6	16	7	18	8	20	9	22	10	3
4	5	9	6	11	7	13	8	15	9	17	10	19	11	21	4
5	9	3	11	4	13	5	15	6	17	7	19	8	21	9	5
6	4	8	5	10	6	12	7	14	8	16	9	18	10	20	6
7	8	2	10	3	12	4	14	5	16	6	18	7	20	8	7
8	3	7	4	9	5	11	6	13	7	15	8	17	9	19	8
9	7	1	9	2	11	3	13	4	15	5	17	6	19	7	9
10	2	6	3	8	4	10	5	12	6	14	7	16	8	18	10
11			8	1	10	2	12	3	14	4	16	5	18	6	11
12			2	7	3	9	4	11	5	13	6	15	7	17	12
13					9	1	11	2	13	3	15	4	17	5	13
14					2	8	3	10	4	12	5	14	6	16	14
15							10	1	12	2	14	3	16	4	15
16							2	9	3	11	4	13	5	15	16
17									11	1	13	2	15	3	17
18									2	10	3	12	4	14	18
19											12	1	14	2	19
20											2	11	3	13	20
21													13	1	21
22													2	12	22

The horizontal lines enclose each pair of parallel coils.
Note that the last coil always starts in slot No. 2.
The coil pitch is indicated in the first line of each table, corresponding to coil No. 1

CHART SHOWING EASY METHOD OF WINDING CHORDED SPLIT-LOOP WINDING.—*Continued*

Coil No.	24 slots		26 slots		28 slots		30 slots		32 slots		34 slots		36 slots		Coil No.
	Start in slot No.	Finish in slot No.	Start in slot No.	Finish in slot No.	Start in slot No.	Finish in slot No.	Start in slot No.	Finish in slot No.	Start in slot No.	Finish in Slot No.	Start in slot No.	Finish in slot No.	Start in slot No.	Finish in slot No.	
1	1	12	1	13	1	14	1	15	1	16	1	17	1	18	1
2	13	24	14	26	15	28	16	30	17	32	18	34	19	36	2
3	24	11	26	12	28	13	30	14	32	15	34	16	36	17	3
4	12	23	13	25	14	27	15	29	16	31	17	33	18	35	4
5	23	10	25	11	27	12	29	13	31	14	33	15	35	16	5
6	11	22	12	24	13	26	14	28	15	30	16	32	17	34	6
7	22	9	24	10	26	11	28	12	30	13	32	14	34	15	7
8	10	21	11	23	12	25	13	27	14	29	15	31	16	33	8
9	21	8	23	9	25	10	27	11	29	12	31	13	33	14	9
10	9	20	10	22	11	24	12	26	13	28	14	30	15	32	10
11	20	7	22	8	24	9	26	10	28	11	30	12	32	13	11
12	8	19	9	21	10	23	11	25	12	27	13	29	14	31	12
13	19	6	21	7	23	8	25	9	27	10	29	11	31	12	13
14	7	18	8	20	9	22	10	24	11	26	12	28	13	30	14
15	18	5	20	6	22	7	24	8	26	9	28	10	30	11	15
16	6	17	7	19	8	21	9	23	10	25	11	27	12	29	16
17	17	4	19	5	21	6	23	7	25	8	27	9	29	10	17
18	5	16	6	18	7	20	8	22	9	24	10	26	11	28	18
19	16	3	18	4	20	5	22	6	24	7	26	8	28	9	19
20	4	15	5	17	6	19	7	21	8	23	9	25	10	27	20
21	15	2	17	3	19	4	21	5	23	6	25	7	27	8	21
22	3	14	4	16	5	18	6	20	7	22	8	24	9	26	22
23	14	1	16	2	18	3	20	4	22	5	24	6	26	7	23
24	2	13	3	15	4	17	5	19	6	21	7	23	8	25	24
25			15	1	17	2	19	3	21	4	23	5	25	6	25
26			2	14	3	16	4	18	5	20	6	22	7	24	26
27					16	1	18	2	20	3	22	4	24	5	27
28					2	15	3	17	4	19	5	21	6	23	28
29							17	1	19	2	21	3	23	4	29
30							2	16	3	18	4	20	5	22	30
31									18	1	20	2	22	3	31
32									2	17	3	19	4	21	32
33											19	1	21	2	33
34											2	18	3	20	34
35													20	1	35
36													2	19	36

The horizontal lines enclose each pair of parallel coils.
Note that the last coil always starts in slot No. 2.
The coil pitch is indicated in the first line of each table, corresponding to coil No. 1.

Shove Through Coils for Closed-slot Armatures.

—For a closed-slot armature, the coils consist of pieces of wire cut into definite lengths. If only one or two armatures are to be rewound, the coils can be wound in shapes shown in Fig. 52C. The dimension B is the pitch of the coil and L the length of each coil side. The ends are then cut off at A. When a mould is used it should be made wide enough so that about 25 coils can be wound at one time, using 2, 3, or 4 wires in hand.   Then one turn will make 2, 3 or 4 coils depending upon the number of wires in hand.

If a number of armatures of the same size are to be rewound, the mould should be shaped as shown in Fig. 52C and the coil wound to shape and then cut at A and A.

Closed slots can be insulated with 0.010-in. fish-paper and shellaced in place.   When the wires of the sides of a coil are started in the slots, the bottom half of the coil is pushed into the slot about ¼ to ⅜ in.   The top

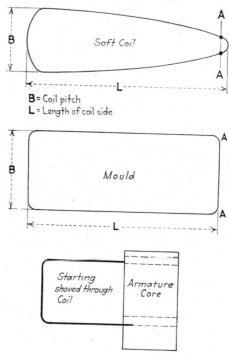

Fig. 52C.—Dimensions of soft coil and mould for shoved-through winding and method of starting coils in slots.

half of the throw coils are left out of the slots.   When enough bottoms have been put in the slots so that when the pitch is counted out, there will be a bottom half of a coil in the same slot that the top half of the coil should go in, then the tops are put in until all the bottom are in. The tops of the throw coils are also put in at this stage.   Then all the coils, tops and bottoms, project into the slot ¼ to ½ in.   The next step is to push each coil in a little at a time going around the armature as shown in Fig. 52C, until all coils have been pushed through to their final position.

CHAPTER VII

I. THE SPLIT V-LOOP WINDING

The split V-loop winding, as shown in Fig. 53, might be called a combination of the windings described in Chaps. IV, V and VI, the split-loop winding and the straight loop winding. This winding is divided on each side of the shaft, and the wire at each end of the coil is formed into loops which are, however, cut before connecting to the commutator. In this winding the two coils on each side of the shaft do not run parallel to each other, as in the split winding, but form a V. Another

FIG. 53.—Completed armature showing end apppearance of a split V-loop winding.

A pair of coils is visible when the armature is wound. This pair forms a V which incloses the shaft. When winding this kind of armature, follow Fig. 54 and the instructions on page 60 for details. The armature shown in the photograph has seventeen slots and is wound with a pitch of 1 and 8, leaving two slots (at the right) between the sides of the V. In Fig. 54 only one slot is included between the ends of the V, while two are shown in this illustration.

distinctive feature is that after the first coil is wound in place a slot is filled as the winder proceeds.

Advantages and Disadvantages of Split V-loop Winding.—This winding has the same advantages and disadvantages as the split winding and the loop winding, where the number of slots is great and size of wire and number of turns is large. While the space between the bottom of the slot and the shaft is small, the split-loop winding will occupy less space than either the split winding or the loop winding. This type of winding and the straight loop winding are independent of the number of

59

slots. The split winding can be used only when the number of slots pitched is divisible by 2. The winding shown in Fig. 53 is a split V-loop winding, the armature having 17 slots and the coils being pitched 1 and 8, leaving 2 slots between the open end of the V, while in Fig. 54 only 1 slot is left between.

Split V-loop Winding Used on Automobile Generator Armatures.— This type of winding is used mostly on automobile generator armatures, where the voltage is low, and hence insulation on the ends may be

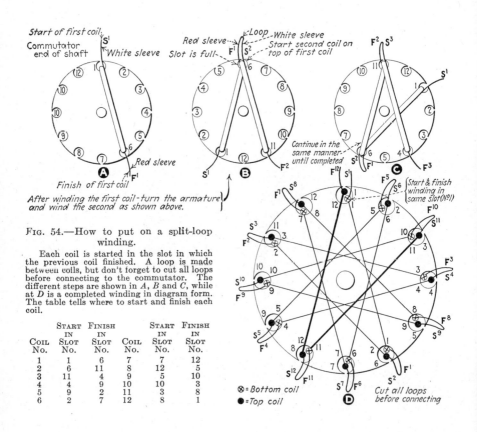

Fig. 54.—How to put on a split-loop winding.

Each coil is started in the slot in which the previous coil finished. A loop is made between coils, but don't forget to cut all loops before connecting to the commutator. The different steps are shown in *A, B* and *C*, while at *D* is a completed winding in diagram form. The table tells where to start and finish each coil.

Coil No.	Start in Slot No.	Finish in Slot No.	Coil No.	Start in Slot No.	Finish in Slot No.
1	1	6	7	7	12
2	6	11	8	12	5
3	11	4	9	5	10
4	4	9	10	10	3
5	9	2	11	3	8
6	2	7	12	8	1

omitted if there is no room for it. However, for a 110 or 220 volt armature, a strip of insulation should always be placed under each coil at the front and rear as explained in the following paragraph.

Steps When Putting Winding on Armature.—Before starting the winding, slip on a number of sleeves of the proper size. For the 12-slot armature shown in Fig. 54, 12 sleeves can be slipped on, alternating red and white. This will leave a white sleeve for each starting lead and a red sleeve for each finishing lead. After 6 coils are in place the wire is cut in order that 12 more sleeves may be put on which will be enough to finish the winding. As shown in A of Fig. 54, the motor taken as an example is a 12-slot machine and the coils have a pitch of 1 and 6. The first coil is started through slot 1 and across the rear end of the armature on the right-hand side of the shaft to slot 6. After the required number of turns is put on, the coil is finished in slot 6, leaving a red sleeve on the loop as shown in Fig. 54. A white sleeve is left on the other side of the loop for the starting lead of the next coil. Note that in this type of winding that the sleeves are left at the end and beginning of each coil and are not put on over the loop as in the loop type of winding. This is done as the loops are to be cut open before connecting, thus the color of the sleeving will identify the starting and finishing leads. Before the second coil is started the armature is rotated until the finishing lead of the first coil is at the top as shown at B and then the second coil is started in the same slot on the top of the first coil. Before starting each coil put a strip of treated cloth insulation underneath to protect it from the other coils. After each coil is finished, continue in this manner, as shown in C of Fig. 54 until the entire armature is wound. As the winding progresses around the armature each slot will fill up, and on completion each slot will contain a starting and finishing lead, as shown in D of Fig. 54. The table under Fig. 54 shows in which slots the different coils start and finish.

Precautions When Inserting Sleeves on Coil Leads.—The following illustration will explain the importance of putting the sleeves on the wire of the coil leads and not over the loop. Great care must be taken to leave a red sleeve on one side of the loop and a white sleeve on the side of the loop that starts a new coil.

Refer to Fig. 54, diagram D. If we were to take the loop F_{10} and S_{11} and consider it the lead of coil 11 and bring it over to the right and the center line of this coil and connect it to the commutator, then put the loop F_3 and S_4 of coil 4 in the next bar to the right, and so on around the armature until all leads are in, we would have the following condition: Coil 11 would be in series with coil 12-1-2-3-4. Note that a series of 5 coils is passed through before returning to the adjacent bar and that when coil 11 is in a proper commutating position, the other coils are in an active field. This would result in sparking and a jerky action of the armature and heating which would burn out the winding if allowed to run any length of time. When the loops are cut lead S_{11} of coil 11 would be brought to the right as before, then lead S_4 placed in the bar to the right, etc., until all starting leads are down. Then top lead F_{11} of coil 11 would be brought over to the left and put in the same bar as lead S_4. This puts coils 11-4-9-2-7-12-5-10-3-8-1-6 in series around the armature each coil being picked up in the order given from adjacent bars which gives each coil its proper position.

II. DIAMETRICALLY-SPLIT WINDING

This type of hand winding is not as frequently encountered as the types described in preceding paragraphs since it is most suitable for a few turns of large size of wire and on most modern motors formed coils are used to meet these conditions.   However, when it is desired to keep a winding away from the shaft in a machine where the end room is scant, this is the type of winding to use.   The armature shown in Fig. 55 is used in a steam-turbine generating outfit for locomotive headlights.   The hollow space between the winding and the shaft is formed by a wooden mandrel on the shaft while winding the armature.

Steps When Winding a Diametrically-split Winding.—In Figs. 55 and 56 a motor is shown wound directly on the half.   That is, with full pitch

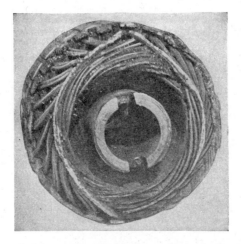

Fig. 55.—How the end of an armature looks when a diametrically-split winding is used. One coil is wound on both sides of the shaft in slots directly opposite each other.   The chalk mark shows the last coil put on.   In Fig. 56 you can see the steps followed in putting the coils in place.

and from this comes the term diametrically-split winding.   The number of slots must be even for this type of winding, since one-half of each coil is wound around the right-hand side of the shaft and the other half around the left-hand side of the shaft in slots which are exactly opposite each other.   Both halves of one coil are in the same slot at the top and in the same slot at the bottom of the armature.   As shown in Fig. 56, the first coil is started in slot 1, leaving a white sleeve for a starting lead. Two turns, or one-half the total turns, are put in slots 1 and 7 across the right-hand side of the shaft, the wire being put down in layers.   Then two or more turns are laid down across the left-hand side of the shaft, through the same slots, 1 and 7.   After the proper number of turns has been put on, the coil is finished in slot 7 and a red sleeve is left on the finishing lead,

One coil fills only half of the slot, and one-half the total number of turns per coil are wound on each side of the shaft. The second coil is started in slot 2, and two turns are taken to the right of the shaft and two to the left, as with the first coil. The second coil starts in slot 2 and finishes in slot 8, as shown in Fig. 56C. The winding is continued in this manner, the start of each coil being always in the slot next to the one where the previous coil was started. When half the coils are in place,

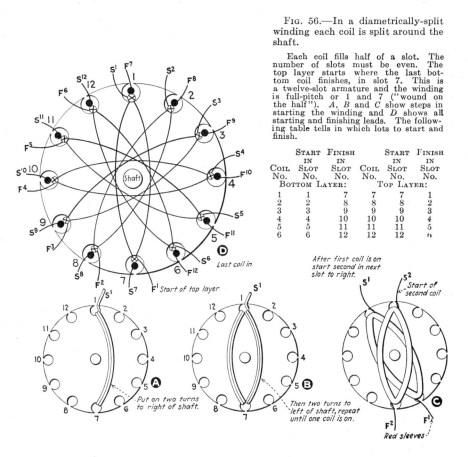

Fig. 56.—In a diametrically-split winding each coil is split around the shaft.

Each coil fills half of a slot. The number of slots must be even. The top layer starts where the last bottom coil finishes, in slot 7. This is a twelve-slot armature and the winding is full-pitch or 1 and 7 ("wound on the half"). A, B and C show steps in starting the winding and D shows all starting and finishing leads. The following table tells in which lots to start and finish.

Coil No.	Start in Slot No.	Finish in Slot No.	Coil No.	Start in Slot No.	Finish in Slot No.
Bottom Layer:			Top Layer:		
1	1	7	7	7	1
2	2	8	8	8	2
3	3	9	9	9	3
4	4	10	10	10	4
5	5	11	11	11	5
6	6	12	12	12	0

there will be one lead projecting from each slot. Six, or half, of the leads on one side are starting leads and six, or half, on the other side are finishing leads. The top layer is started in the slot which contains the finishing lead of the last coil in the bottom layer. This is slot 7. The winding is then continued as before and when complete all the slots will be full and each will have a starting lead and a finishing lead. The last coil should be tied down on each side by means of heavy cord threaded underneath the other coils.

III. PROGRESSIVE-SPLIT-HAND WINDING THAT SAVES TIME IN REWINDING ARMATURES

A progressive-split-hand winding for small armatures will save time when the number of slots is not divisible by four and the coils are wound full pitch. It must not be attempted with a chorded pitch. The use

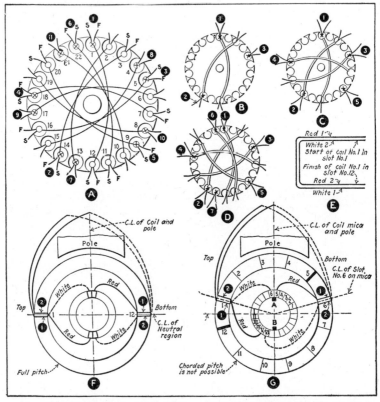

Fig. 57.—Diagrams explaining how a progressive-split winding is put on.

    A shows the sequence of winding which is also shown in an accompanying table (page 67). The armature has 22 slots and 66 bars and the pitch is 1 and 12, full pitch. The figures in the small black circles are the coil numbers in the order of putting them in place. The crosses indicate where coils are started. *B*, *C* and *D* explain steps in putting on the coils. *E* shows how the leads are marked with sleeving. Red denotes a bottom lead and white a top lead. The correct method of connecting up the commutator is indicated in *F*. From *G* it is clearly seen that a chorded pitch is not possible with this type of winding. The heavy lines at slots 12 and 5 indicate the coil position when bars 5 and 6 are under the brush.

of this winding will be illustrated in the rewinding of a 1-hp. direct-current armature with 22 slots and 66 bars and a pitch of 1 and 12 (full pitch). In winding, eleven coils were wound on, each slot being filled as the winding progresses. Six wires in hand are used while in an ordinary loop winding three wires would be used and twenty-two coils wound.

CHART FOR PROGRESSIVE-SPLIT WINDING WHEN NUMBER OF SLOTS IS DIVISIBLE BY 4

Coil No.	12 slots		16 slots		20 slots		24 slots		28 slots		32 slots		36 slots		Coil No.
	Start in slot No.	Finish in slot No.	Start in slot No.	Finish in slot No.	Start in slot No.	Finish in slot No.	Start in slot No.	Finish in slot No.	Start in slot No.	Finish in slot No.	Start in slot No.	Finish in slot No.	Start in slot No.	Finish in slot No.	
*1	1	& 7	1	& 9	1	& 11	1	& 13	1	& 15	1	& 17	1	& 19	1
2	9	3	11	3	13	3	15	3	17	3	19	3	21	3	2
3	↔ 5	11	5	13	5	15	5	17	5	19	5	21	5	23	3
4	12	6	↔ 15	7	17	7	19	7	21	7	23	7	25	7	4
5	8	2	8	16	↔ 9	19	9	21	9	23	9	25	9	27	5
6	4	10	2	10	20	10	↔ 23	11	25	11	27	11	29	11	6
7			12	4	12	2	12	24	↔ 13	27	13	29	13	31	7
8			6	14	4	14	2	14	28	14	↔ 31	15	33	15	8
9					16	6	16	4	16	2	16	32	↔ 17	35	9
10					8	18	6	18	4	18	2	18	36	18	10
11							20	8	20	6	20	4	20	2	11
12							10	22	8	22	6	22	4	22	12
13									24	10	24	8	24	6	13
14									12	26	10	26	8	26	14
15											28	12	28	10	15
16											14	30	12	30	16
17													32	14	17
18													16	34	18

* The top line gives the coil pitch.   ↔ Indicates where adjacent coil is picked up instead of the 1 and 3 count.

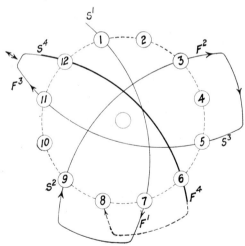

FIG. 57A.—This diagram refers to the chart for progressive-split winding when number of slots is divisible by 4. S_1 is start of first coil and F_1 is finish of first-coil.   The first three coils are in place showing start of fourth coil or the 1 and 2 count as indicated by the sign (↔).   The dotted line shows how the rest of the coils are put on when the 1 and 3 count is used again.

Drawing *A*, Fig. 57 shows the complete winding and the accompanying table gives the sequence of putting on the coils.   A circle with a cross is used to indicate the start of a coil, and the small black circles enclose figures which indicate the coil numbers. As stated above, this type of winding fills the slots, starting with the first coil in. In winding, therefore, the leads must be marked so that each slot will contain one start or bottom lead and one finish or top lead.

CHART FOR PROGRESSIVE-SPLIT WINDING WHEN NUMBER OF SLOTS IS NOT DIVISIBLE BY 4

Coil No.	10 slots		14 slots		18 slots		22 slots		26 slots		30 slots		34 slots		Coil No.
	Start in slot No.	Finish in slot No.	Start in slot No.	Finish in slot No.	Start in slot No.	Finish in slot No.	Start in slot No.	Finish in slot No.	Start in slot No.	Finish in slot No.	Start in slot No.	Finish in slot No.	Start in slot No.	Finish in slot No.	
*1	1	& 6	1	& 8	1	& 10	1	& 12	1	& 14	1	& 16	1	& 18	1
2	8	3	10	3	12	3	14	3	16	3	18	3	20	3	2
3	5	10	5	12	5	14	5	16	5	18	5	20	5	22	3
4	2	7	14	7	16	7	18	7	20	7	22	7	24	7	4
5	9	4	9	2	9	18	9	20	9	22	9	24	9	26	5
6			4	11	2	11	22	11	24	11	26	11	28	11	6
7			13	6	13	4	13	2	13	26	13	28	13	30	7
8					6	15	4	15	2	15	30	15	32	15	8
9					17	8	17	6	17	4	17	2	17	34	9
10							8	19	6	19	4	19	2	19	10
11							21	10	21	8	21	6	21	4	11
12									10	23	8	23	6	23	12
13									25	12	25	10	25	8	13
14											13	27	10	27	14
15											29	14	29	12	15
16													14	31	16
17													33	16	17

* The top line gives the coil pitch. There are half as many coils as slots. This chart is a true progressive-split winding with a 1 and 3 progressive count throughout.

In any ordinary split winding having two, three and so on, times as many bars as slots the armature would be wound with two, three and so on, wires in hand and a white sleeve would be put over all the wires in hand to denote a finish. Likewise, a red or black sleeve would be used for the start, but in this type of winding twice as many wires are used. For instance, in the winding illustrated there are six wires in hand. Then to distinguish a top coil from a bottom one, the wires are divided into two sections of three wires per section before starting to wind. One section would first have a white sleeve put on over the three wires, then a red sleeve. The other section would have the sleeving reversed; that is a red first, and a white last (see *E* Fig. 57). By following this plan, when the coil is wound in there will be a white and a red sleeving projecting from each slot. Thus the leads are separated into three starting and three finishing leads in each slot.

Winding in Coils of a Progressive-split Winding.—Drawings *B, C* and *D* of Fig. 57 explain the method of winding in the coils. At *B* the first two coils are shown in place. Coil 1 is wound in slots 1 and 12, and coil 2 is started in slot 14, skipping one slot. The start of each succeeding coil is located in the same manner. Call the slot in which the last coil is finished No. 1, and count over to No. 3 in a clockwise direction. This is where the term "progressive" originates. At *C*, four coils are shown in place, and at *D* six coils are shown, also the starting point of the seventh coil. It will be noticed at any time during the winding that between the last two coils put in, there will be one slot intervening on each end of the coils. The sequence of winding the coils is given in the following table.

SEQUENCE OF WINDING SHOWN IN FIG. 57

Coil number	Slot number	
	Start	Finish
1	1	12
2	14	3
3	5	16
4	18	7
5	9	20
6	22	11
7	13	2
8	4	15
9	17	6
10	8	19
11	21	10

This table accompanies the diagrams in Fig. 57.

Drawings *F* and *G* (Fig. 57) explain how the leads are connected to the commutator and why this type of winding must be full pitch. In *F* the coil is shown in the neutral region with the leads brought over to commutator bars just on each side of the center line of the coil. The leads of coil 1 are laid down across the top of the commutator, while those of coil 2 are laid down under the commutator. The two leads from one coil are separated by the center line of the poles which indicates that the coils and lead throw are correct.

In *G* the coil pitch is chorded, 1 and 6, on a twelve-slot armature. With the coil in the proper commutating position as shown, the bottom lead of coil 1 is put in bar 5 and the top leads are brought over to bar 6. This makes conditions correct for proper commutation. Now when all the bottom leads have been put down in this way, half the coils will have the correct lead pitch and the other half will be considerably out as coil 2 shows. The leads of coil 2 will be two bars out of true and when bars 5 and 6 are under brush *B,* the coil will have assumed the position indicated by the heavy slot lines 5 and 12. Thus it is readily seen that to wind correctly, the coil pitch must be full.

The following table gives the number of slots with which this method of winding can be used and the coil pitch. The lead throw depends upon the brush position as in any other type of winding.

COIL PITCH FOR ARMATURES WITH DIFFERENT NUMBERS OF SLOTS

Number of slots	Coil pitch
10	1 and 6
14	1 and 8
18	1 and 10
22	1 and 12
26	1 and 14
30	1 and 16
34	1 and 18
38	1 and 20
42	1 and 22

Points to Watch While Winding.—It is important with this winding that the leads are marked correctly. To do this one-half of the total number of wires in hand when winding are used for one coil and the other half for the second coil. Use a red sleeve to denote a start or bottom lead and a white sleeve to denote a finish or top lead. Then on one-half of the wire put on about four or six sleeves, first a red then a white, red, white, etc. On the other half put on a white sleeve first, then a red, white, red, etc. When starting to wind each coil leave a red and white sleeved bundle of leads at the start and a white and red sleeved bundle of leads at the finish, thus making a start and finish lead at every slot.

CHAPTER VIII

WINDING AUTOMOBILE STARTER AND GENERATOR ARMATURES

For low-voltage armatures operating at 6 and 12 volts from a storage battery, in general the same types of windings can be used as on other small direct-current armatures. When such an armature is received, it should be inspected for the type of winding used, the insulation, size of wire, and connections to the commutator. All of this information should be recorded as explained in Chap. II. When the old armature is stripped, it should be thoroughly cleaned and after the winding has been applied, the commutator should be trued up and turned and the whole armature given a careful testing, then varnished and baked.

Cleaning Automobile Armatures.—After removing the old winding, armatures can be quickly and thoroughly cleaned by the use of some good varnish remover made by varnish companies. A solution composed of 25 per cent alcohol and 75 per cent benzole is good for loosening the varnish of old insulation so that it can be scraped from the slots. Alkali solutions such as hot caustic soda will also loosen the old insulation without injury to the laminations but will creep between the laminations when they are loose and after the armature is rewound and may cause trouble by eating small holes in the insulation *unless* the core is *thoroughly washed and baked* after being cleaned with this solution.

Insulation Required.—For small automobile armatures a combination slot insulation can usually be used consisting of 0.004 in. fish paper and 0.006 in. empire cloth shellaced or glued together. This will give a thickness of about 0.010 in. which is sufficient. Sheets of each kind of insulation can be purchased in a size 24 by 36 in. and glued together so as to be cut to the dimensions required by the slots with a large sheer like the one described on page 221. In addition to these sheets of combination insulation it is advisable to carry in stock rolls of 0.005 and 0.008 in. fish paper and 0.008 in. red fiber for strip insulation. This red fiber strip insulation can be purchased in rolls of narrow width, the dimensions 12 to 15 in. in diameter and $2\frac{7}{8}$ in. wide being the most convenient size for strip insulation using this material. The strip insulation is applied as described in Chap. III.

When armatures are dipped in liquid Bakelite after being rewound and then baked, the insulation between ends of coils can be omitted and also the slot wedges in the top of the slots. It is advisable to use as heavy a thickness of slot insulation as the winding space will allow for mechanical protection.   This should be from 0.010 to 0.015 in.   When wedges are not used, trim the slot insulation flush with the top of the slot and if a good appearing job is desired, use a fish paper wedge about 0.010 in. a little dished and slipped in the top of the slot to bind together the cell insulation ends and close up the slot.   This applies to Bakelite dips only since the Bakelite will hold the wires together and prevent them from flying out.   A separator is not required between top and bottom coils either and the sleeving over the leads can be omitted unless it is required to identify the leads when connecting them to the commutator.

When a Bakelite dip is used and the armature coils are made up of strap copper, the coil insulation may be as follows: When an even number of coils is used, one-half the set can be left bare; when a odd number is used, it will be one less than one-half.   The other half of the set can be insulated as shown in Fig. 57*B*.

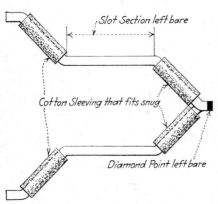

This insulation consists of cotton sleeving that will fit snugly on the copper strap and cut to lengths that will insulate both rear ends from the end of the slot section to the beginning of the diamond point and on the front end from the slot section to the beginning of the lead bend. For this winding a slot insulation of 0.007 or 0.010 or 0.015 in. fish paper (as thick as winding space will allow) should be used.   Between the top and bottom coils a 0.007 or 0.010 in. fish paper or untreated fuller board separator should be used.   Or better

Fig. 57*B*.—Insulation for strap copper coils when Bakelite dip is used.

still when space permits, use a piece of soft cord (such as flax) and wind it zig zag back and forth from the commutator end through the slot to the rear, then around the tooth to the next adjacent slot and through it to the front and repeat.   The diameter of this cord should be selected so that when the top coil half is driven down it will flatten the cord to the slot width.   This soft cord acts as a wick and helps to suck in the liquid Bakelite when dipped into it.   It also helps to hold the coils in place, without the use of wedges.   If a fish paper separator is used it should be cut to the width of the slot inside the winding cell of insulation and should be a snug fit.   It should also extend at least ¼ in. beyond the end of the bend of the slot portion of the coil at each end.

Taking Data from Automobile Armatures.—To determine the turns per single coil, first count the number of slots and bars.   The number of single coils per slot will be equal to the number of bars divided by the total number of slots. To find the number of wires in parallel per single coil, lift all the wires to one commutator bar and count them. Do not count wires used as fillers or dummies. Then one-half the number of active wires per bar will be the number of wires in parallel per single coil.

To find the turns per coil, if the winding is not too old and brittle, find the top coil, that is the one that is exposed across the rear end from slot to slot and cut it open on the rear end. Be sure to cut only one coil.

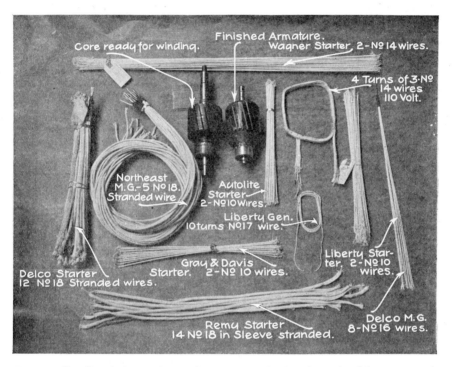

Fig. 58.—Bundles of wire can be supplied to winders in these forms for different types of armatures.

The bundles show single coils and groups of single coils for automobile starter armatures. With wires cut to length, there is little chance for a winder putting the wrong number of turns in any coil.

Then count the total number of wires in this bundle and divide this by *a number* which is found as follows: Divide total number of bars by total number of slots and then multiply this by number of wires in parallel per single coil. Then dividing total number of wires cut through by the number thus found, will give the number of turns per coil. This number can also be found by lifting all leads until the front end of a coil is found. Then cut open the top of the slot insulation and find the top lead and unwind the coil counting each turn. The first method is the quickest and when once understood can be applied to all windings.

Size of Wire for Coils.—The wire required for automobile armatures will range in size from No. 40 to No. 8 and it is usually advisable to supply it to winders in reels of about 10 lb. each, making up these small reels from the larger reels in the stock room so as to reduce the quantity of wire at the winding benches and reduce the time that the winder would spend running around after the wire required for a job. Many armatures require the use of from 2 to 14 wires in parallel and in such cases it is convenient to supply the wire required to the winders in bundles instead of on reels. It is an easy matter to determine the length of wire required for a single job and this length can be put up in bundles by a helper in the stock room and save much of the winders time. Typical bundles of wire for different armatures are shown in Fig. 58. When armatures require a large number of turns per coil, say 50 to 100, and a number of such armatures are regularly wound, a winding machine such as shown in Fig. 39, page 36, will save much time and quickly pay for itself.

Varnishing and Baking.—The varnishing operation should be preceded by drying out for 30 minutes in an oven at about 150°F. The armature should then be dipped in a good insulating varnish kept at a temperature of about 100°F. After soaking for about 10 to 15 minutes or until no bubbles show on the surface of the varnish, remove the armature and allow it to drip for 45 minutes over the varnish tank. Then place the armature in an oven and allow it to remain there over night or at least eight hours.

To remove the varnish from the shafts, the armature can be centered in a small lathe, and a tool with a hinged joint inserted in the tool post and swung down on the shaft so as to scrape the varnish off as the tool post carriage is moved along. A piece of emery cloth will quickly smooth up the job.

Winding 32-volt Armatures.—When winding 32-volt armatures that operate from a storage battery and are used in applications on farms in connection with a farm lighting set the same procedure as used for automobile 6- and 12-volt armatures can be followed.

Layer Winding for Automobile Armatures.—On some automobile generator armatures a type of hand winding is used known as a layer winding. This is a useful winding when the turns in the coils are from 1 to 9 of fairly large wire and the end room is scant. The armature shown in Fig. 58*A* has a layer winding. It is a four-pole armature and is connected up as a wave winding.

It will be impossible to use such a winding on an armature if the number of slots and poles and the pitch do not satsify the following equation:

(Number of poles × pitch) plus or minus 1 equals the number of slots.

If the sign is minus, the winding will be progressive; if it is plus, it will be retrogressive. In Fig. 59 there were four poles and twenty-seven

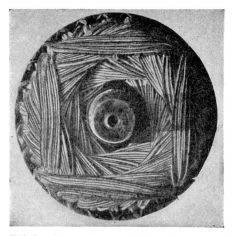

Fig. 58*A*.—This hand-wound layer winding takes very little end room.

As a usual thing a machine of this kind is wound by inserting previously-formed coils. In this case, however, there was not room and therefore the motor was wound by hand. The number of turns per coil is small and the wire is large. To get the idea of putting on such a winding look at Fig. 59.

Fig. 59.—How a layer winding is put on an armature.

This winding is used where the coils have few turns of large wire, but the end room is so scant that formed coils cannot be inserted. The first layer consists of four coils which step around the armature, the end of the last coil being in the slot next to the start of the first coil. The second layer passes around the armature in the same manner, the coil ends lying on top of the first layer (see Fig. 58*A*). When completed the armature connects into a wave winding. Such a layer winding is possible only when the following equation holds true: (Number poles × pitch) ± 1 = number of slots. In the armature shown this equation is as follows: $(4 \times 7) - 1 = 27$. This is a progressive winding. If the sign had been + instead of −, the winding would be retrogressive. For instance $(4 \times 7) + 1 = 29$ would indicate a retrogressive winding. The number of layers equals the number of slots divided by the number of poles as $27 \div 4 = 7$ layers in this case. The following table shows the slots in which the coils are started and finished:

Coil No.	Start in Slot No.	Finish in Slot No.	Layer
1	1	8	
2	8	15	1
3	15	22	
4	22	2	
5	2	9	
6	9	16	
7	16	23	2
8	23	3	
9	3	10	
10	10	17	
11	17	24	3
12	24	4	
13	4	11	
14	11	18	
15	18	25	4
16	25	5	
17	5	12	
18	12	19	
19	19	26	5
20	26	6	
21	6	13	
22	13	20	
23	20	27	6
24	27	7	
25	7	14	
26	14	21	7
27	21	1	

slots. Therefore the pitch is 1 and 8, or 7 slots. This makes a progressive winding. Twenty-nine slots would make a retrogressive winding.

The distinguishing feature of this type of winding is that four coils are visible across the end of the armature. Also the wires are laid down in layers, the bottom layers being close to the shaft and each succeeding layer being put on further away from the shaft, as shown in Fig. 58A.

Steps When Winding a Layer Winding.—At the start, put several sleeves on the winding wire, alternating red and white. Start in slot 1, leaving the white sleeve for the starting lead. Wind across the back of the armature on the right-hand side of the shaft to and through slot 8

Fig. 60.—Special power operated holders for winding layer wound armatures. Note the tools used.

leaving the finishing lead in slot 8 with a red sleeve. In winding the first coil bend it in toward the shaft as shown in Fig. 59. Start the second coil in slot 8, in which the first coil was finished, and wind through this slot and slot 15 in the same manner as the first coil. Continue in this manner with the third and fourth coils, which brings the finish of the fourth coil in slot 2. Coil 5 will start the second layer of the winding in slot 2. The coils of this layer should not be bent as close to the shaft as the coils of the first layer, as shown in Fig. 59. The other coils are put on in the same manner, continuing according to the table shown with Fig. 59. The coils of each succeeding layer are farther and farther from the shaft.

Making Ends of Coils Wind in Layers.—There is a trick in getting the ends of the coils to wind in layers without pounding. This trick is as follows: The first turn across the end of the armature is put in the middle of the space which the complete coil will occupy.   Then the following turns are laid on opposite sides alternately; that is, the second turn to the right, third to the left, fourth to the right, and so on.   Allow

Fig. 61.—Winding 6-volt armatures for automobile starting motors.

The coils are formed by machine out of bare strip copper.   Every other coil is insulated on the ends as shown.   A .010-in. fish paper cell is used with a .010-in. insulating strip ("willie") between top and bottom coils in the slot.   The whole armature is dipped in Bakelite.   Wedges and bands are not required.   A girl winder puts on insulation, inserts coils and puts leads into commutator slots in about 20 minutes.

the wires to bunch up in the slots, but start to fan them out as close to the slot ends as possible.

Connecting Coil Leads to Commutator.—In connecting a layer winding to the commutator, the same method is used as already described for the split and split-loop windings.   When connected, this winding forms a four-pole wave winding.

CHAPTER IX

HOW TO DETERMINE THE POSITION OF COMMUTATOR ON THE SHAFT

To determine the position of the commutator when the brushes are on the center line of the poles, the following formula may be used.

1. If $(pb \div s)$ is an odd number, the center line of the slot should be on the center line of mica.

2. If $(pb \div s)$ is an even number, the center line of the slot should be on the center line of a bar.

In these formulas, p is the lead pitch, b is the number of bars and s is the number of slots.

The connection and winding shown in A of Fig. 62 is called "wound and connected on the half." A chorded-pitch winding (see Chap. VI) with the brushes on the center line of the poles is shown in B, Fig. 62. When the coil is under commutation, it is in the position shown; that is, on a line parallel to the horizontal center line of the shaft. The connections of the coils to the commutator are shown in the lower part of diagram B. The winding is called "chorded and connected on the half." The position of commutator with reference to slots is determined as in the previous case by formula $(pb \div s)$, etc.

Commutator Position for Full-pitch Winding.—A full-pitch winding with the brushes on the center line of the neutral region is drawn in C of Fig. 62. The connections to the commutator are shown in the lower part of diagram C. This forms what is called "wound on the half and connected straight-out winding." The leads are connected to the bars directly in front of the slot.

The position of the commutator in a motor with brushes at the neutral zones between the poles is determined by the following formula:

If $(f + p) \times (b \div s)$ is an odd number, the center line of the slot should be on the center line of a mica. If this is an even number, the slot center is on a center line of a bar. In these formulas f equals full pitch, p equals the pitch used, b equals the number of bars and s equals the number of slots.

Commutator Position for Chorded-pitch Winding.—A chorded-pitch winding with the brushes on the center line of the neutral region is illustrated in D of Fig. 62. The upper sketch in D shows the coil in the proper position for correct commutation. In order to connect this coil to the bars that are in contact with a brush, it is necessary to give the leads a

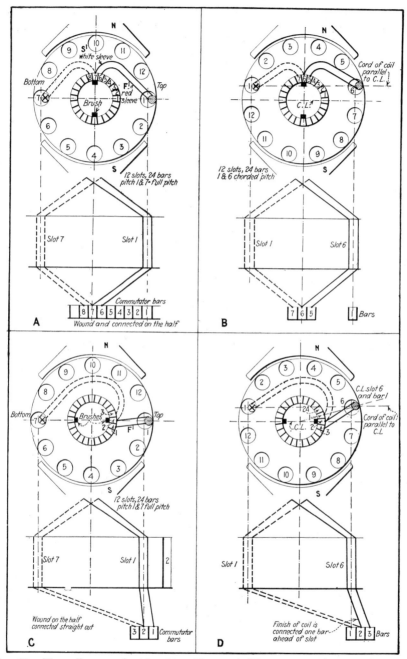

Fig. 62.—These diagrams show brush positions and different connections of coils to the commutator.

Before taking off the old winding a drawing should be made showing the winding methods followed. At *A* is a full-pitch winding and the brushes are on the center line of the poles. At *B* the pitch is chorded and the brushes are on the center line of the poles. *C* shows a full-pitch winding with brushes on the center of the neutral zone. *D* illustrates a chorded pitch with brushes on the center of the neutral.

slight throw as shown. This is very important, and when connecting or taking data on an armature of this type, care should be taken to get the line-up correct. If the coil is by error connected to bars 24, 1 and 2, then when slot 6 is in the neutral region and bar 1 in contact with the brush, the bottom half of the coil in slot 6 would be under the pole and in a magnetic field, which would cause sparking at the brushes and heating of the armature. The formula in the paragraph just ahead of this one may be used to get the commutator in the right position.

In some cases where the leads are incorrectly connected; that is, thrown back so that both halves of the coils are under the poles, one-half under a north and the other half under a south, the motor will tend to rotate and then stick. This is due to the brushes short-circuiting an active coil. The foregoing applies to the other types of connections as well.

Checking Position of Commutator with Armature in the Motor.— These examples and Fig. 62 are given to enable the winder to check up his data and to understand the principle of connecting. When in doubt before connecting the commutator, put the armature in the field, then turn it so that one coil will lie in the correct commutating position, which should be on the center line of the neutral region for a full-pitch winding, as shown in *A* and *C* of Fig. 62. With a chorded-pitch winding, the centers of each slot containing a half of the coil should lie on a straight line parallel to the neutral region center line, as in *B* and *D* of Fig 62. When the coil is in the correct position note which bar the brush is making contact with, mark it and then bring the leads out to this bar, using it as the center point, as bar 2 in *D* of Fig. 62. A properly wound loop winding is very easy to connect, as the leads are all put down in one layer. The leads can be put down in any position to suit the brush position.

Distance Commutator Should Be Pressed on Shaft.—The distance that the commutator should be pressed on to the shaft is an important item that should be recorded before removing commutator for repairs or replacement. If pressed on too far there will be excessive end play, the winding space between core and commutator will be reduced, the brushes will not bear on the full surface and grooves will be worn in the brushes which will break off their corners.

Lining Up Armature Slots or Teeth with Commutator Mica or Bars.— The alignment of the armature slots or teeth with respect to the commutator mica or bars, for all types of armatures, will follow the general rules outlined below.

1. With the coil pitch even, and the lead pitch even, the center line of the tooth will line up with the center line of the mica.

2. With the coil pitch odd, and the lead pitch odd, the center line of the slot will line up with the center line of a bar.

3. With the coil pitch even, and the lead pitch odd, the center line of the tooth will line up with the center line of the bar.

4. With the coil pitch odd, and the lead pitch even, the center line of the slot will line up with the center line of the mica.

The above rules apply when the center line of the armature coil is used as a base for lining out. When the coil pitch is odd, the center line of the coil will fall on the center line of a slot, and when the coil pitch is even, the center line of the coil will fall on the center line of a tooth.

CHAPTER X

CONNECTING UP HAND-WOUND ARMATURES

The process of connecting the leads to the commutator is an important step in the rewinding of any armature. A careful study of Chaps. II and XI in connection with this chapter will be of considerable help in getting a good understanding of the process of connecting up the windings of small hand- and machine-wound armatures. In this chapter the most important and peculiar points to remember when connecting the direct-current windings described in preceding chapters are taken up. When these points are observed the mistakes that invariably spoil a good

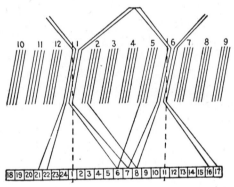

Fig. 63.—A simple working diagram for connecting coils to the commutator. Any slot can be called No. 1, then bar No. 1 will be on a line with the center of this slot as shown by the dotted line through slot 1 to bar 1.

winding job can be avoided. In Fig. 63 a connecting diagram is shown for a 12-slot, 24-bar armature. This sketch gives a good idea of the proper manner in which the individual coils should be picked up. Notice that the last coil in slot 5 is connected in series with the first coil in the adjacent slot 6. The series connection continues on to slot 7, 8, etc. Also note that the top and bottom leads of the coil shown in full are bent in towards the center of this coil.

The whole problem of connecting becomes a process of properly locating the coil sides in the proper commutating field and bringing the leads of this coil around to the commutator bars that are in contact with one brush and also picking up each individual coil in proper sequence, as shown in Fig. 63.

With hand- or machine-wound small armatures, a standard system of marking the leads should be adopted and carefully carried out. This can be done with different colors of sleeving as explained in Chap. VII, page 61, and in the following paragraph. This will not only save time but add accuracy to the connecting process.

How to Use Sleeves for Marking Coil Leads of Loop Windings.—With loop windings having as many bars as slots, no sleeving is necessary for fan-motor armatures and others up to $\frac{1}{6}$ hp. Above this size use a white sleeve on all loops. When there are twice as many bars as slots there will be two loops per slot. Then put a white sleeve on the first loop and a red one on the second loop and repeat this for each slot. The loops will then be put down in the following order to the commutator: White, red, white, red, etc.

When there are three times as many bars as slots, there will be three loops per slot. In this case put a white sleeve on the first loop, a red one on the second, and a black one on the third loop. Then put the loops down in the following order: White, red, black, white, red, black, etc.

These directions apply when one wire in hand is used and the wire is not cut until the last coil is in place.

Marking Coil Leads When Wound with More than One Wire in Hand.—When the armature is wound with as many wires in hand as the number of bars exceed the number of slots, use a white sleeve for the starting or bottom leads. For fan armatures and others up to $\frac{1}{6}$ hp., no sleeving is necessary on the finishing or top leads. For armatures of larger capacity use a red sleeve for the finishing or top leads. When using more than one wire in hand, use a large enough sleeve, so that all the wires can be put in the one sleeve. Do not use friction tape as a covering for the leads because the tape binds the wires together too tightly and makes it hard to shift the position of the wires when putting down the top leads. The tape also takes longer to apply.

Location of Brushes for Full and Chorded Pitch Windings.—The majority of motors have the brushes either on the center line of the poles or on the center line of the neutral region between poles. In some few special cases the brushes are advanced or given a backward lead to bring a part of the coil under commutation into a weak field. Figure 62, Chap. IX, shows the combinations usually encountered as follows:

1. Full pitch with the brushes on the center line of poles (*A* Fig. 62, Chap. IX).

2. Chorded pitch with the brushes on the center line of poles (*B* Fig. 62, Chap. IX).

3. Full pitch with the brushes on the center line of the neutral region (*C* Fig. 62, Chap. IX).

4. Chorded pitch with the brushes on the center line of the neutral region (*D* Fig. 62, Chap. IX).

In *A* of Fig. 62, Chap. IX, coil 1 is shown under commutation and the leads brought over to the center line of the coil. The lower part of diagram *A* shows the same coil connected to the commutator. It will be noted that there are two coils per slot, and that three bars are connected to the four leads coming from these coils. The two bottom or starting leads connect to bars 8 and 7, while the two top leads connect to bars 7 and 6. Bar 7 has a top and bottom lead attached to it. This puts the two coils in series. Likewise one coil per slot will take up two bars; three coils per slot four bars; four coils, five bars, etc.

Filling Hollow between Coil Ends and Commutator.—After the commutator is pressed on the shaft, fill the hollow between the end windings and the commutator with friction tape, up to the level of the bottom of the slot in the commutator necks. (See Fig. 31*A*.) This makes a bed for the bottom leads to rest on. Such a bed in any type of winding will prevent the leads from breaking off at the rear of the commutator. Figure 65 shows an armature being connected after filling up this hollow. Note that this armature is wound with large wire and that two or three turns of friction tape is used to mark the top or finishing leads. This tape is removed when connecting to the commutator.

Connecting Leads of First Coil to Commutator Bars.—Determine the position of commutator bar No. 1 to which the starting leads of coil 1 are to be connected, as explained with Fig. 62 (Chap. IX) under the headings "Commutator Position for Full-pitch and Chorded-pitch Windings" on page 76. Then fill in the hollow between the coil ends and the commutator, and separate the loops of coil leads from each slot into as many sections as there are bars times slots. Then take any one slot to start with (as slot 1) and a white sleeved loop and put this down in the proper bar (as bar 1) after untwisting the wires and skinning the part that is to be put into the commutator neck. Next take a red sleeved loop and put it down in the next commutator neck. Care must be taken to put the loops down in the same sequence that they were wound on the armature. This is one of the pitfalls of connecting loop wound armatures and it is, therefore, important that the winder be careful in marking the leads or loops with the proper color of sleeve while winding.

An example of incorrect connections which may result from failing to put different colored sleeves on the loops when there are more bars than slots is shown in Fig. 64. This illustrates a three coil per slot winding where the armature has three times as many bars as slots. In Fig. 64, *A* is the first coil wound in the slot and has a white sleeve. In this same sleeve is a finishing lead of the last coil wound in the adjacent slot to the left. This lead is not shown connected to the commutator. *B* is the second or red sleeved coil and *C* the third and last coil with a black sleeve. If the white loop is connected to bar 1, and the black loop to bar 2, and the red loop to bar 3, as shown in the left sketch of Fig. 64, there will be two coils *A* and *B* in series between bars 1 and 2. This will give a drop twice as high as normal measured with a voltmeter as shown. With the voltmeter leads across bars 2 and 3, the meter will measure the drop through one coil *B*. But when the meter is across bars 3 and 4 two coils, *C* and *B* are in series, resulting in a high reading. This is what is termed a reversed lead resulting in a high, low, high, reading, and can be caused by the winder using the wrong sleeve or the connector putting down the leads in wrong sequence.

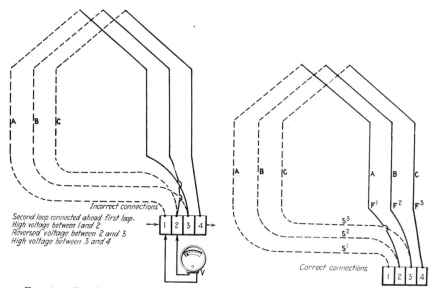

Fig. 64.—The left hand diagram shows a possible error in winding. The correct method is shown in the right hand diagram. The left-hand drawing shows what may happen if different colors of sleeving are not used when there are more bars than slots.

When laying out the lead pitch (See Chap. II, page 16), before starting to connect, it is advisable to use the last coil wound on, as the complete coil is visible and its leads can be traced and put down in the proper direction.

Connecting Leads of First Coil When There are Several Leads in One Sleeve.—When the loop winding is put on by hand, and the wire cut at the end of each coil, each white sleeve contains all the starting leads and each red sleeve all the finishing leads. The first step after filling the hollow between the coil ends and the commutator, is to pick out all the red sleeves, or finishing leads, and bend them back against the armature core, as shown in Fig. 65. Then select the last coil and find its bottom (starting) leads by placing one end of a test lamp lead on the finishing lead of this coil, which is easily found by inspection and lighting out the white sleeved or starting leads until the one that lights is found. Then put any one of the leads in this sleeve down to the marked bar.

Connecting Leads of First Coil When There are Two or More Coils per Slot.—With a winding having two coils per slot, the following system should be followed in laying down the first lead. The armature is turned until the last coil is in the position of the coils shown in Fig. 62 (*A-B-C-D*) page 77.   Then if the bottom leads are on the left when looking at the commutator end, lay out the bars as in Fig. 62*A*; that is, counting from right to left.   Then put any one of the two leads in the last coil sleeve, in the bar marked off for the lead pitch, as bar 7 in Fig. 62*A*. Then put the remaining lead of this sleeve into the adjacent bar to the

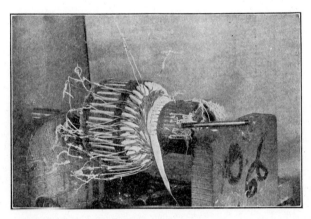

FIG. 65.—In this diagram the bottom or starting leads are shown connected to the commutator with the top or finishing leads bent back during this operation.   Note also the insulation between coil terminals.

left.   If the bottom leads are on the right-hand side, then lay out the bars as above and put the first lead in the pitch bar.   The next lead is put in the adjacent bar to the right.   This applies to any type of connection; that is, straight out, etc.   The rest of the leads are put down in regular rotation; that is, the lead in the slot to the right of the one started in, is put in the two bars to the right of the first two.   No attention need be paid to the order in which the wires (after the first one) in any of the bottom sleeves are laid down.

When there are three coils per slot any one lead in the proper bottom sleeve can be put in the pitch bar.   Then another lead is put in a bar to the left and the third lead in the bar to the right.   This procedure is followed for both right- and left-hand windings.

When there are four coils per slot and bottom leads to the left, put any one lead in the proper sleeve in the pitch bar, then put one lead in the bar to the right and remaining two leads in the two adjacent bars to the left.   With the leads to the right put one lead in the bar to the left and the two in the two bars to the right.

For five coils per cell put one lead in the pitch bar and two to the left and two to the right.   Figure 66 shows all cases.

After all the bottom leads are in place, put a layer of friction tape over these leads, as shown in Fig. 65.   This insulates the two layers of leads from each other.   A bias cut tape makes the best job.

Test to Locate Top Leads before Connecting Them to Commutator.— With the straight loop winding (that is, where the lead wires are not cut from start to finish) it is not necessary to test the leads, as a top and bottom lead is put down together.   But in a winding when the wire is cut after each coil is put on, the top leads must be tested out while putting them down to the commutator.   For this purpose a convenient test lamp should be provided on the connecting bench.

The following procedure can be followed for cut-loop, chorded-split loop and diametrically-split loop windings.

To start, turn the armature until the last coil is in the position shown in Fig. 62, page 77.   Call this coil 1, and the pitch bar bar 1.   Then put one of the test leads on bar 1, as shown in Fig. 67.   With the other test lead touch each of the finishing leads of coil 1 until a light is obtained. This is the finishing lead of coil 1 and is shown at a in Fig. 67.   When the bottom leads are on the left, place the top lead found by the test in the bar to the right or lead a is put in bar 2 as in Fig. 67.   If the bottom leads are on the right, put the top lead in the bar to the left.   Then with one test lead still on bar 1 find the next top lead that lights, as b Fig. 67. Put this lead in the bar next to a.   Continue to light out the top leads as above.   Move the test lead on bar 1 only when convenient to do so, then slide it along in the same direction that the top leads are being picked out and keep it at least three bars behind the last top lead put down.   For connecting a wave winding see page 89.

In Fig. 67, if lead a had been put in the bar to the left of bar 1, a "long connection" would be made.   This would reverse the polarity of a generator and the direction of rotation of a motor.   Note that in this connection that the top and bottom leads cross each other at the rear of the commutator.   This is the only manner in which it is possible to reverse a lap-wound armature when rewinding.

Connecting Leads of First Coil for Split V-loop Winding.—For the split V-loop winding the loops must be cut open and the leads projecting from each slot separated into two sections; that is, top and bottom or start and finishing leads.   After this the leads are put down in the same manner as for the chorded-split winding.

In connecting the special windings described in preceding chapters be sure to follow the instructions regarding the method of marking and bringing out the leads as described with each special winding.

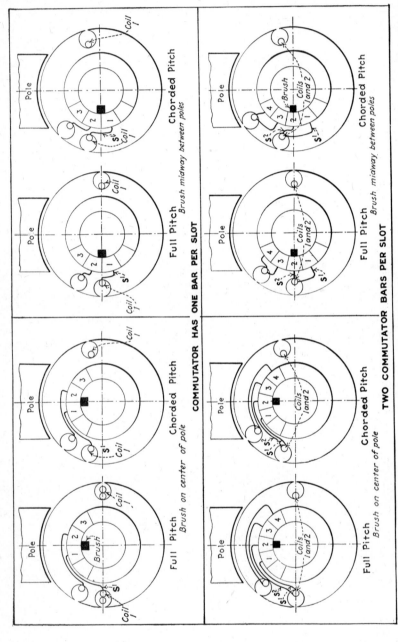

FIG. 66.—The diagrams on this page and the following one show how the starting (bottom) leads of coils are connected to the commutator. The four rows of diagrams show the methods used with coils wound respectively with one, two, three and four wires in hand.

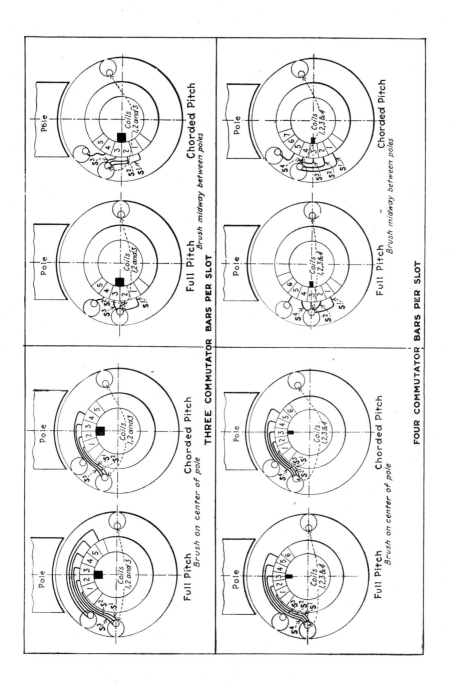

Checks to Make after Connecting Up Commutator.—After a motor is connected, there are a number of checks which should be made. When the coil connections are not correct and an attempt is made to run the

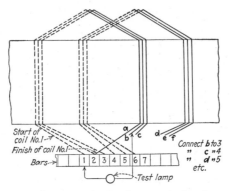

Fig. 67.—Lamp test to locate top leads when connecting them to commutator.

This is the method for connecting any split, split-loop or diametrically-split winding. The starting leads are laid down in one layer to the proper commutator bars. Then the finishing leads are found with a test lamp and connected to the bar just ahead of the starting lead (to the right in this drawing). There is only one slot between the sides of the V. There are twelve slots, and the pitch is 1 and 6.

Fig. 68.—Soldering leads of the armature coils to the commutator by the use of wire solder.

A gas blow pipe permanently attached to a standard is used to supply the heat. The flame plays directly on the outer ends of the commutator bars while solder is applied to the terminals in the slots. This method of heating insures a sufficiently high temperature in both the bottom and top of the slot.

machine, there will be considerable sparking. The armature will heat up and have a jerky movement or it will tend to stick at each tooth and will develop very little torque. On a shunt or compound motor the speed may increase, the percentage increase depending upon the error in the connections. With a series motor the armature may run slow and the field and armature windings become very hot in a short time. Mistakes are easy to make and cause much trouble hence great care should be taken to get the windings and connections correct.

Connecting Top Leads to Commutator for Wave Winding.—In any wave winding, a series of coils equal to half the number of poles will encircle the armature. This series must end either one bar ahead or one bar behind the bar started on, depending on whether the winding is progressive or retrogressive (see page 73, Fig. 59). The following test will locate the top leads when connecting the commutator: Lay down in the commutator all bottom leads and then determine the commutator pitch by counting from a marked bar, as No. 1. Place a test-lamp lead on this marked bar and touch the top-coil leads until the proper one lights out. This one is to be placed on the bar corresponding to the pitch already found. Then place one test-lamp lead on this bar containing a bottom and top lead and touch the top leads in order until another lights out. This will be the next top lead to be connected to a bar. The connection will be to a bar one ahead or one behind the bar first marked for a four-pole winding, depending on whether the winding is progressive or retrogressive. The third top lead to light out will connect one bar ahead or one bar behind the first top lead connected, depending on whether the winding is progressive or retrogressive, and so on, until all top leads are connected (see also page 19, Fig. 23).

Soldering Leads to Commutator.—Figure 68 shows one method of soldering the leads to the commutator after connecting and testing. This method employs a flame from a gas torch played directly upon the commutator thus heating the bars and allowing the solder to run. Another method is to use a large iron; that is, one that will hold its heat. Place this iron on the brush surface of the commutator and apply solder to the commutator surface until solder will melt and run into the necks. This and the first method gets solder all over the commutator surface but is not a serious disadvantage since the commutator has to be turned and polished in any case and it does not require an extra cut to remove the solder.

CHAPTER XI

TESTING ARMATURES WHILE AND AFTER WINDING

In the rewinding of all types of hand-wound armatures there are a number of defects and troubles that can occur. Details will be given in this chapter for locating the most common ones which are as follows:

1. Grounds.
2. Reversed coil leads.
3. Open circuits and short circuits.
   (*a*) Between coil turns.
   (*b*) Between top and bottom coils.
   (*c*) Between commutator bars.
   (*d*) Between coil leads.
   (*e*) Between coil ends. A short circuit between coil ends cuts out groups of coils.

In rewinding hand-wound armatures, a variety of cores and sizes are received. The condition of the cores varies; some cores can be well insulated and others are hard to insulate properly. On some cores the slot or end room is scant and considerable pounding is required to get the wire into place. When fine wire is used, there is a chance of its breaking; therefore, a 110-volt test lamp should be provided at the winder's bench or winding machine so that the winder can test each coil as he finishes it, thus detecting grounds or opens before passing the defect.

Points during Winding When Tests Should Be Made.—In order to detect any of these defects while winding an armature as soon as possible after the defect occurs, it is well to have a procedure of testing that will perform this function. The following method of testing armatures is recommended for use in repair shops rewinding the average range of small armatures:

1. After the armature has been stripped and before winding, test the commutators for grounds and shorts.
2. Wind and wedge the armature.
3. Test for grounds and shorts, using a growler to locate them.
4. Connect the armature and then before soldering leads to the commutator, make a bar-to-bar test using a millivoltmeter.
5. Solder leads, dip and bake, and turn commutator.
6. Give the armature a final bar-to-bar test.

The reason that a bar-to-bar test with a millivoltmeter is recommended after connecting and before soldering the leads, is that shorts between leads, as well as reversed and crossed leads occur at this stage, and it is easier to raise the leads to locate and remedy the defects when the leads are not soldered. The reason for the test after finishing the armature is that when soldering and turning the commutator particles of solder may run down between the bars at the back of the commutator thus shorting the bars, or in turning the commutator the tool may drag small particles of copper across the mica which also shorts the bars.

Testing Commutator for Grounds.—The first step after the armature has been stripped, and before winding, is to test the commutator for grounds and shorts. To test the commutator for grounds a piece of

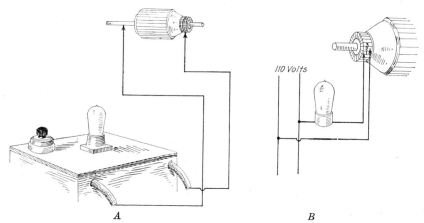

A *B*

Fig. 69.—To test a commutator for grounds, wrap a bare copper wire completely around it, making sure that the wire touches all bars.

This test is shown at *A*. Apply one test lead of the testing transformer to the shaft or core and the other to the wire around the commutator. At *B* is shown the method of testing a commutator for shorts between bars. This is done by putting a 110-volt test light in series with one lead from the power supply and applying the leads to adjacent commutator bars. If the bars are shorted the light will glow.

bare copper wire is wound around the complete commutator, making sure that the wire touches all bars. Apply one test lead to the shaft or core and the other to the wire around the commutator, as shown at *A*, Fig. 69. For armatures up to and including ½ hp., a test to ground of 900 volts alternating current for one minute is sufficient. For armatures above this size, use twice the line voltage plus 1,000 volts for the test to ground; that is, for 100- to 150-volt armatures the test voltage is 1,200 volts; for 250- to 275-volt armatures the test voltage is 1,500 volts; for 400- to 450-volt armatures, use 2,000 volts. This test should be applied for one minute.

Testing Commutator for Shorts.—The next step is to test and clear the commutator of shorted bars. This is done with a 110-volt test lamp, putting the leads of the test lamp on adjacent bars as at *B*, in Fig. 69. The carbonized mica will glow or sputter depending upon the resistance of the shorts; in some cases of dead short, the test light will come up to full brilliancy. Most short circuits between bars can be cleared by dig-ging out the dirt and carbonized mica with a knife or ground hack-saw blade. The hole should then be filled with a good commutator cement. A good cement can be made from plaster of paris and shellac. These two ingredients should be mixed together into a thick paste, which can be used to fill the hole in the commutator. Where there are a number of bad spots it will be found more satisfactory to put in all new mica segments or in the smaller sizes of motors, to supply a complete new commutator. The important thing is to be absolutely sure that the commutator is free from all defects before starting to wind.

Testing Winding for Grounds before Connecting to Commutator.— If the armature shows a ground, after winding and wedging and before

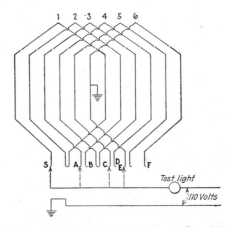

Fig. 70.—How to locate grounded lead in straight loop winding, before connecting leads in commutator.

After cutting open the loop AB, if the test light glows with test lead on S, the ground is in section S to B. If light remains dark move test lead to A, C and E, consecutively, cutting open loops about four slots ahead so as to sectionalize the winding until the grounded section of the winding is found, as at E

connecting the leads to the commutator, the following procedure should be used for locating the grounded coils. There are two cases: one is the straight loop winding in which the wire is not cut from the start to the finish of the winding, and in the other case, each slot has a number of leads projecting from it, half of these leads being top or finishing leads, the others being bottom or starting leads.

In the case of the straight loop winding, the set-up shown in Fig. 70 should be used to locate the grounds. One test lead is fastened to the core or shaft and the other test lead is touched to one end of the winding as at S in Fig. 70. Then a loop about four slots away is cut open as at B. If the ground is in the section between S and B, the test lamp will not go out. If the ground is in the other section of the winding, the circuit will be broken and the light will go out. In this case, touch the test lead to *A*, cut open a loop four slots away, as at *D*. Repeat until the ground is located in a section of four coils, then starting with the first coil of this section, cut open the loops until the grounded coil is found. In Fig. 70, coil 6 is the grounded coil. After locating this coil, the remainder of the loop winding should be tested to make sure that there is only one defective coil.

In the other case referred to, each slot has a number of leads projecting from it, half of them being top or finishing leads, the other half being bottom or starting leads. The first step is to separate the top leads and bend them back, toward, but not touching the core. The bottom lead should be pulled out straight and about ¼ in. of the insulation should be removed from the end of each lead. Then tie the leads together into separate bunches by pieces of bare copper wire and apply high voltage between each of these bunches and ground. One of these bunches of wire will show a ground. Remove the tie wire from the bunch that shows a ground and test each lead separately with a test lamp, one lead of which is on ground, until the grounded coil is found.

Test for Locating Grounds after Leads Are Connected to Commutator.—If the winding is tested for grounds after wedging and before connecting to the commutator, the finished winding will be clear from grounds. However, if the winding shows a ground after connecting the leads to the commutator, the following method will locate the defect:

The set-up for this test is shown in Fig. 71. The test line with a lamp bank in series with it is connected to bars directly opposite, as at 1 and 10. With a millivoltmeter on two adjacent bars at 2 and 3 adjust the lamp bank until approximately one-quarter scale reading is obtained on the meter. Then remove the millivoltmeter leads from bars 2 and 3 and connect the lead to the core as shown. With the other lead touch the commutator at a point midway between the two line leads, as bar 4. Make this connection lightly and quickly, watching the meter scale. If the pointer of the meter goes off the scale try bar 5, bar 6, etc. If this does not bring the pointer down on the scale, try bars on the opposite side of bar 4. The reason for the high reading when the meter leads are touched to bar 4 is as follows: Coils 1, 2, 3, 4, 5, 6, 7, 8 and part of 9 are in series to ground; hence the meter measures the drop across the series of coils between bar 4 and ground. When the meter lead is moved to bar 5, as at *C*, the drop is reduced by one coil. As the lead is moved toward the bar to which the grounded coil connects, the meter readings will become lower until bar 9 is touched. This will give the lowest reading. If bar 10 is touched the reading will become larger. Decreasing readings indicate that the grounded coil is being approached while increasing readings denote that we are working away from the defective coil.

After locating the grounded coil in the manner just described, test it by disconnecting from the commutator the top lead of the grounded coil

and a lead on each side of this lead.   Test the coil to ground and also
the other section of the winding to make sure that all grounds have been
located.   A telephone receiver can be used in the test described, in place
of the millivoltmeter.   A loud noise in the telephone receiver corre-
sponds to a high meter reading.

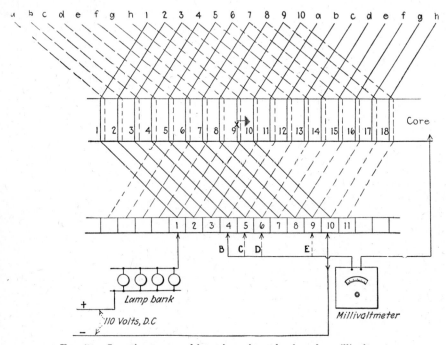

Fig. 71.—Locating a ground by using a lamp bank and a millivoltmeter.

The millivoltmeter is first placed across two adjacent bars, as bars 2 and 3, and the lamp bank
adjusted so as to permit current enough to pass through the winding to give a quarter-scale deflection
on the millivoltmeter.   One lead of the millivoltmeter is then grounded to the core as shown and the
other test lead is successively connected to commutator bars 4, 5, 6, etc., as at B, C, D, respectively.
As the bar to which the grounded coil is connected is approached, the millivoltmeter readings will
decrease and as you work away from the grounded coil the readings will increase.   The lowest reading
indicates the bar to which the grounded coil is connected.

Checking Coil Connections for Reversed or Crossed Leads.—

Reversed or crossed leads often occur while connecting the leads to the
commutator; hence these defects should be located before soldering the
commutator connections.   There are two cases of reversed leads:
In one case a voltmeter will show up the fault; in the other case it will not.
In diagrams A, B and C of Fig. 72 is shown a reversed coil or a case in
which the top and bottom leads have been interchanged.   In diagram A,
the flow of current from the test leads L_1 and L_2 is from left to right
through all the coils except coil 2, over which the arrow is shown reversed.
The only way in which this type of reversed lead can be detected is by
means of a compass.

Inspection of diagrams *B* and *C*, Fig. 72, will show that a voltmeter or telephone receiver will not locate this fault.   When using a millivoltmeter in the bar-to-bar test, as in diagram *B* of Fig. 72, place the millivoltmeter leads on bars 1 and 2.   This measures the drop over one coil, the direction of the flow of current being indicated by the arrow through the meter in the diagram.   With the millivoltmeter leads on bars 2 and 3, as shown in diagram *C*, the drop over coil 2 is measured.   In this case, the current through coil 2 is reversed, but the flow through the meter remains the same, therefore, there is no indication of trouble.   If an armature with a coil in this condition were put in a motor frame and run, the coil would cause sparking every time it passed from under the brush.   The correct way to locate this kind of a defect is to place a compass over the armature

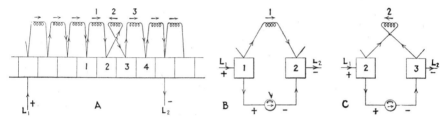

Fig. 72.—A case of reversed leads that will not show up with the drop of potential or millivoltmeter test.

In diagram *A* is shown the connections for the ordinary millivoltmeter test.   Current goes in commutator at L_1 and out at L_2.   The current goes in the same direction through all the coils except coil 2.   With the millivoltmeter across bars 1 and 2 as shown in diagram *B* a deflection will be obtained. With the millivoltmeter across bars 2 and 3 as shown in diagram *C*, a deflection in the same direction will be obtained.   Although the current through the coil is reversed, the millivoltmeter reads the same as in the case of coil 1 because it merely measures the drop of potential across the coil and not the current passing through it.   The correct way to locate reversed leads is by the use of a compass as explained in the text.

slot while direct current is being passed through the windings.   The armature should be revolved slowly and as the slot having the defective coil passes under the compass, the compass needle will reverse. This trouble can be caused by the winder putting on the wrong colored sleeve on the start and finish of one coil; that is, by interchanging colors.

Checking for Reversed Coil Leads Due to Use of Wrong Colors of Sleeves.—Another case of reversed coil or crossed leads occurs in loop windings and is caused by putting the wrong colored sleeves on two loops. This case is shown in diagrams *A*, *B*, *C* and *D* of Fig. 73.   In diagram *A*, the bottom lead of coil 1 and the top lead of coil 2 have been connected to bar 3, and the bottom lead of coil 2 and top lead of coil 3 have been connected to bar 2.   This reverses coil 2 as is shown by the arrows over each coil.   When making a bar-to-bar test with the millivoltmeter leads on bars *x* and 1, the drop over one coil (coil *x*) will be obtained.   Call this a normal reading.   When the meter leads are put on bars 1 and 2, a reading that is twice normal will be obtained, but the pointer will point in the same direction. Diagram B shows the reason for this double reading. The top lead of coil 1 connects to bar 1, and its bottom lead to bar 3; the top lead of coil 2 also connects to bar 3, and the bottom lead of coil 2 is connected to bar 2. Hence, coils 1 and 2 are in series between bars 1 and 2. When the millivoltmeter leads are placed on bars 2 and 3, as in diagram C, the drop of one coil (coil 2) is measured and a normal reading is obtained, but the pointer points in the opposite direction. The reason for the reversed reading is that the lead of coil 1 makes bar 3, positive, just as if L_1 were directly attached to bar 3. When the milli-

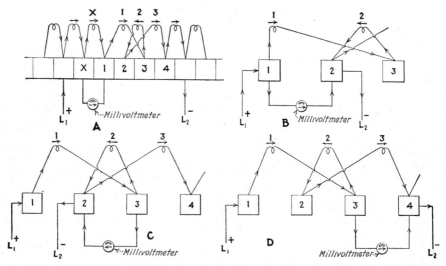

Fig. 73.—Another case of reversed coil leads that sometimes occurs in loop windings.

This condition is shown in diagram A. On passing a current through the winding and with the millivoltmeter leads across bars x and 1 as shown in diagram A, a normal deflection will be obtained on the meter. With the meter leads on bars 1 and 2 as shown in diagram B, a reading twice normal will be obtained, because the meter is across coils 1 and 2 in series. With the meter leads on bars 2 and 3 as shown in diagram C a reversed reading will be obtained. The reason for the reversed reading is that the lead of coil 1 makes bar 3 positive just as if L_1 were directly attached to bar 3. When the meter leads are placed on bars 3 and 4 as shown in diagram D, a reading twice normal and in the correct direction will be obtained. This is because the meter is measuring the drop of potential over coils 2 and 3 in series.

voltmeter leads are put on bars 3 and 4, as in diagram D, a reading of twice the normal amount and in the correct direction will be obtained. This is because coils 2 and 3 are in series between bars 3 and 4. Hence, when making a bar-to-bar test, this type of defect is indicated by obtaining the following sequence of readings: first a double reading, then a normal but reversed reading and finally, a double reading in the proper direction. A telephone receiver would give a high, followed by a low, and finally a high sound. The meter is more accurate, however, as it gives one more indication; that is, the direction of the current flow.

Tests for Locating Short Circuits.—The remaining types of defects that are likely to occur while winding and connecting armatures, are short circuits. Each type of short circuit has different characteristics and different methods must be used for locating them. The most common short circuit is a short between turns; that is, when one or more turns form a closed circuit. This affects only one coil. Using a milli-voltmeter in the bar-to-bar or drop-of-potential method of testing, a short circuit between turns in a coil will give a lower than normal read-

Fig. 74.—Using a growler to test a small armature for shorts.

If the iron keeper which is placed over the top slot is attracted, the coil in that slot is defective. In the foreground at the left is a portable testing transformer which is used for testing the winding and commutator for grounds.

ing on the millivoltmeter scale. The magnitude of the reading depends upon the amount of the coil that is shorted out. A zero reading will be obtained when the coil is completely short-circuited, in other words a dead short.

Use of a Growler for Locating Shorted Coils.—The best method of locating shorted coils is to use a growler like the one shown in Fig. 74. An armature should be tested for short circuits by means of a growler after winding and wedging and before connecting the commutator leads to the commutator.   Then any shorts that show up after connecting are either in the commutator leads or in the commutator.

Shorts between Coil Turns.—When using the growler, as shown in Fig. 74, shorts between turns will cause the metal keeper to be attracted to two slots; that is, the slots in which the top and bottom halves of each coil lie.   By studying the effect of each type of short separately, it soon becomes easy to determine and locate any shorts that may occur in the winding.   For example, assume a 14-slot armature, coil pitch 1-and-7 and that the growler test shows signs of shorts in four slots.   Assuming that the coil turns are shorted and that the slots marked from the growler test are spaced 1, 4, 7, and 10, then slots 1 and 7 contain one coil and slots 4 and 10 contain the second coil.   The coil pitch and what can be seen of the coil helps to locate the bad coil.   With the bar-to-bar test the

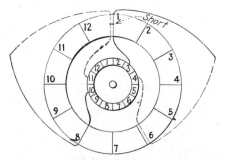

Fig. 75.—Method of locating shorts that occur between top and bottom halves of coils in the same slot.

In the growler test the iron keeper was attracted in slots 1, 6 and 8.   The coil pitch of the winding shown is 1 and 6.   Take any slot which has shown signs of being shorted in the growler test, for instance, slot 1.   Then count each way from this slot a distance equal to one coil pitch and if the two slots reached are the remaining ones that showed signs of being shorted from the growler test, the two coils are shorted together in the slots from which the count was started.   Counting a coil pitch each way from slot 1, you reach slots 6 and 8 which were the other two slots that showed signs of being shorted; hence the short between the two coils must be in slot 1.

millivoltmeter will give a low reading when it reaches the two bars to which the lead of the shorted coil connects.   This locates the coil without any further test.   Shorts between coils in the same cell in a loop winding would come under the head of shorted turns, although the shorts are between coils, and if the two loops from the slot were cut open a light would be obtained between the two coils, although the circuit had been broken.

Shorts between Top and Bottom Halves of Coils.—The next type of short is one that occurs between top and bottom halves of coils in the same slot; this is commonly called a short between top and bottom coils. This is done to distinguish this type of short from the short between the coils in the same cell in a loop winding.   This type of short forms a closed path, similar to a figure 8 and will affect two and three slots, depending upon the type of winding and the coil pitch.   With a diametrically-split winding two slots directly opposite would be affected.   With the chorded-loop, split-loop, and split V-loop windings, three slots would be affected.

Finding Slot in Which Short Is Located.—To find the slot in which the short is located, take any one slot that the growler shows as shorted and

Fig. 76.—Here is a good arrangement of a test bench for armature testing. The millivoltmeter is mounted on an upright wood panel.   The test light is a little behind and to one side of it, and the growler is directly in front of the tester.

Fig. 77.—Small motor test board wired for 110- and 220-volt alternating-current and direct-current test circuits. See Fig. 77A for wiring diagram.

calling this slot No. 1, count over to the right and to the left a distance equal to one coil pitch.   Then if each count falls on a marked slot as shown from the growler test, the short is in the slot called No. 1, but if the count does not fall on a marked slot on both sides, take any other

marked slot and call it No. 1 and repeat the right and left count.   This
method is shown in Fig. 75.   With the bar-to-bar test, a low reading will
be obtained between bars 10 and 11, and 3 and 4, but this would not
indicate anything more than that there were two shorts in the winding.

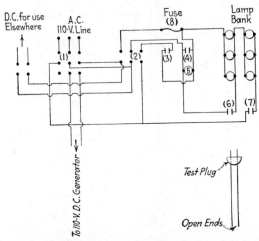

Fig. 77*A*.—Wiring diagram for test board shown in Fig. 77.

(1) Double-throw, triple-pole switch.   (2) Single-throw, triple-pole switch with fuses.   (3), (4), (5),
(6), and (7) Lamp sockets with female end of attachment plugs.   (5) Lamp socket.   (8) Fuse block
using fuse wire.   Plug in (3) is in series with alternating-current line only; in (4) is across line alternating current or direct current; in (6) uses first lamp for direct current; in (7) use both lamp banks for
alternating current only.   Socket (5) is across the line for alternating current or direct current.

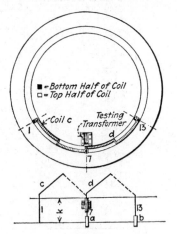

Fig. 78.—How a growler is used in testing the stator winding of small alternating-current
motors.

From the above, it is obvious that the growler is the best means of detecting and locating shorts.

Determining Whether Short is in Winding or in Commutator.—The
growler will also show whether a short is in the winding, or in the com-

mutator. If two commutator bars show up as being shorted from the millivoltmeter test, put the armature on a growler and bridge the two bars with a knife, taking care that the coil to which these bars connect is in the active field of the growler. Then break contact with one bar. If a spark is seen at the time of breaking contact, the short is in the wind-

Fig. 79.—Panel board for testing small stators for shorts, grounds, and unbalance. A wattmeter is used to check between phases and a voltmeter as a check on line voltage.

ing; if no spark is obtained, then the two bars are shorted and the trouble is in the commutator.

Locating Shorts between Coil Leads.—Shorts between leads occur mostly on armatures that are wound with more than one wire in hand and in which more than one wire is used per sleeve. Shorts of this kind are caused by the wires in the sleeve getting twisted. When pounded on while connecting, the insulation is broken, thus shorting the two coils. This acts the same as a short between turns

This trouble occurs mostly in the top layer of leads, for the bottom leads are usually put down as they come from the slot. The top leads have to be twisted and interchanged and sometimes the twist is pulled back close to the core. The very act of pulling the twist tight often results in a short.

Locating Shorts between Coil Ends.—Twisting and pulling of coils may be the cause of shorts between coil ends on any type of hand winding. This is the hardest type of short to locate because one coil in crossing the end of the core from slot to slot, passes over a number of other coils, both top halves and bottom halves. There is no regularity about the occurrence of the attracted slot or bars when using the growler. A number of slots will show signs of shorts and they cannot be reduced to a regular order, as explained previously. You can be sure that the trouble is between coil ends, sometimes, by moving the end windings with the hand. If the trouble can be made to disappear and reappear, this proves where the trouble is, but if this method fails the following will locate the trouble:

Remove all the top leads; then take a test light and attach one lead of the test circuit to any one top lead with a piece of bare, copper tie wire. Have this wire long enough to reach around the commutator. Then with the other test lead touch the top lead adjacent to the one to which the first test lead is permanently attached. If a light is obtained, it indicates a short between these two coils. In this case, tie the two leads together with the tie wire and at the same time mark both leads so they can be found later. If no light is obtained, tie both top leads together with the tie wire without marking the leads. Then touch the test leads to the next top lead. After this tie this lead to the first two leads by the tie wire. Repeat this process with each top lead until the starting point is reached, marking every top lead that shows a light. These marked leads are the ones that connect to the coil shorted across the coil ends. With a bar-to-bar test, all kinds of readings would be obtained on the millivoltmeter, depending on the degree of contact and the number of places shorted. No definite results would be obtained with a bar-to-bar test in this case.

Reasons for Variations in Readings with Bar-to-bar Test.—With the drop-of-potential or bar-to-bar test with a millivoltmeter, a short circuit in a coil will give a very low reading and also a poor contact will give a high reading. When making tests on hand-wound armatures there are a number of causes that contribute to high and low readings. When testing an armature that has the commutator leads connected but not soldered, if the leads fit easily in the neck, consistent readings may not be obtained because poor contact may increase the resistance of the coil under test. Hence a series of high and low or irregular readings will be the result. Other things that may cause a variation in the readings are a large number of turns per coil, the use of small sized wire in the coil, or one or two turns may have been left out of the coil.   Sometimes a cord or tape band put on tightly over the leads just back of the commutator will cause the leads to make better contact in the neck and give more consistent readings in the bar-to-bar test.   When a low reading is obtained in the bar-to-bar test and if there is any doubt about it being a short, use the growler.

Strip and Rewind When Troubles Cannot Be Located.—When a number of troubles show up when testing a winding and trouble is experienced in finding them, it is always advisable to strip the armature and rewind it completely.   Much time and expense will thus be saved and a better job the result.

PART II

REWINDING PROCEDURE FOR SMALL ALTERNAT-
ING-CURRENT MOTORS

CHAPTER XII

TESTING AND LOCATING FAULTS IN SMALL ALTERNATING-CURRENT MOTORS WHEN RECEIVED FOR REPAIRS

Before starting to dismantle a small alternating-current motor that comes into a shop for repairs, it should be given a thorough general inspection. For the reason that the first cost of a new motor in this class is very low, the repair costs must be kept as low as consistent with good workmanship. In some cases the repairs required will exceed the cost of a new motor or the motor will not be worth repairing. A general inspection will locate most mechanical faults and electrical troubles such as an oily switch, bent or sticking switch parts, etc. By switch is meant the centrifugal cutout switch used in the starting circuit of split-phase motors. This inspection will reveal worn bearings, starting or running windings burned out, or water-soaked coils. These troubles are easily found but sometimes a motor which is apparently in good condition may not operate properly.

How to Locate Troubles When Motor Will Not Start.—When a motor has been found in good condition after a general inspection, it should be tested with twice normal voltage (alternating current) from ground to the windings. If the windings hold up under this test and the trouble does not show up, it must be located in other ways. If the bearings are O. K. and the windings and connections are good, but the motor will not start, bring the motor up to speed and throw it on the line. The motor may be brought up to speed by winding a length of cotton tape or heavy cord around the shaft and then giving it a quick pull. After the motor has been started in this manner and thrown upon the line and it operates without heating or unusual noises, the running winding is in good shape, but the failure to start is probably due to an open circuit in the starting winding. To find this, remove the end bells and the rotor. Check each section of the winding with a test lamp from the leads to the switch, switch to the coils, and across each coil until the open circuit is located.

If the motor will not start after being rotated by the tape method, but tends to jam and hum, there is probably a short circuit in the running coils. In such a case, remove the end bells and rotor and connect the running winding across the line. Place the blade of a screw driver against the iron in the center of each coil and pull it up and away from the iron to test the magnetic strength of each coil. The coil which has the least pull is the short-circuited one. In making this screw driver test, do not

107

leave the current on the windings too long or they will burn out. A small growler such as used for testing larger motors (Fig. 78) may be made up for testing the stators of small motors. Such a small growler is described on pages 7 and 223.

How to Locate Troubles When Motor Starts but Will Not Pull Load.— If the windings seem to be in good condition but the motor will not pull its load, inspect the rotor to see if all the bars are making good contact. If poor contacts are found, resolder the rotor. Sometimes a motor will start but will not come up to speed on account of the fact that the springs on the centrifugal switch are too light or weak, and fly out before the rotor reaches the pull-in or running speed.

If the trouble cannot be determined by any of these methods, it may be well to read the following chapters to learn how the windings are put on and connected. An understanding of the windings will often help the repair man to know just what the trouble is.

Troubles with Starting Circuit Switch.—When the switch in the starting circuit sticks in the open position and the motor is left on the line in this condition for any length of time the running winding will be burned out before the fuse will blow. When the switch sticks in the

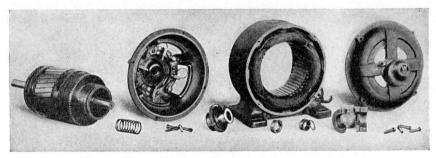

Fig. 80.—A ½-hp., single-phase, repulsion motor showing short circuiting device that should be carefully inspected when the motor fails to operate properly.

closed position the motor will start and run, but the starting coils are across the line and will be burned out if left on any length of time. A starting winding is easier to replace than a running winding as the former is wound on top of the running coils. Quite often when a starting coil is burned out it also ruins the running coils. This happens when the motor is allowed to run with a sticky switch.

Causes for Repulsion Motor Failing to Start.—With the repulsion type of motor, failure to start is quite often due to the brushes being worn short, thus weakening the spring tension. A slight pressure of the centrifugal device may cause the brushes to move out of contact with the commutator before the pull-in speed has been reached. To test for this fault put small blocks of wood under each spring, use blocks about ⅛ to

¼ in. thick. This will restore the spring tension. Another cause of failure to start in this type of winding is that the brushes are off neutral. To reset them proceed as follows: Take a spare set of brushes and pare them down to a width of about $\frac{1}{16}$ in. It is not necessary to pare the complete brush, the full length in contact with the commutator, to a depth of ⅛ in. being sufficient. With these brushes in place, locate the approximate neutral by inspection; that is, trace the leads of the coil that has its sides in the magnetic neutral region. The brushes should make contact to the bars that the coil leads connect to. Then with full line voltage applied to the windings, rock the brush arm until a point is

Fig. 81.—Parts of a small single-phase motor that has been taken down for cleaning and thorough overhauling.

reached where the armature will not start to rotate. Mark this point on the brush arm and collar, as this is the dead neutral. If the brush arm is shifted about ¼ in. either side of this mark, the armature should revolve either clockwise or counter-clockwise depending upon which side of the neutral the brush arm mark is placed or, in other words, moving the brush arm from one side of the neutral mark to the other will reverse the direction of rotation.

Locating Troubles in Universal Type of Motor.—There are two distinct types of the universal motor. One is the straight series motor with laminated fields and this type can be inspected in the same manner as the ordinary type of direct-current motor. (See Chap. I.) The second type is the compensated type such as is used in drills, etc. This motor has the field put in the stator in the same manner as in an induction motor.

The greatest trouble experienced with the universal motor is the shifting of the field or stator within the frame thus throwing the brushes off neutral.   In small commutating types, the brushes are sometimes located back of the neutral point and the coil pitch is chorded.   Therefore, the best method of relocating the brushes is to arrange the front end bell so that it can be turned a little at a time and fastened in place each time so that the motor can be run.   Use direct current whenever possible and shift brushes until a point is found where the motor delivers its maximum torque and runs with the least sparking and heating.   When this point is found, note the distance that the screw holes in the end bell have been moved from corresponding holes in the frame; then turn the stator or field within its frame a like amount and in the same direction.

Split-phase motors have two distinct windings; a main running winding and a high resistance starting winding which are connected to the circuit as shown in Fig. 82.   The direction of rotation of the motor is reversed by interchanging the terminals of either one of these windings,

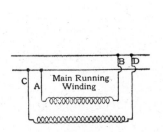

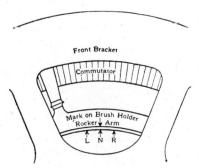

Fig. 82.—This diagram shows the connections to interchange when the direction of rotation is to be changed.

Fig. 83.—Neutral marking on rocker arm of a repulsion-start motor.

but not both; that is, *C* and *D* may be interchanged or *A* and *B* may be interchanged.   The reason for the reversal is the same as in a two-phase motor, one of the phases is reversed by interchanging the leads.

Repulsion-starting motors have an armature winding, a commutator and brushholder similar to direct-current machines, the brushholder being short-circuited through the rocker arm.   Reversal of the direction of rotation of these motors is accomplished by shifting this rocker arm relative to the supporting bracket, as shown in Fig. 83.   An arrow is stamped on the movable brushholder, which may be put opposite any one of the three marks on the stationary bracket.   The middle one of these marks is known as the neutral and, when the brushholder is in this position, the motor will not start in either direction.   When the brushholder is shifted to one side or the other of this neutral, as indicated by the marks *R* and *L*, in Fig. 83, the motor will run right hand or left hand respectively.

Shading-coil motors have only a single winding connected to the line, and it is obvious that reversal of the terminals of this one winding will not reverse the direction of rotation, since the motor operates on alternating current. The obvious method of reversing the direction of rotation of such motor is to shift the short-circuited starting coils to the other side of each of the main poles. This, however, is quite difficult to accomplish

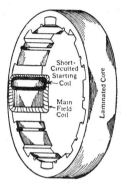

Fig. 84.—Field construction for a single-phase motor using a shading coil for starting.

and it is usually much easier to reverse the motor by taking off both end brackets and turning the complete stator end for end relative to the rotor; or else by taking out the laminated core with the windings in it, and reversing it end for end relative to the rotor.

Series motors of the commutator type are reversed by reversing the direction of current through either the armature or the field, just as in a series direct-current motor.

CHAPTER XIII

INFORMATION TO RECORD FOR SMALL ALTERNATING-CURRENT MOTORS BEFORE STRIPPING THEM

The information in Chap. II on procedure and forms for recording information and data needed for rewinding small direct-current motors, for the most part holds for small alternating current motors also. In this chapter information is given that applies particularly to small alternating current motors.

When it is known that the motor has to be rewound, the first thing to do is to record the winding and nameplate data. A very good plan is to use individual file cards for each motor as mentioned on page 10, Chap. II, something like the one shown in A, Fig. 85. In recording the nameplate data for a small alternating-current motor, the following information should be included. When all of this information is not shown on the nameplate, it should be obtained from the manufacturer so as to build up a card file of complete information for future use and save time in determining the data for every motor of the same design as it comes into the shop for repairs.

(1) Manufacturer's name and address; (2) horsepower; (3) voltage; (4) amperes per terminal; (5) number phases; (6) cycles; (7) r.p.m. at full load; (8) 40° temperature rating and 50° temperature rating; (9) style number; (10) serial number; (11) frame number.

After this data is recorded, put down details of the kind of connection, the number of coils and the other information shown on the card forms of Fig. 85. Ways to determine all of this information are described in the following paragraphs.

After the card has been completely filled out and the job is completed, it should be filed according to make, as Westinghouse, General Electric, Robbins & Myers, etc. Under each make these file cards should be sorted into types such as CA, AR, etc., and finally subdivided according to horsepower. When a file of this kind has been built up it can be consulted whenever a motor is brought into the shop for rewinding and if the motor is identical with one which has been wound before, the information may be followed and thus save the time necessary to work up the same information again.

How to Get Winding and Connecting Information from an Old Motor.—After the nameplate data has been put down, the number of slots, the bore and length of the stator iron should be recorded and the

A

Customer K.C. Master + Co.   Order No. 2326
Make
Serial No. 56699   Style No. F-5   Type S T   R.p.m. 1725   Volts 110   Cycles 60
No. Slots 36   No. Poles 4
Running Coils: No. 4   Connection Parallel
Turns 30-1. No.20 S.C.+ En. In. per turn 57 Total Lb. 2
Starting Coils: No. 4   Connection Parallel
Turns 57-1 No.30 S.C.+ En. In. per turn 32 Total Lb. $\frac{1}{4}$
Wanted 5-1-22 Issued 4-5-22 Completed 4-29-22

B

RUN $\frac{1}{1}$ 2 2 1 0 0 1 2 2 $\frac{1}{2}$
START   2 1 X X X X X 1 2

Back of card filled like this for skein winding.

C

SLOT NO.	1	2	3	4	5	6	7	8	9	10	11	12	13	14	15	16	17	18	19
RUNNING WINDING	30/	60	60	30	·	·	30	60	60/30	30/60	60	60	30	·	·	30	60	60	30/30
STARTING WINDING		114	57	·	·	·	114	57	·	·	·	57	114						

For hand winding back of card may be filled like this or as shown below.

RUN $\frac{30}{30}$ 60 60 30 0 0 30 60 60 $\frac{30}{30}$
START 114 57 X X X X X 57 114

C

Customer   Order No.
Make   Hp. $\frac{1}{4}$ Volts 110   Cycles 25
Serial No.   Style No.   Type   R.p.m. 1440
No. Slots 24   No. Poles 2
Running Coils: No. 2   Connection Parallel
Turns 42-1 No.20 S.C.+ En. In. per turn 120 Total Lb. 2 $\frac{3}{4}$
Starting Coils: No. 2   Connection Parallel
Turns 42-1 No. 25 S.C.+ En. In. per turn 118 Total Lb. $\frac{1}{2}$
Wanted   Issued   Completed

D

Run $\frac{1}{2}$ 2 2 2 1 0 0 0 1 2 2 2 $\frac{1}{2}$
Start $\frac{1}{2}$ 2 2 2 1 0 0 0 1 2 2 2 $\frac{1}{2}$

E

Customer   Order No.
Make   Hp. $\frac{1}{6}$ Volts 220   Cycles 60
Serial No.   Style No.   Type   R.p.m. 1720
No. Slots 36   No. Poles 4
Running Coils: No. 4   Connection Series
Turns 37-1 No.20 S.C.+ En. In. per turn 65 Total Lb. 3
Starting Coils: No. 4   Connection
Turns   No.   In. per turn   Total Lb.
Wanted   Issued   Completed

Run 2 2 1 0 0 1 2 2 0 2 2 1 0
         C   D   A
Start 2 2 0 0 0 4

FIG. 85.—A convenient form of card for recording winding and name-plate data when stripping small alternating-current motors.

A convenient way to record such data is to use 3- by 5-in. cards as shown. At A is the face and at the right the back of the card. The back is filled in to indicate the number of times the skein is placed in the different slots of a skein-wound stator. The same winding is indicated at B and C which show the back of a card filled in by two different methods. The top illustration at right of A shows a more complete method which contains the same information as shown in C. The figures indicate the number of turns in the slot. For a beginner it may be better to follow the method shown at the right of A as this indicates more clearly the number of turns in each slot. At D are data for a two-pole motor. At E is information taken from a skein-wound four-pole motor in which the coils do not overlap.

connections checked, whether series or parallel, etc. Then, to make the stator easy to strip and to take data from it, connect it across full line voltage and allow current to flow through the windings (both running and starting) until they smoke and become hot. This will loosen all the varnish, oil, etc. and allow the wires to be pulled apart.

The information on the starting windings should be taken first because they are usually on top. Most starting windings are skein wound. In getting the information, lift up the ends of starting coils so that you can see how many slots are skipped from one side of the coil to the other and the number of times the skein is put through each slot. Record this information. In *A* of Fig. 85, the starting winding skipped five slots as

REPAIR JOB TAG	WORK REQUIRED
JOB NO.	CHECK IN SQUARES
	☐ NEW WINDINGS --- { START ☐ / RUN ☐
CUSTOMER	☐ NEW COMMUTATOR
	☐ REPAIR COMMUTATOR
MFGR'S NAME	☐ NEW STARTING SWITCH
H.P. VOLTS	☐ REPAIR STARTING SWITCH
AMPS PER TERMINAL	☐ NEW ROTOR
NO. PHASES CYCLES	☐ NEW SHAFT
FULL LOAD R.P.M.	☐ NEW BEARINGS
MOTOR { SERIAL / NUMBERS { TYPE / FRAME	☐ NEW BRUSHES
	☐ VARNISH AND BAKE
DATE WANTED	☐ PAINT FRAME
DATE COMPLETED	☐ OTHER WORK AND MATERIALS
WINDERS NAME	USED
HOURS LABOR	

Fig. 86.—Front and back of a tag showing the data that should be recorded before a small motor is stripped. This tag should be attached to the motor until repairs are completed and the job tested out.

indicated by the dots and slots 7 and 13 each contain one side of the skein. In slots 6 and 14 the skein is put through twice. The starting coils do not overlap each other.

It is very important before removing the winding of a repulsion type of motor, to mark the slots in which a pole group starts. The motor must be rewound so that the general line of the pole will be in the same position in reference to the brush as it is in the original winding. The reasons for this are given on page 122, Chap. XV.

The data for the main or running winding is recorded next. This may be either a hand or skein winding. It is easy to determine which it is by inspection. The skein winding will show the ends crossing each other, whereas the hand-wound coil will have a neat, uniform appearance. The data in *A* of Fig. 85 shows that in the main winding, the slots 4 and 7 have thirty turns. Slots 2, 3, 8 and 9 have sixty turns, indicating that two turns of the skein were in these slots. The dividing line in slots 1 and 10 indicates that the coils overlap. The data also show the position of the running winding in reference to the starting winding. All of this information should be put down on the winding card. The card forms *B* and *C* of Fig. 85 show the winding data put down in a more simple manner. This may be followed when a man has had considerable rewinding experience.

Information Needed for Hand and Skein Windings.—It is a good practice to employ the following rule for hand windings: Put down the

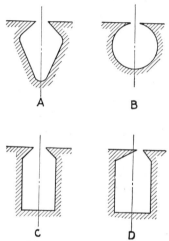

Fig. 87.—Different shapes of slots used in stators of small alternating-current stators. *A* is the most common shape and requires care in winding since the wedged shape of the bottom of the slot tends to allow the insulation to break and forcing of the top coil in the slot will often ground the bottom half of the coil. *C* is another shape of slot often used. *B* is the next most frequently used shape of slot in old fan motors. It is a good slot to wind and insulate. *D* is a slot with the opening close to the slot side and off center. It is hard to insulate and wind.

number of turns per slot as shown in *A* and the upper part of *C* in Fig. 85. For skein winding put down the number of times the skein passes through each slot, as shown in *B* and the lower *C* of Fig. 85. Put the main winding data on top and the starting winding at the bottom. When coils overlap denote it by using a diagonal dividing line, as shown. Note that in all these cases the length of the skein and the pounds of wire total is put down. The length of skein is the length of the completed skein and not the length of the entire wire before it is wound into the skein.

The card form *D* in Fig. 85 is the data for a two-pole motor. Card form *E* of Fig. 85 is the data for a skein-wound four-pole motor in which the coils do not overlap. The data in this case indicate that one slot is skipped between each adjacent running coil and the starting winding is passed through the slot four times. Also, the skein is passed through slots C and A twice, and through slots D and A twice, making four in A, two in C and two in D. If desired, this particular winding could be reconnected for eight consequent poles.

Six Points to Note before Stripping a Stator.—In addition to the information outlined in the preceding paragraphs, the following points should be noted concerning the winding before it is stripped: (1) How windings are connected to starting switch and line. (2) Coil pitch in slots. (3) Sizes of wire used. (4) Kind of insulation on wires, whether single or double cotton covered or enameled. (5) Thickness of slot insulation and the kind used. (6) Whether coils fit tight or loose in slots. This should be noted to see if the slot insulation thickness or covering on the wires can be increased.

CHAPTER XIV

INSULATING THE CORE AND THE WINDING

As in the case of a small direct-current motor, the slots of the stator of an alternating-current motor must be thoroughly cleaned of all old insulation and varnish and all burrs and rough edges removed with a file. The slots are then ready for their insulation. Several methods of insulating the slots of small motors are in use; namely, fish-paper cell only; fish-paper and treated cloth cells; a combination cell only.

Insulating Slots with Fish-paper Only.—When a fish-paper cell only is used it should be about 0.015 in. thick and should be cut to extend at least $\frac{1}{8}$ in. beyond the fibre punchings. It should be of such width as to come just to the edge of the tooth tip; that is, it should not obstruct the slot opening when putting the wires into the cell. The cell should, of course, be formed to fit the slot if possible. After the slot is wound a $\frac{1}{32}$ or $\frac{1}{16}$ in. thick fibre strip of suitable width should be inserted in the top of the slot under the teeth and between the teeth and the fish-paper cell. This fibre wedge should extend at least $\frac{1}{8}$ in. beyond the punchings.

The starting winding of split-phase motors should be insulated in the slots from the main winding by a fibre strip as wide as the slot, or by an additional fish-paper cell. Where an additional cell is used, the first fish-paper cell into which the main winding is wound should be folded over and the second fish-paper cell placed on top. The starting winding should be insulated from the main winding on the ends with drilling or light canvas in case considerable shaping is necessary to form the windings. Where shaping of the end windings is not necessary, no insulation is required between the main and starting windings except that provided on the individual wires and by the insulating varnish which is applied to the completely wound stator.

Insulating Slots with Fish-paper and Treated Cloth.—Cut insulating cells of 0.007-in. fish-paper for the slots. These should be about $\frac{1}{8}$ in. longer than the slot and should come just below the top of the slot. In addition to this a tan treated-cloth slider of the same shape should be used in each slot, or 0.007-in. fish-paper may be employed as a slider. When the coils overlap, a treated-cloth cell for the top coils should be cut $\frac{1}{2}$ to 1 in. longer than the slot in order to protect one coil from another. After the wires are inserted, the treated-cloth cell should be cut off flush with the slot and folded over, and a fiber wedge inserted as in the case when the fish-paper cell only is used.   Also, in slots that contain both a running and a starting coil, as in the case where fish-paper only is used, put a treated-cloth (0.005 to 0.007 in. thick) cell between the two coils.   It is good practice to use 0.010 in. asbestos paper between the running and starting coils.   The reason is that the starting winding is, nine times out of ten, the one which burns out when the motor stalls. In some cases the starting winding is completely roasted out.   If there is no insulation between this winding and the running coils, the heat will burn the insulation off the running winding, which will cause short circuits and burn out of the entire winding.   The use of asbestos paper will confine the burning to the starting winding alone.   This is the top winding and the easiest to remove and rewind.

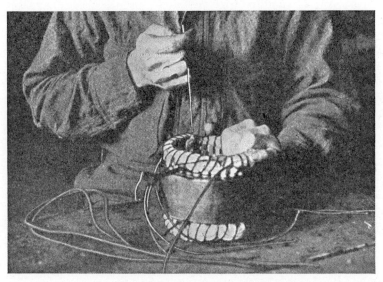

Fig. 88.—Method of tying the running and starting windings together after the stator has been wound and all the leads are in place.

When cutting the fish-paper for the slot cells, be sure that the grain of the paper runs parallel to the length of the slot.   If a treated-cloth cell or slider is used in connection with the fish-paper cell, the latter can be cut off flush with the top of the slot.   The only material then projecting through the slot opening will be the two sides of the treated-cloth slider.   It is important in a skein winding to have some insulation projecting from the slot to protect the wire as it is fed into the slot.

Insulating Slots with Combination Cell.—With hand-wound stators a combination insulation (see page 27, Chap. III) cell can be used cut flush with the top of the slot so that the full opening of the slot is available. The combination cell should be inserted so that the fish-paper side is next to the iron to protect the treated-cloth insulation. It is easy to guide one wire into the slot without damaging the insulation on it.

Varnishing and Baking Winding.—All small motors should be dipped in varnish and baked, after they are completely wound and insulated.

Fig. 89.—Single-phase motor with new winding completed and ready for final assembly of parts.

Any good grade of insulating varnish which does not bake too hard will be satisfactory. Some insulating varnishes require a longer time to bake

Fig. 90.—Note how the windings of this single-phase motor are bound together and the way the leads are brought out.

than others, and some require higher temperatures than others, but in no case should the temperature exceed 250°F. and the length of the baking time should never be less than four hours. About eight hours is a safe time. Before immersing the wound primary into the insulating varnish it should be heated for two hours at 120°F. to permit it to dry out thoroughly. It should then be immersed immediately into the insulating varnish and allowed to remain there until bubbles cease to rise. Then remove and allow to drip from 30 to 45 min.

Tying Ends of Coils with Cord.—It used to be the practice to tape the ends of coils with cotton tape. Usually this is not needed but the ends must be tied together with a cord. However, in cases where the winding is exposed to dust, etc., the ends should be taped.

Figure 88 shows the method of tying the running and starting windings together. This is usually done after the motor has been connected and all the leads are in place. The cord used is about $\frac{1}{32}$ in. in diameter. To facilitate the cord being pushed through the space between slots and the winding close to the core, a needle can be used, made by bending a piece of bare No. 17 copper or banding wire into a hairpin and twisting the free ends together.

On fan motor stators, enamel-covered wire is sometimes used, but on the stators used in the larger motors, single cotton and enameled wire is more satisfactory.

End Rings to Protect Overhanging Coils.—To protect the overhanging coils from rubbing against the iron of the core and producing grounds, a $\frac{1}{16}$-in. fibre ring should be cut to fit the ends of the stator core and shellacked to the iron.

CHAPTER XV

HOW TO MAKE UP A SKEIN AND WIND IT IN SMALL ALTERNAT-ING-CURRENT STATORS

In practically all small, alternating-current motors, single cotton-and enamel-covered wire can be used. After the length of the skein is determined from the data recorded when the stator was stripped as described in Chap. XIII, page 115, it is wound by means of the shuttle shown in Figs. 91 and 92. The pegs are set at the proper distance and the shuttle is turned on its axis until the proper number of turns are put on. Then the skein is taken off and wound into the stator slots.

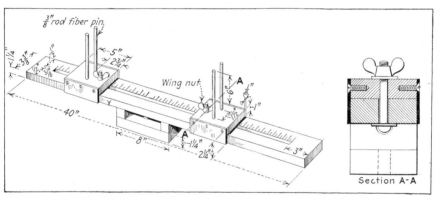

Fig. 91.—Construction details for an adjustable shuttle for winding skeins.

Winding a Skein on the Stator.—The drawings in Fig. 93 show the different steps in putting a skein in the stator slots. Figure 94 shows a two-pole stator with one coil in place and the second coil partly wound. This also shows what is known as a split-skein. When the size of wire is larger than No. 19 and the total turns per skein make a bunch ½ in. square or larger, the skein is wound in two sections to make it easier to handle. The winding of a split-skein is described on page 126.

The different steps shown in winding the skein in Fig. 93 follow the data in A and B of Fig. 85, page 113. At A, of Fig. 93, the skein is shown started in slots 4 and 7 with the lead end of the skein at the bottom of the drawing. This satisfies the center part of the data shown in A, of Fig. 85. This data is 1-0-0-1, so that the winding is in slots 4 and 7. Two slots in between are skipped.

How to Start Winding in Proper Place on a Stator.—In most cases it is necessary to start the winding at a certain point on the stator. With the repulsion type of motor the coils must be put back in place in the same arrangement as the original coils. If they are shifted with reference to the brush rigging, it may be difficult to fit the brushes so that the motor will operate correctly. The neutral mark and the rotation mark on the brush shell will have to be relocated. If the coils are shifted too much the motor cannot be made to operate properly.

Fig. 92.—This illustration shows how the shuttle in Fig. 91 and the reel of wire should be mounted when winding skeins.

In any type of motor, care must be taken to start the winding at such a point that when completed it will not rub against the studs or bolts which pass through the core and hold it together. Figure 94 shows how a coil should be placed so that the thick or high part of the completed winding falls in between the studs. If this is not done the high part of the winding will rub on the bolt when the motor operates and this will result in grounding the winding. Figure 94 shows a two-pole stator,

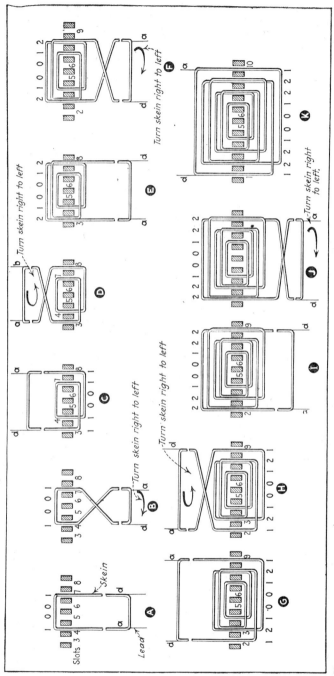

FIG. 93.—Steps from start to finish when putting on a skein winding. This is the running winding of the motor for which data is shown in forms *A* and *B* of Fig. 85 (Chap. XIII).

which is one of the hardest to wind and shape. The upper coil shows the proper position for a two-pole coil in reference to the studs. The lower coil, which is just started, is in the proper position for a completed four-pole winding A general rule for locating the coils for two poles and four studs is that the outer coils should lie in the slots midway between the studs. For four poles and four studs the outer coil, or the last one wound on, should lie in the slot above the studs.

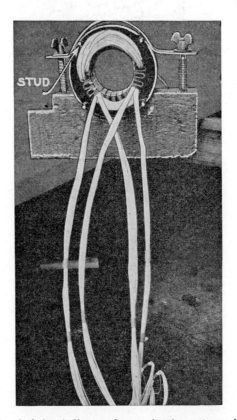

FIG. 94.—A skein winding partly completed on a two-pole stator.

The top coils represent one-half of the running winding, which is already in place. The other half of the winding has been started below. This is a split skein winding. One-half of the winding is shoved through the opening at a time and then the other half is brought through and placed in the same slot. Notice how the coils are placed with reference to the studs which hold the end bells of the motor in place. This picture also illustrates a convenient holding clamp.

The first turns of the skein should be shaped to conform to the curvature of the stator bore. They should be bent down to allow room for the starting winding to be placed on top of them. Figure 94 illustrates this method of shaping the coils. Care must be taken to keep kinks and twists out of the wire. Also each coil must be pressed tightly against the core and against any other layers of coils which have been put in before.

If this is not done there will not be enough of the skein left to make the last turn of the skein.

After the first turn is put in the slots as shown in *A* of Fig. 93, the skein is twisted as shown in *B*. The right-hand side of the skein is twisted over the left-hand side so as to make the side *a* change place with the side *d*. The skein is then bent over and pushed through the opening in the stator and the side *a* is threaded into the slot 8, while the side *d* is threaded into slot 3, as shown at *C*. The skein is twisted again at *D*, and pushed through the hole in the stator and threaded again into the slots 3 and 8. This leaves the winding as shown at *E*, which satisfies

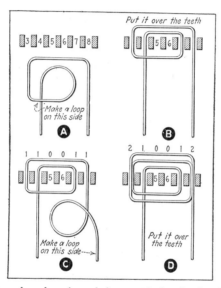

FIG. 95.—How to make a loop in a skein or a single-wire, handwinding when fitting the coil turns into the slots. This is an easier method of winding than that shown in Fig. 93 for the entire skein (when used) need not be pushed through the opening in the stator.

the directions 2-1-0-0-1-2. At *F* the skein is twisted ready to push through and thread into slots 2 and 9 as has been done at *G*. Another twist is made at *H* and the skein is brought back through slots 2 and 9, as shown at *I*. The remaining length of skein is given another twist at *J* and threaded into slots 1 and 10. This completes the coil and satisfies the entire winding data, which is 1-2-2-1-0-0-1-2-2-1. It makes no difference which way the skein is twisted each time as the polarity of the coil will not be affected, nor will the coil sides neutralize each other after a change of twist.

Easy Method for Winding a Skein.—The method of putting on a skein winding which has just been described, is the one which involves the least possibility of making mistakes. A study of this method should result in a clear understanding of the principles of skein winding and of

the position of the skeins upon the stator.   There is, however, a quicker
and easier method of winding a skein which may be used by an experienced winder.   This method does not require pushing the entire skein
through a small stator opening.   Instead, a small loop is made in the
skein and this alone is shoved through the opening, after which it is
fitted into place in the slot.   The drawing in Fig. 95 shows this method
and Fig. 101 (Chap. XVI) shows the same principle in use with a
single wire in a hand winding job.   In winding with this method a twist
or a loop similar in shape to the small letter e is put first in one side of the
coil and this loop is slipped through and the wires are placed in the proper

Fig. 96.—Mould for winding skeins. Note that there are two grooves for each size
of skein permitting the winding of two skeins of the same size or one split-skein. In
winding a split-skein, one half is wound in one groove and the other half in the other groove
and the two halves tied together separately.   This mould is split through the center so as to
be adjustable for different sizes of skeins.

slot.   Then the loop is made in the other side of the coil and the second
loop is slipped through.   A little practice will enable a winder to master
this method.

When a Split-skein Can Be Used.—As already mentioned, when the
wire is larger than No. 19 and the skein is over $\frac{1}{2}$ in. square, it should
be wound in two sections to make it easier to handle.   When winding the
skein upon the shuttle, half of the total turns are wound on.   Then the
skein is tied in two places with a cord or tape.   Without cutting the wire,
the rest of the skein is wound upon the first section with a space between.
The crossover of the single wire from the first section to the second

section should be made at the end of the skein opposite to the lead end. This crossover end is put in the motor first. The winding is started in the same way as when winding a skein which is not split. After the winding is in the first two slots, however, before the first twist is made the two halves of the winding are separated. Then the twist is taken in the top half of the skein and this is shoved through the opening of the stator, and the coil sides are put in place in the slots. Then the other half of the skein is twisted and it is shoved through and the coil sides put in

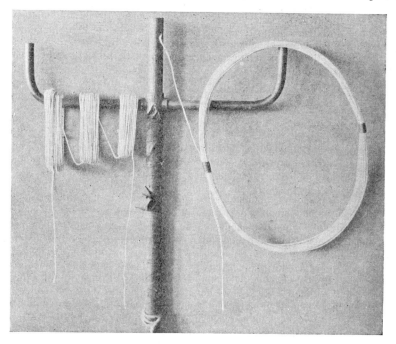

FIG. 97.—This illustration shows coils wound as a three-gang group and as a skein. Note the connections between the gang wound coils.

place on top of the preceding ones. In Fig. 94 the upper section of the skein is shown crossed ready to put through the slot. After both sections are put through the slots, the stator is turned around and the operation repeated. This time the lower section of the skein is on top.

With the split winding as well as the simple skein winding, instead of shoving the entire skein through the slot the simpler method can be used as already described. This is the method in which a small loop only is shoved through the opening.

When putting the main winding in the slots in which the starting winding also will go, room must be left for the starting winding. Two or more loose fitting fiber wedges should be put into the slot into which the starting winding goes.

When putting in a skein winding after each twist there will be a tendency for the wires in each section to cross and twist. When this occurs, work such crosses and twists into the slot just finished. This can be done with finger and thumb.

How to Bring Out Stator Leads.—To determine which side of the stator the leads will come out on with a skein winding, count the number of times the skein passes through the slots on one side of any pole. In Fig. 85, form *B*, the left-hand side of the running winding data, (top line) shows 1-2-2-1, or a total of six. With an even count the leads will come out on the opposite side started on. In Fig. 93*A*, the leads point towards the bottom of the page in starting and at the finish, as in Fig. 93*K*, the leads point upwards. With an odd total, the leads will come out on the same side started on.

How to Calculate the Length of Skein to Use.—When the length of a skein cannot be obtained from the old winding or the motor has been stripped without saving a complete skein, the length required can be roughly obtained by trial with a single wire. This wire should be laid

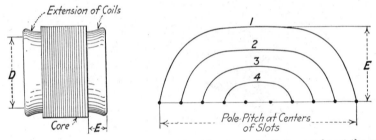

Fig. 98.—Diagram for finding the length of end loops of coils that extend past the ends of the slots.

in the slots exactly as the skein of wire will be laid, making proper allowance for the building up of the skein ends from slot to slot. Then remove the wire and measure it. Make up a trial skein of this length and wind it in the slots. One more correction in length will usually be enough to make the skein fit and this can then be used for making up the others. This is a quicker and about as satisfactory a way of getting the length of skein as to spend the time to calculate it.

When a winding is so burned or damaged that a complete skein cannot be removed and saved, the number of times a skein is looped through each slot and the number of turns in the skein and the distance the ends of the winding extend out from the ends of the slots should be noted. Then measure the average diameter (*D*) of the stator; that is, from the center of the slot depth on one side to the center of the slot depth on the other as shown in Fig. 98. The pole pitch can then be calculated from the formula:

Pole pitch = $(3.14 \times D) \div$ number of poles. When D is measured in inches, the pole pitch will also be in inches and represent the distance from the center of one slot to the center of another a pole pitch apart. Then compare this distance with the nearest slot centers that fit this distance on the stator and layout the actual distance in inches as checked on the stator, on a straight line as shown in Fig. 98. Mark this line, pole pitch at slot centers, as shown. Then mark the distance the complete

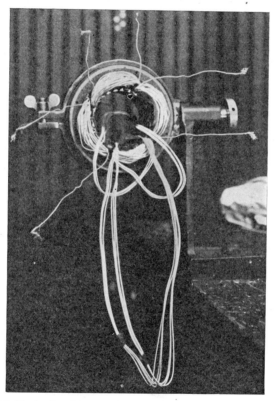

Fig. 99.—This illustration shows a split-skein being wound in the slots. The skein has been split into three sections. The first or bottom section is shown twisted and being wound into the slots first to reduce the piling up of the ends.

winding extends from the end of the slot as E and draw in the lines representing the number of times the skein is looped through the slots. Bend pieces of bare wire the length of lines 1, 2, 3 and 4 and measure them. Then multiply each of these lengths by the number of times the skein is looped through each slot and add up these dimensions. This will give the length of the skein projecting out one end of the slots. Multiply this by 2 and this is the length of both ends. The length of skein in the slots when added to length at the ends will make up the total length of

skein. This length in the slots is found by measuring the length of slot
and multiplying by the number of times the skein is put through the core
and then by two to include the two slots the skein is put in every time it
is put through the core.   From these dimensions a trial skein must be
made up and wound in the slots.   If too short or too long, a correction
must be made and the skein wound in again.   It will thus be seen that
this method is a cut and try one as in the case where one wire is used to
make up a trial skein.

CHAPTER XVI

HOW A HAND WINDING IS PUT ON A STATOR

When winding a small-alternating current motor stator by hand, one wire is threaded in at a time. The wire is unwound from a reel and cut at the finish of each coil. This type of winding is resorted to when the wire is large or when the slots are high and narrow. In a hand winding, the wire is formed into a loop like the letter "*e*," as shown in Fig. 101. This loop is formed usually with the right hand, and then pushed through the stator opening and grasped with the first finger and humb of the

Fig. 100.—Completed single-phase stator with starting winding skein wound and running or main winding hand wound. These windings are shown tied together with cord.

left hand and at the same time guiding the wire into the proper slot on the side of the pole furthest from the winder, as in Fig. 101, which shows the wire ready to enter the slot. Then the left hand guides the wire into the proper slot on the near end of the pole, the wire being held in its proper place across the back end with the left hand, while the wire is pulled tight with the right hand.

Starting Hand-wound Coils.—Hand-wound coils are started in the two inside slots in the same manner as a skein winding. When these two slots are filled the next two are started. As may be seen from *A*, Fig. 102

131

slots 3 and 5 are first filled, then slots 2 and 6, and last, slots 1 and 7. The last section of coil *B* also overlaps coil *A* in slot 7. In the winding shown in *A*, Fig. 102, the wire is cut after each coil is in place and the sleeving is put on. The coil ends are later connected up to form poles. (See Chap. XVII.) Each succeeding coil is wound in the same direction. For instance, the wire is started in slot 1 and wound across the back to slot 5 and then in succession to slots 2, 6, 1 and 7, making clockwise wind-

ings in all cases. Likewise coils *B*, *C* and *D* are all wound in the same direction.

How to Keep Wires from Climbing above Core.—To keep the winding from climbing up above the core, it is a good plan to use pieces of round cold-rolled steel, cut in 8-in. lengths. These should be about ⅛,

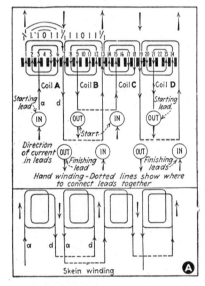

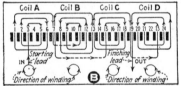

Fig. 101.—This is the way the loops of a hand winding are slipped through the opening and into the slots. A skein winding may be put on in the same manner after the winder has had some experience.

Fig. 102.—These diagrams show the out-and-in-method of connecting a skein or hand winding.

In the upper part of *A* is shown the method of connecting up a skein winding after it is in place. At the lower part of *A* is a diagram showing the connections for a hand-winding in which the wire is cut between coils. Note that in both of these cases when the current is assumed to come "out" of the finishing lead of one pole, it passes "in" on the starting lead of the next pole. The coils are all wound in the same direction, clockwise. It is not necessary to cut the leads of a hand winding if it is put on as shown in *B*. In this case, the first coil is wound clockwise, the second counter-clockwise, the third clockwise and the winding is continued in this manner. It will be noted that the coils form alternately north and south poles.

³⁄₁₆ or ¼ in. in diameter. They should slide easily into the slots but be too large to pass out of the opening at the top of the slot. These bars are placed in the slots reserved for the starting winding and the wire is wound underneath them as shown in Fig. 103. The wire goes up to the bars but the slot holds them down so that there will be room for the start-

ing winding.   The dotted lines in Fig. 102 indicate the way the leads
are connected together to get the right polarity.

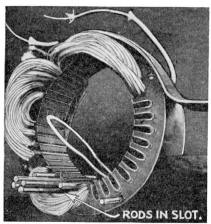

Fig. 103.—In hand winding steel rods are placed in the slots which are to be left vacant when putting on the running winding.   The wire is wound around underneath these rods, which hold the coils down and reserve room for the starting winding to be put on later.

Fig. 104.—How the completed running and starting coils look after being bound together with cord.   This is a ⅛-hp., four-pole, 60-cycle, 110-volt motor.   The running coils are hand-wound, while the starting coils are skein-wound.

Fig. 105.—A single-phase, ¼-hp. motor with the windings on the rotor.
The main winding is hand wound and the starting winding skein wound.   The switch shown at the left is in the form of a collector ring having two rings and three terminals.   One terminal has both a starting and a running lead connected to it, another a running lead and the third a starting lead. The starting circuit is broken when the motor reaches about 75 per cent of full speed.

Winding Coils without Cutting the Wire between Coils.—It is

possible to eliminate some of the soldered joints between coils of a hand
winding by winding alternate coils in the opposite direction and not

cutting the wire between coils, as shown in *B*, Fig. 102. Coil *A*, in *B* of Fig. 102, is wound in the same direction as coil *A*, in *A*, of Fig. 102, but the wire is not cut at the finish of the coil in *B*, Fig. 102. It is brought around to slot 11 of coil *B*, then across the back of the stator to slot 9

Fig. 106.—Putting the running winding on a small stator. The starting coils are skein wound and put on as soon as two running coils are in place.

The skein coils hang on the rack in front of the winder. Note the rack for the wire reel under the bench and the device to keep the wire from springing over the edge of the reel. The *L* shaped piece of iron with a hole for the wire, mounted on the side of the reel sags the wire and keeps it from uncoiling. Also note the tin gutter along the edge of the bench to prevent small tools from rolling to the floor.

and successively through slots 12, 8, 13 and 7. This coil *B* is wound counter-clockwise as indicated by the small circles with arrows. Coil *C* is wound in the same direction as coil *A* and likewise coil *D* is wound the same as coil *B*. This method of winding saves cutting the wire and soldering, and does not require checking and grouping of coils later on.

In Fig. 105 is shown a type of single-phase motor in which the rotor carries the running and starting windings, while the stator forms the squirrel-cage winding. The rotor is hand wound, both running and

Slot No.	1	2	3	4	5	6	7	8	9	10	11	12	13	14	15	16	17	18	19	(20)	21	22	23	24	25	26	27	28	29	30	31	32	33	34	35	36
Main Winding	1/1	2	2	1				1	2	2	1/1	2	2	1			1	2	2	1/1	2	2	1			1	2	2/1	2	2	1			1	2	2
Starting Winding				1	1	1	1							1	1	1	1							1	1	1	1						1	1	1	1

A

Slot No.	1	2	3	4	5	6	7	8	9	10	11	12	13	14	15	16	17	18	19	20	21	22	23	24	25	26	27	28	29	30	31	32	33	34	35	36
Main Winding	1	1	1				1	1	1	1	1	1			1	1	1	1	1	1			1	1	1	1	1	1			1	1	1		1	1
Starting Winding			2	1/1	2					2	1/1	2					2	1/1	2				2	1/1	2				2	1/1	2					

B

Fig. 107.—Chart showing distribution for a 4-pole, 36-slot motor.

starting windings and to eliminate leads, the coils are wound without cutting the wire between them as shown in Fig. 102*B*; that is, every other coil is wound in an opposite direction.

Slot No.	1	2	3	4	5	6	7	8	9	10	11	12	13	14	15	16	17	18	19	20	21	22	23	24	25	26	27	28	29	30	31	32	33	34	35	36
Main Winding	1/1	2	1		1	2	1/1	2	1		1	2	1/1	2	1		1	2	1/1	2	1		1	2	1/1	2	1		1	2	1/1	2	1		1	2
Starting Winding			2	1/1	2				2	1/1	2				2	1/1	2				2	1/1	2				2	1/1	2				2	1/1	2	

Fig. 108.—Chart showing distribution for a 6-pole, 36-slot motor.

Figure 106 shows a winding bench used in a large factory. The girl in the foreground is putting in a hand winding. Note the loop in the wire and the wire rack at the foot of the bench, also note that the starting coils are put in as soon as two running coils are in place.

Slot No.	1	2	3	4	5	6	7	8	9	10	11	12	13	14	15	16	17	18	19	20	21	22	23	24
Main Winding	1/1	2	2	1					1	2	2	2	1/1	2	2	1					1	2	2	2
Starting Winding			1	2	2	2	1/1	2	2	1					1	2	2	2	1/1	2	2	2	1	

Fig. 109.—Chart showing distribution for a 2-pole, 24-slot motor.

The remarks regarding the location of the winding in reference to the field stud bolts, given in Chap. XV, page 122, also apply to a hand winding.

Slot No.	1	2	3	4	5	6	7	8	9	10	11	12	13	14	15	16	17	18	19	20	21	22	23	24
Main Winding	1	1			1	1	1	1				1	1	1	1			1	1	1	1		1	1
Starting Winding			1	1		2			1	1					1	1					1	1		

Fig. 110.—Chart showing distribution for a 4-pole, 24-slot motor.

How Starting and Running Windings Are Distributed in Slots.—

The pitch of coils as wound in the slots varies with number of slots and number of poles of the motor stator. For a 36-slot, 4-pole stator the arrangements shown in Fig. 107*A* and *B* can be used. The arrangement shown in *A* of Fig. 107 is most common for the reason that the starting winding is less concentrated. When the distribution shown in *B* of Fig. 107 is used the starting winding would not have as advantageous a distribution as in *A*, and a smaller size of wire would be required for the main winding because the number of wires per slot would be larger for the same effective number of turns and consequently the copper loss

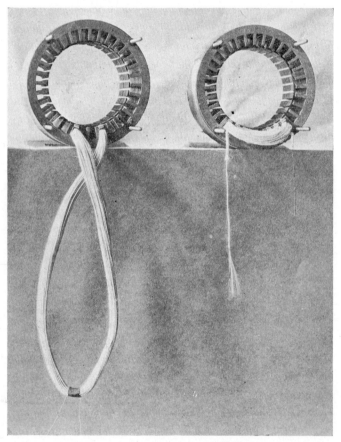

Fig. 111.—The start (left) and finish (right) of a skein winding for one pole group. Note the twist in the skein before inserting it through the slots the second time.

would be higher. Under some conditions of pole and slot combinations it may be satisfactory to use a winding distribution so that adjacent main poles do not lap. In *A* of Fig. 107 the main winding of one pole is shown wound in slots 1, 2, 3, 4 and 7, 8, 9, 10, and the starting winding in slots 3, 4, 5, and 6. The numbers in the squares of the arrangement diagram indicate the number of times the skein passes through each slot.

In Fig. 108 the winding arrangement for a 6-pole motor with 36 slots is shown. Figure 109 is for a 2-pole motor with 24 slots and Fig. 110 for a 4-pole motor with 24 slots. These are the number of poles and slots most used.

When a skein is used the length of skein (See Chap. XV for finding the length required) for the starting winding is found in the same way as

Fig. 112.—The start of a hand winding in a single-phase stator.

Note that the wire from the reel is held in the operator's right hand and the loop made in the wire as it is put into the slots is caught and held by the first finger and thumb of the left hand. The left hand guides the wire around the coil ends and into the proper slot, then the wire is pulled tight with the right hand. The slack is then pulled from the reel and another loop formed and pushed through the stator with the right hand as before. Note the position of the coil in reference to the stud bolts. Also note the wooden pin through the stator slot at the center of the coil used to prevent the wire from climbing above the stator bore. A convenient stand and holder is shown in this illustration.

for the running winding and is put on last above the running winding in the slots as shown in the diagrams of winding arrangements. It is usually located with respect to the running winding so that the pole center of the starting winding is midway between the pole center of the main winding. This is a resistance winding and its length should be the same in a rewound motor as in the original winding so that its resistance will not be materially changed.

In most cases the starting winding for a single-phase motor is skein wound and the main or running winding hand wound with a single wire.

Mould and Hand Winding.—The mould-winding method is sometimes employed in winding small motors of the induction type. It takes its name from the fact that the pole coils are first wound on a mould, and then placed in the slots.   In most cases one pole set of coils is wound together so that individual coils do not have to be connected together after being placed in the slots.   As far as the final results are concerned, the mould type of winding has the same general appearance as the hand type. Any mould-wound small motor can be hand wound; that is, one wire at a time wound in by hand—when it is repaired.   The winding diagram of both the gang- and mould-wound, and hand-wound motors is the same.

The starting windings of motors with either mould-wound or hand-wound main windings are generally skein wound, although they too may be mould-wound, but they should not be hand wound because the resistance of the starting winding is very important and, in the case of a hand winding, would vary too much.   When the starting winding is mould-wound, and no mould is available for rewinding, it is necessary to measure the entire length of the starting winding coil of one pole of the motor to be rewound and to wind the same amount of wire into the slots.

Main Features of Single-phase Motors.—Single-phase motors can be roughly divided into two classes: (1) The split-phase type having two windings, one used while starting and the other when running, with a squirrel cage rotor; the repulsion-start type having one running winding with a wound rotor.

In the split-phase motor the starting winding is of high resistance and small inductance while the running winding is of high inductance and low resistance.   These two windings are placed in the stator 90 electrical degrees apart; that is, the center of a starting winding lines up midway between the centers of two coils of the running winding and is cut out of the motor circuit by a centrifugal switch just before normal speed is reached.

In the repulsion-start motor, the primary winding is on the stator and is similar to the running winding of the split-phase motor.   The rotor has a commutator and brushholder similar to a direct-current motor, except that the brushholder is short-circuited through the rocker arm. The stator usually has a bipolar winding.   The stator winding is connected to the single-phase supply and the motor starts because of the repulsion between closely approaching poles of like sign on the stator and rotor.

The shading-coil type of motor has a main field winding connected to the single-phase supply in connection with which a small bare copper short-circuiting winding is used on the field pole.   This shading coil is off dead center with respect to the main field flux while the current in the rotor winding is symmetrical with respect to the main field.   On starting, the pole produced in the rotor winding is repelled by the similar pole produced in the field winding, tending to cause the rotor to turn toward the shading coil and thus start the motor.   The objection to this type of motor is that it runs only in one direction and cannot be reversed.

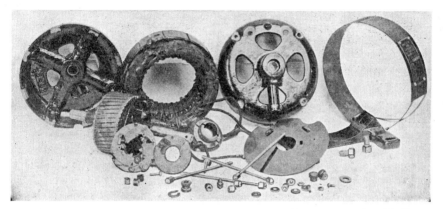

Fig. 113.—Completed stator winding ready for assembly of rotor and end bells.

In some designs both end brackets can be taken off and the complete stator turned end for end in respect to the rotor.   This will reverse the direction of rotation.

In the case of the split-phase motor, its direction is reversed by interchanging the terminals of either the starting or running windings, but not both.   The repulsion-start motor is reversed by shifting the brushholder to one side or the other of the neutral position on the rocker arm.

CHAPTER XVII

CONNECTING A SKEIN-WOUND OR A HAND-WOUND STATOR

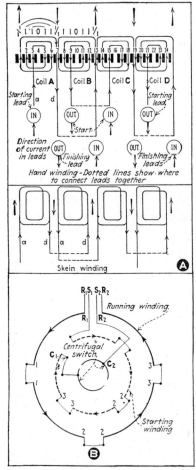

FIG. 114.—In the upper part of A is shown the method of connecting up a skein winding after it is in place. At the lower part of A is a diagram showing the connections for a hand winding in which the wire is cut between coils.

Note that in both of these cases when the current is assumed to come "out" of the finishing lead of one pole, it passes "in" on the starting lead of the next pole. The coils are all wound in the same direction clockwise. A consequent-pole motor having four coils and eight poles is shown at B. The diagram shown here is for a series connection.

After a winding is in place on the stator, the next job is to connect it up. An easy way to tell which leads should be connected together, is to use what is called the *in-and-out* rule. When one has learned to apply this rule it will not be necessary to use a compass test for polarity.

Connecting Up Coils of Hand-wound and Skein-wound Stators.— Diagrams A and B in Fig. 114 will help to explain this method, which applies to both the running and starting windings of either hand-wound or skein-wound stators. First, take the running coils and bring out the leads as shown in diagrams A or B, Fig. 114. The starting and finishing leads of each coil should be brought out to the same side of the stator. The drawing A shows how the leads on a skein winding will appear. To make sure that the leads a and d belong to the same coils, test them with a test lamp. Then take any convenient lead to start with and assume that the current is flowing into the coil through this lead as is assumed for the lead in slot 3 of A, Fig. 114. Then the current must flow out of this coil through the finishing lead in slot 7. Now the problem is to know which lead and which coil the lead in slot 7 should be connected to. If the current in slot 7 is *out*, then the current in slots 7, 8 and 9 must also be coming *out* as shown by the arrow. Then the starting lead of coil *B* is *out*, whereas an *in* lead is desired to take the current coming from coil *A*. The lead of coil *B* which is in slot 13 is an *in* lead and, therefore, the lead *d* of coil *A* in slot 7 is connected with the lead *d* of coil *B* in slot 13. Follow this *in-and-out* rule throughout and the connections will be correct.

To state the rule briefly, connect an *out* lead to an *in* lead of the next adjacent coil. Or it may be worded in this fashion: Connect a starting lead to a starting lead and a finishing lead to a finishing lead. Then if a starting lead is picked out for the first lead of the entire winding, the last lead will also be a starting lead. The last lead will be a finishing lead if a finishing lead is picked out for the first lead. With a skein winding the leads to the left can be called the starting leads.

How to Determine Direction of Rotation.—By using the above rule for connecting the coils, it is possible to have the motor run in any desired

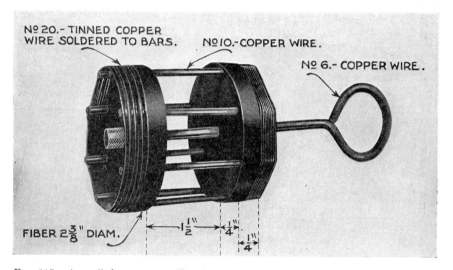

Fig. 115.—A small dummy rotor like this can be used to tell the direction of rotation.
    When this rotor is held inside the opening it will revolve in the same direction as the real rotor will turn when it is put in the motor. This little rotor may be used for testing the direction of rotation of large motors. It is held inside the stator close to the iron and moved around the core.

direction. If a starting coil is connected so that it has the same polarity as an adjacent running coil, the rotor will turn from the starting coil toward the running coil. The reason for this is that when connected to the line, the current in the starting coil is at a maximum a short time before the current in the running coil is at a maximum. This means that the shifting or revolving magnetic pole produced by a combination of the starting and running windings travels from the starting winding to the running winding of the same polarity. The rotor is dragged around in the direction in which this magnetism moves. To test the direction of rotation after the stator is connected, a small dummy rotor may be made

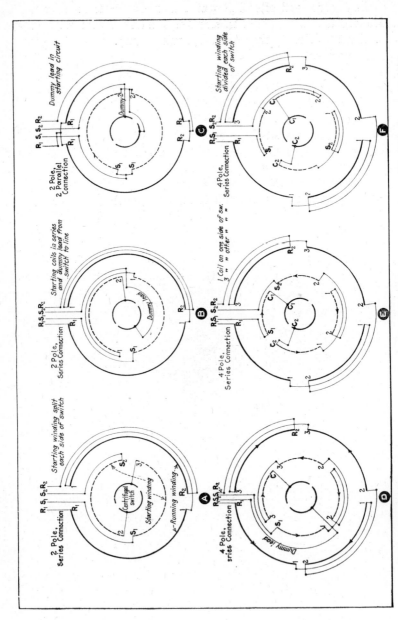

Fig. 116.—Connections for split-phase stators of small alternating-current motors. (Continued on page 143.)

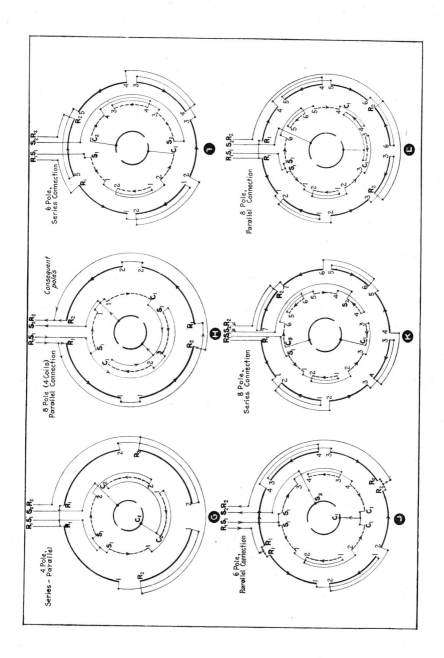

up as shown in Fig. 115. Starting and running windings are connected to the line as they would be in starting conditions and this dummy rotor is held inside of the stator. It will revolve in the direction in which the motor would turn. If it is necessary to reverse the direction of rotation the starting leads should be interchanged.

Connecting Various Types of Single-phase Motors.—Figures 116, 117 and 118 show the connections for various types of single-phase motors. In Fig. 116 are ordinary connection diagrams for motors of two, four, six and eight poles. These diagrams also indicate the different methods of connecting the starting winding. In all the diagrams the heavy full lines represent the main windings and the dotted lines the starting windings. The small split inner circles indicate the centrifugal switch

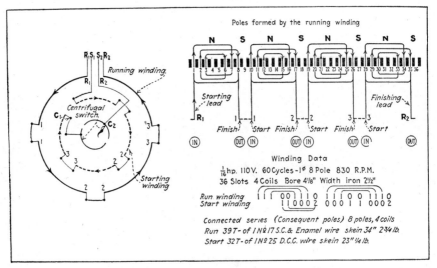

FIG. 117.—A winding diagram for a consequent-pole motor having four coils and eight poles is shown with a series connection of coils at the left.

which is in the circuit of the starting winding. The diagram *A*, in Fig. 116 shows one starting coil connected on each side of the switch, while *B* shows the two coils in series on one side of the switch, while a dummy lead is brought from the other side of the switch. For four-pole motors, the diagram shown at *F* in Fig. 116 is probably the best one to use.

The drawing in *C* of Fig. 118 shows how to connect a small hand-wound compensated repulsion-type motor (type R I, General Electric Company). Note that there is no connection between the compensating winding and the line.

The stator of a four-pole single-phase (Westinghouse, type AR) repulsion-type motor is shown in Fig. 119. This is a coil-wound machine with a concentric winding of six coils in each group. The sixth coil in each group overlaps the sixth coil in the adjacent group. Six different sizes of coils are required and four of each size. Each coil is threaded in, starting with the smallest coil, then the ends are taped from slot to slot. Four leads are brought out for series or parallel connections.

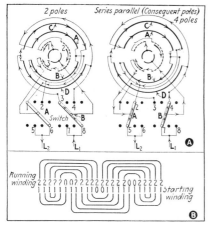
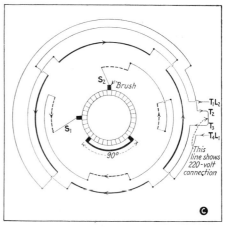

Fig. 118.—A special two-speed winding and connections for a repulsion-type motor.

The two-speed winding shown in *A* and *B* may be connected by means of the switch for either two poles or four poles. The drawing (left) shows the position for two poles, which gives the higher speed. This shows a parallel connection. The right-hand diagram is also a parallel connection, but the polarity of alternate coils has been reversed, and this forms a four-pole consequent winding, which gives the lower speed. The starting connections remain the same in both cases. The relative position of the running and starting windings is shown in *B*. At *C* are shown the connections for a repulsion type motor. This is a General Electric motor, type R1 526-4, 110 to 220 volts, $\frac{1}{2}$ hp., four-pole, single phase, 60 cycles, 1,800 r.p.m. For 220 volts, connect T_2 and T_3 together, and connect T_1 and T_4 to the line. For 110 volts connect T_1 and T_2 to one line and connect T_3 and T_4 to the other line. The armature has a two-circuit wave winding.

Fig. 119.—A coil-wound stator of a single-phase motor.

This differs from the usual repulsion motor in that the coils are wound before being placed in the stator. The motor is a four-pole single-phase machine. It has six coils per pole in a concentric chain winding. The sixth coil of each group overlaps the sixth coil of the adjacent group. Six sizes of coils are used of each size. Each coil is threaded in and then the ends are taped from slot to slot.

A consequent-pole motor having four coils and eight poles is shown in Fig. 117. The diagram shows how the coils are connected together to form the consequent poles and the winding data is given below in this diagram. A special two-speed winding, which may be connected for either two poles or four poles, is shown in Fig. 118, *A* and *B*. A motor of this kind is used on wood-turning, dental lathes, etc. The drawing *A* shows the connections and the switch position for the two poles which give the higher speed. The running winding is in two sections and eight leads are brought out. The starting winding consists of three coils as shown, one long coil and two short ones. The diagram *A* shows a parallel connection, while *B* is also a parallel connection but the polarity of alter-

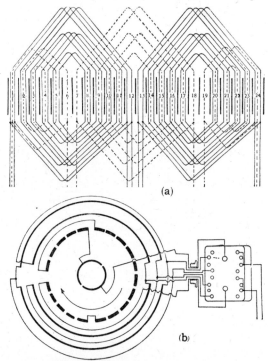

Fig. 120.—In this diagram (a) shows how the leads are brought out for connection to a pole-changing switch for a two-speed motor. (b) shows connections of main and starting windings to a pole-changing switch for a two-speed motor.

nate coils has been reversed, thus forming a four-pole, consequent winding which gives the lower speed. The starting connections remain the same in both cases. The relative position of the running and starting windings is shown in *C* of Fig. 118.

The stator windings of the single-phase repulsion motors are generally connected in two sections, as shown in Fig. 118*C*. This is done to enable the motor to operate on 110- or 220-volt circuits; that is, for 110 volts the two sections are connected in parallel and for 220 volts they are put in series.

Changing Single-phase Motor for Operation at Two Speeds.—The procedure to follow in changing a single-phase motor which has a starting and main winding so as to operate at two speeds by means of a pole, changing switch can be illustrated by the following details for a ⅙-hp. single-phase, 60-cycle, 110-volt motor connected to operate at 1,700 and 3,400 r.p.m. The main winding is wound with two coils as in a two-pole motor except there are two wires in parallel and eight leads are brought out for connection to the pole-changing switch, as shown in (*a*) of Fig. 120. The starting winding consists of one coil with two-pole pitch or throw and two coils with four-pole pitch or throw, six leads being brought out from these three coils for connection to the pole-changing switch, as in (*a*) of Fig. 120. The leads from the main and starting windings are connected to the pole changing switch as in (*b*) of Fig. 120. With the motor leads at the left of the pole-changing switch in (*b*) of Fig. 120 numbered from top to bottom, connecting lead 1 to one side of the line and lead 3 to the other gives the four-pole connection or the

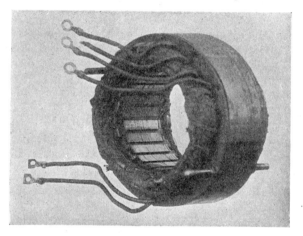

Fig. 121.—Stator of a single-phase motor that has six leads brought out. The two bottom leads go to the starting switch. Two of the top four leads are the starting winding leads and the other two the running winding leads that connect to the line.

consequent-pole arrangement. By connecting leads 2 and 4 across the line the two-pole connection will be obtained. The pole-changing switch is so arranged that the starting winding is connected across the line with the switch in either the two- or four-pole position. The two solid outside coils in (*a*) of Fig. 120 in each pole indicate the two coils which are wound in parallel as mentioned above. The operation of the motor as a two-pole or four-pole motor is the same as any series- and consequent-pole arrangement. The starting winding, however, functions along slightly different lines and an analysis of the flux from the various starting winding coils for the two connections of the switch will indicate that its operation is the same as a two-pole motor with one coil missing in the one case and a four-pole motor with two coils missing in the other case.

CHAPTER XVIII

REWINDING SMALL UNIVERSAL MOTORS

The small universal motor as used in adding machines, fans, drills, etc., can be divided into three classes: (1) the straight series type; (2) the series type with shifted brushes; (3) the compensated series type.

The Straight Series Type of Universal Motors.—This is the most simple in construction. It has laminated pole pieces, which is an absolute necessity on alternating-current work to eliminate heating of the iron circuit. When carrying an alternating magnetic flux, the armature ampere turns will be considerably higher than the field ampere turns. This is necessary to improve power factor and reduce core losses, and is one of the most important characteristics of this type of motor. The

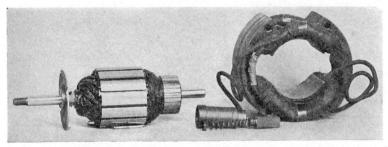

Fig. 122.—Field and armature of a series type of universal motor used in portable drills and grinders.

One lead of one field coil connects to the line, the other is connected to the adjacent coil. The lead from the other coil connects to a brush holder. The other brush holder is connected to the other side of the line. The field coils are therefore in series ahead of the armature.

greater the number of turns in the field circuit, the higher will be the reactance, which causes the current to lag behind the impressed voltage thus reducing the power output. With a high ratio of armature ampere turns to field ampere turns, the armature reaction is greater, which will distort the field and introduce commutating difficulties, due to strong armature and weak fields. The coil under commutation is in a magnetic field that tends to oppose the reversal of the current, thus causing sparking. On alternating current the current induced in the shorted coil is governed by the resistance of the coil.

The method used in the small, straight series type of universal motor to reduce sparking, is to use a brush having high contact resistance. Therefore, to get consistent good operating results with this type of universal, use the grade of brush specified by the maker of the motor.

Straight Series Universal Motor with Distributed Field and Shifted Brushes.—In this type the winding resembles the stator of a single-phase motor without the starting windings. That is, instead of one coil per pole, the coil is spread out in a number of slots. With this type of field the brushes are shifted *against rotation.* This uses part of the field as a compensating winding, thus reducing the armature reaction and improving the power factor.

With this type of winding the brush position and armature lead throw are very important and should be carefully marked and checked when dismantling for repairs. However, a distributed winding has a higher impedance than a single field coil, so that for a small motor this type might be less efficient than a straight series type of good design.

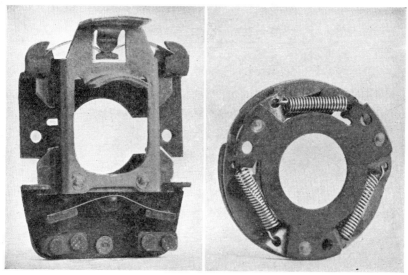

Fig. 122*A.*—This illustration shows the stationary and rotating elements of the centrifugal switch used on a Westinghouse single-phase motor.

The weights on the rotating part work between the two projections shown on the upper part of the stationary element. When these weights fly out the switch is opened. Then when the rotor slows down and stops, the weights spring back and close the switch ready for the starting of the motor again.

The Compensated-series Universal Motor with Two Independent Windings.—The main winding is usually concentrated in one coil per pole, and the compensating winding distributed over the pole face as in large direct-current generators. The polarity of the compensating winding should be the same as the main field adjacent to it, *against* the *direction* of *rotation,* and when the rotation is reversed, the polarity of the compensating winding must also be reversed.

This type of winding compensates for armature reaction and results in high power factor and fair efficiency and makes the universal motor applicable in larger size motors, but there is still present the high value of current in the short-circuited coil. On the large single-phase universal motors, used in railway work, a compensating winding is used and resistance leads are placed in the bottom of the armature slots and in series with the coil and the commutator. Thus the resistance of the coil under commutation is increased, which improves the operation.

Fig. 123.—Inserting a coil in the stator of a small universal motor.

From the foregoing remarks it is obvious that it is the armature reaction, impedance of the field and the current in the coil under commutation that decides the type of winding that will be used in a universal motor for any given application. In general, the lower the full-load current the simpler will be the winding. Where heavy currents are required a full-compensated, two-winding field with preventive (resistance) leads will be required.

Points to Remember When Stripping a Universal Motor.—When stripping the winding of a universal motor, that is, one which operates on either direct-current or alternating-current, it is important to remember that in winding the fields of this type of motor, the coils must be put back in their proper positions in relation to the brushes. The field core of a universal motor can usually be put back only in one position in the frame. Most of the cores are built up of laminations riveted together. The core is fastened to the motor frame and held in position by two set screws which project into two corresponding holes drilled in the stator core.

If the stator winding is stripped without paying any attention to the position of the main field coils in reference to these line-up holes, the proper position will have to be found by trial. This can be done satisfactorily, (see page 156) but the extra time and trouble can be saved if the slots containing the main coils are marked before the old winding is removed.

When rewinding universal motors without noting very carefully the throw of the coils and the connections to the commutator, for the old winding, some difficulty may be encountered in locating the proper bars and coil connections for a particular brush position.

Some small universal motors operate with the brushes located a little back of the neutral position, the amount of this shift depending upon the design of the motor. When rewinding such a motor the only safe rule to follow is to note carefully the throw of the coils in the original winding and the connections to the commutator and connect the new winding in the same way. These small armatures are usually wound with a coil span slightly less than the number of slots divided by the number of poles. This is done to make winding easy and save end room. For such windings the neutral point for the brush position is at the location of the coil ends on the commutator when the two sides of the coil are at equal distances from the center of the pole face.

Kinds of Windings Used on Universal Motors.—There are two general kinds of windings used on the stators of universal motors. One of these is similar to the field winding of a series motor while the other has, in addition to such a winding, a compensating winding. The smaller universal motors, such as those used in fans, vacuum sweepers, drink mixers, etc., are simply series motors with a laminated field. The punchings are usually shaped as shown in Figs. 123 and 124. The field coils are wound in the same way as any mush direct-current field coil. They are left soft and flexible so that they can be sprung over the pole horns as shown in Fig. 124. After the field coils are in place, two fiber or heavy cardboard strips are put in on top of them to act as wedges to hold the coils in position.

For the straight, series type of universal motor, the armature is usually connected between the two field coils.   One lead of each coil is

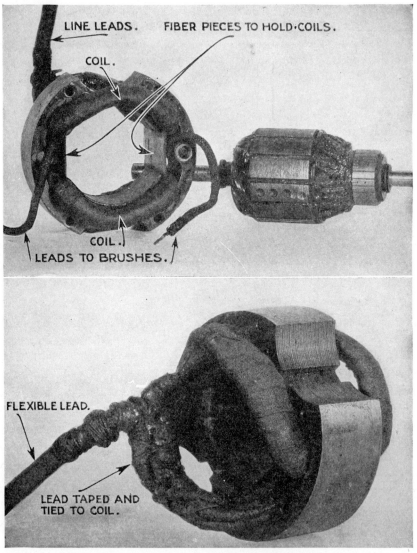

FIG. 124.—A small universal motor without compensating field.   Note how the leads have been taped and tied with string to prevent breaking in service.

connected to the line and the other lead of each coil is connected to the brush holder.   This eliminates a field connection inside the motor.

In Fig. 125 another motor of the single-series type is shown.   In this motor, however, the field windings are distributed in 24 slots.

Compensating Windings for Universal Motors.—In the larger universal motors compensating windings are required to cut down the voltage induced in the coils which are short-circuited by a brush. This voltage is induced by the alternating flux regardless of the brush position. The magnitude of the voltage will depend upon the impedance of the coils. In the small motors the resistance of the coils is usually high enough to limit the induced current to such a low value that a compensating winding is not required to obtain satisfactory commutation. But in most of the

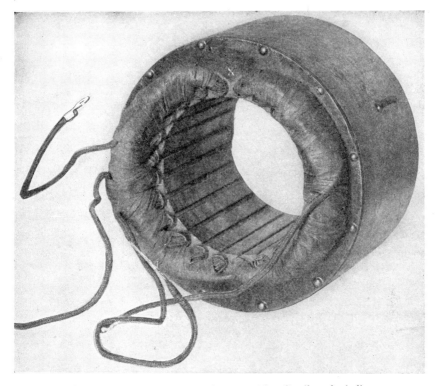

Fig. 125.—Stator of a universal motor with a distributed winding.

This stator has no compensating winding but the main winding has many turns of fairly small wire whose resistance limits the amperage on direct current. The motor is part of a drill made by the Chicago Pneumatic Tool Company. It is type 3B, which is rated at 240 volts and 1,500 to 2,000 watts full load. It has twenty-four coils each having twenty-four turns of No. 22 silkenite wire. The pitch is 1 and 7.

larger machines the coils consist of a few turns of a large size of conductor. Hence the resistance is low and a compensating winding is necessary.

This compensating winding is connected in series with the armature and displaced 90 electrical degrees from the main field. It is usually distributed over a number of slots in the pole face, while the main winding consists of only one or two coils per pole. A compensating winding of this kind opposes the magnetism generated by the alternating current

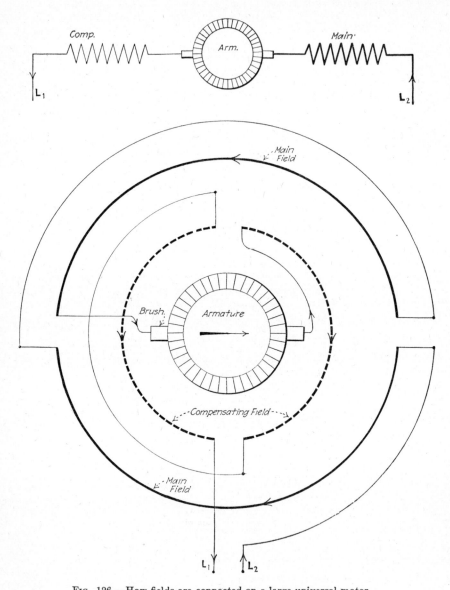

FIG. 126.—How fields are connected on a large universal motor.

This motor has a compensating field. The data which was taken when the motor was stripped before rewinding is shown in Fig. 127.

in the armature. It thus prevents the induction of current in the coils under commutation and thus eliminates sparking at the brushes.

A compensating winding is used in the stator of the blower motors used in connection with the main motors on the locomotives of the New York, New Haven and Hartford Railway. These motors operate on 600 volts direct current in the city limits and 1,200 volts, alternating current outside. The armature is similar to any ordinary lap wound direct-current armature and the stator has a distributed, strap copper, two-layer, diamond shape lap winding. It is similar in appearance to any induction motor stator but the stator winding is divided into two sections—a main and compensating winding and with this motor the brushholders are fixed. Therefore, when stripping the stator, the slots in which the leads of each winding are brought out should be marked and a diagram drawn to enable the winder to pick up the windings in proper relation to the brushes. A shift of one slot will cause trouble. An example of such trouble is given on page 157.

Winding Coils in Compensated Universal Motor.—The field core construction used in the compensated type of universal motor is prac-

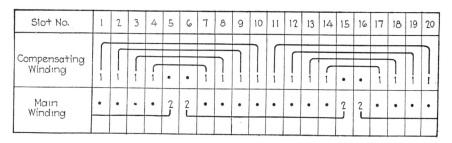

Slot No.	1	2	3	4	5	6	7	8	9	10	11	12	13	14	15	16	17	18	19	20
Compensating Winding	1	1	1	1	•	•	1	1	1	1	1	1	1	1	•	•	1	1	1	1
Main Winding	•	•	•	•	2	2	•	•	•	•	•	•	•	•	2	2	•	•	•	•

Fig. 127.—Data for stator of a universal motor with a compensating winding.

This is the motor whose connections are shown in Fig. 126. When stripping the winding the following data was put down. No. of slots (20). No. of poles (2). Compensating coils (8). Connection, series. Turns (34). One No. 19 single-cotton and enamel wire. Total weight (1½ lb.). Main coils (2). Connection, series. Turns (34). One No. 22 single-cotton and enamel wire. Total weight (½ lb.).

tically the same as that of a single-phase stator. The core is laminated and there are many slots, usually partly closed. The two main field coils are wound up on a form in the same manner as the field coils of larger shunt motors. The field coils on a universal motor, however, are threaded into the slots without being taped. When the coils are in position in the stator the ends projecting beyond the core are taped from slot to slot. In shaping these coils on the stator they must be kept below the iron so they will not close up the compensating slots. The compensating winding is put in place in the same way as a single-phase stator is wound. This winding is usually of the skein type

In Fig. 126 are shown the connections of the main and compensating fields to the armature. The main winding is on one side of the armature while the compensating winding is on the other, all three of them being in series. In Fig. 128 is shown the armature, stator field and brush holder of a compensated universal motor.

Determining Brush Position by Trial.—If it has not been possible to determine the correct location of the coils with reference to the brushes, the proper brush position can be found by trial. To do this, press the stator in place in the frame, judging the brush position as closely as possible. Then put in the armature and put the end bells in place. Now try out the motor by connecting it to the line. If it sparks or heats, remove the screws from the end plate at the commutator end and shift this plate around until the motor operates satisfactorily on both alternat-

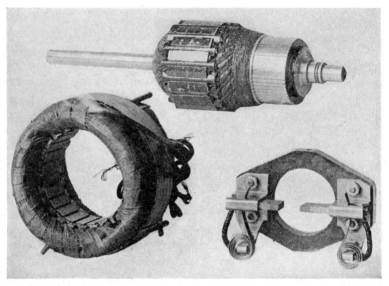

Fig. 128.—Lap wound armature, field and brush holders for a compensated universal motor.

ing current and direct current. Then make a mark on the field frame showing how much the screw holes on the end bells have been shifted away from the corresponding holes on the field frame. After this remove the end bell and make a chisel mark on the stator and its frame at the same place. Now press the stator out of its frame and shift it in the opposite direction and by the same amount as the end bell was shifted to get perfect commutation. The chisel marks can be used for guidance in doing this. Then press the stator back into its frame when it is in this correct position.

Two Unusual Features of Universal Motors.—One of the distinguishing features of a universal motor is that the armature will have a larger diameter in comparison than the armature of a straight direct-current motor of the same hp. rating. The field will have short, stubby pole pieces. These two features of construction are accounted for by the fact that the ampere-turns of the armature are greater in number than the ampere-turns of the field. It is for this reason that a compensated winding is required on the larger sizes to neutralize the magnetism developed by the armature winding.

Another feature of the universal motor is that usually with the same applied line voltage it will have a greater torque on direct current than it will on alternating current. The higher the frequency of the supply, the less will be the torque. On direct current the voltage drop in the field is due to the resistance of the coils alone, while on alternating current a greater voltage drop results from the impedance of the coils which is the resultant of both resistance and inductive effects. In fact, some of the series commutator type of motors have been designed to operate on either 300 volts direct current or 600 volts alternating current. Under both of these conditions the motor torque is practically equal.

Insulating Slots and Inserting Coils.—The insulation for slots and the method of inserting the skein wiring in them is the same as described in Chaps. XIV and XV.

Possible Trouble When Slots Containing Main Coils Are Not Marked. The following experience will illustrate the difficulties that arise when the slots containing the main field coils or the slots in which the leads are taken off these coils (top and bottom) with reference to a perpendicular line bisecting the center of the stator are not marked. A four-pole, 300-volt alternating-current and 150-volt direct-current motor was completely rewound without checking up and marking the original position of the main coils in the old winding. When an attempt was made to run this motor, it sparked at the brushes and the winding heated up excessively. Tests showed the winding clear of shorts, grounds and opens.

This motor stator had 40 slots, and a two-layer winding with diamond shaped coils made of two turns of $\frac{1}{16}$- by $\frac{1}{2}$-in. bare copper strap. Each turn was insulated so that one strap could be threaded in at a time. The pitch was 1 and 10. The coils were connected up into two separate windings; one the main field or torque winding, and the other, the auxiliary or compensating winding. When it was discovered that trouble was due to the failure to check up the position of the main field winding before the motor was stripped for rewinding, the procedure to determine the correct winding from the one put on was as follows:

The main winding was traced out and marked with chalk. Then the front end bracket was put on and the brushes were not found on the center lines of the main poles as they should have been. This meant that the stator must be reconnected or stripped and rewound again. The first course was found possible. The diagram in Fig. 129 shows the corrected winding as finally reconnected.

It was found that the winder made the mistake of using the bottom lead in slot 14 as S_1 instead of the bottom lead in slot 11 as shown in the corrected winding. Since the rest of the winding was picked up in the proper order, the completed winding was four slots out of line, which had the effect of shifting the main poles 27 mechanical degrees. The brushes were set on the center lines of slots 6-16-26-36 which should also be the center lines of the main or torque poles. Instead the winder had made the pole centers on slot 9-19-29-39. This brought a coil short-circuited

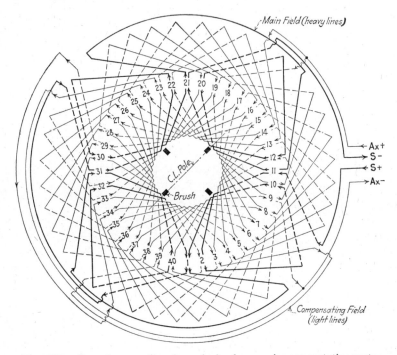

Fig. 129.—Correct connections for a single-phase, series commutating motor.

This is a four-pole motor for 300-volts alternating current or 150-volts direct current. It has 40 slots and 40 coils of two turns each. (Only one is shown.) Full lines represent top half of coil, the dotted lines the bottom half. Pitch is 1 and 10. Center line of brushes should pass through the center line of slots 6, 16, 26, and 36.

by the brush in an active field which resulted in large currents being induced in these main coils and cause the heating and sparking experienced.

The practice should be followed when rewinding stators of single-phase universal motors, of marking the slots in which the coils containing leads for the main winding lie whenever such a motor is stripped. This can be done by using a small steel stamp with the slot number. A drawing should then be made showing the correct coil layout, as in Fig. 129, with the same numbering so that the winding can be replaced in its proper position and the connecting leads easily located.

CHAPTER XIX

REWINDING A COMPENSATED-SERIES MOTOR

The following details describe a method of winding a single-phase, compensated-series motor with form-wound coils. The reasos for then compensated winding are given in Chap. XVIII. These form-wound

FIG. 130.—Series type of universal motor used in a vacuum cleaner. One field coil is connected to one brush holder while the other field lead and brush holder are connected to the line

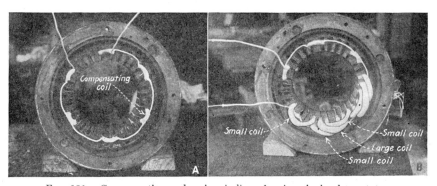

FIG. 131.—Compensating and main winding of series, single-phase stator.

At *A* the compensating winding is shown in place. The six compensating coils are placed around the six large teeth. At *B* is shown part of the main winding. This consists of eighteen coils, six of the coils being twice as large as the remaining coils. Note how the upper side of the first main coil is held in place during winding by several wedges placed over it in the slot.

coils are of the same dimensions but some of them have twice as many turns as the other. An unusual feature of the stator is that some of the teeth are wider than others.

The stator for which the winding information is given in what follows has 30 slots and 24 coils. There are 18 main coils and 6 compensating coils. Every fifth tooth has twice the area of the others, as shown in Fig. 131. The compensating coils are wound around these six large teeth.

Winding Compensating Coils on Stator.—The compensating coils are wound by hand on the stator, every alternate coil being wound in the opposite direction, as shown in *D* of Fig. 132. The wire is not cut at the

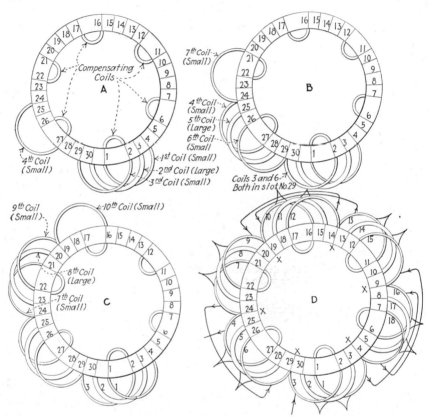

Fig. 132.—Steps in winding single-phase stator of a compensated-series motor.

end of each coil but is carried over to the next coil, thus doing away with soldered connections. The first compensating coil is started in slot 1 and finished in slot 2. Then the second coil is started in slot 6 and finished in slot 7. This is repeated around every large tooth, as shown in *A* of Fig. 132.

Winding Main Coils on Stator.—A part of the main winding is shown in place on the stator in *B* of Fig. 132. This winding consists of 18 coils. Six of these coils have twice as many turns per coil as the remaining twelve coils.

This winding is a combination of a winding with two slots per coil (single-layer) and a winding with one slot per coil (double-layer). A study of *B*, in Fig. 131, will show that each coil with the larger number of turns completely fills two slots. Each small coil is put in so that one side is in the same slot as one-half of a compensating coil; the other side overlaps another small coil. These small coils in turn are made to overlap each other in every sixth slot.

Figure 132 gives the steps in putting on the main winding. The compensating coils are indicated by the short loops inside the small circle.

Fig. 133.—Armature, field and brush holds of a compensated series type of universal motor. The stator has a distributed field and tapped compensated winding displaced 90 degrees.

The first main coil to be put in is a small coil. It is placed in slots 1 and 4. Slot 1 contains also one-half of a compensating coil. These two coil halves completely fill slot 1. The second main coil is a large coil and is put in slots 30 and 3, completely filling these slots. The third main coil (a small one) is put in slots 29 and 2. Slot 2 contains one-half of a compensating coil; therefore it is filled when the third main coil has been put in. The fourth main coil is put in slots 24 and 27. This is a small coil and fills up slot 27 which already contains one side of compensating coil.

In *B* of Fig. 132, a continuation of the winding is shown. The fifth coil is a large one and is put in slots 25 and 28 working in the opposite direction to the first group. Coil 6 is put in slots 26 and 29. Slot 26 also contains one side of a compensating coil. Slot 29 already holds one side of coil 3; therefore coils 3 and 6 overlap each other in slot 29 and this slot.

Coil 7 is started in slots 21 and 24 filling both slots, as slot 21 holds one side of a compensating coil and slot 24 contains one side of coil 4, as shown.

Fig. 134.—A gang mould for winding coils in a group without cutting the wire between them. Four sets of coils are being wound at once with each mould winding a different size of coil. For a 4-pole motor using three coils per group, the complete set of coils can be wound at one time.

The next drawing, *C*, of Fig. 132 shows the third group in place and the start of the fourth pole group. At *D* all the coils are in place with the groups connected. Note that coil 18 overlaps coil 1 in slot 4; also that twelve small coils fill eighteen slots. The winding is so distributed that these small coils overlap each other at six points and in twelve other slots they are put on top of the compensating coils. The six large coils fill the twelve slots.

The main coils can be wound on the same mould, the only difference being in the number of turns per coil. In the original winding the three coils per group were wound on what is known as a **gang mold** (Fig. 134).

This is a mold with three center pieces and with thin barriers between. The three coils are wound without cutting the wire. From three coils only two leads are brought out, start and finish, which does away with twelve stub connections. However, when only one motor is to be rewound the extra time required to make a gang mold is much greater than that required to stub up the groups.

The armature of the motor is wound similar to any standard direct-current wave-wound armature.

CHAPTER XX

SINGLE-PHASE FAN MOTOR WINDINGS

Since the single-phase fan motor is widely used and found in many types and designs, a knowledge of the developments in the construction and design of fan motor windings will be of assistance in handling repair work on the older as well as the newer types. What follows has been taken from an article published in the *Electric Journal* by E. W. Denman.

Commutator-type Series Fan Motors.—In the earliest stage of their development, it was found that fan motors wound for use on a direct-current circuit could be used on single-phase alternating-current circuits, but required a much higher voltage with severe sparking occurring at the brushes. To make a series motor operate on alternating current the

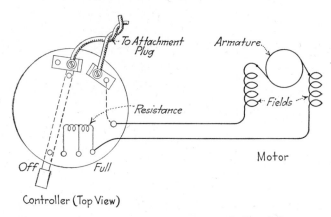

FIG. 135.—Diagram of an early type of series fan motor winding of the commutator type.

reactance of the field was decreased by decreasing the number of turns in the field coils, and to get a good torque with a minimum amount of current, many armature conductors had to be used. Figure 135 shows the diagram of a series motor with the armature connected between the two field coils. All commutator-type motors for small fans are two pole for simplicity and low cost. The first fan motors were series motors with one coil to energize the field and a few manufacturers still make this type. For this motor one of the field coils in Fig. 135 would be omitted.

Speed control in the original series motors was obtained by shifting the brushes from the neutral position. Later designs use resistance in series with the motor winding to lower the voltage impressed on the motor, and this lowers the speed. Taps at different points on the resistance were taken off to give the desired speed of the fan. This method of control is shown in Fig. 135, the resistance being on the controller. The first motors were provided with a ring wound armature and a punched laminated field. The laminated field was necessary as at that time practically all alternating-current circuits operated at 133 cycles, and the high iron loss in a solid pole due to the high frequency was not permissable on account of the high temperature rise.

Induction-type Fan Motor.—The next step in fan-motor development was an induction motor. To operate the fan near the desirable speed of 1,600 r.p.m. on 133 cycles, it was necessary to have ten poles in the field. The poles were concentrated and a coil placed on alternate poles connected in series, all of the same polarity. This winding was called a consequent-pole winding. The poles without coils formed a return path for the magnetic flux from the energized poles. To obtain

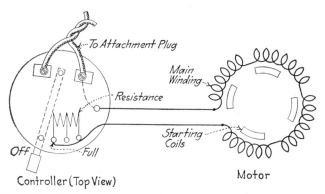

FIG. 136.—Induction motor winding with shading coils for starting.

a phase displacement of the flux in the pole, or otherwise cause a rotating effect of the flux to give a starting torque, the trailing edge of the pole was shaded; that is, a band of copper was placed around a portion of the pole which retarded the flow of the flux in this section, while the flux in the remaining portion of the pole was in phase with the current in the field coils.

The rotors used in induction motors for fans have always been of the squirrel-cage type; that is, if the iron were removed the copper winding would be in the form of a squirrel cage. As compared to rotors of power motors, fan-motor rotors have relatively high resistance to give a reduction in speed of the fan when the flux density in the field poles is decreased. Speed change on induction fan motors is obtained by reducing the voltage impressed upon the field winding, which decreases the current and this decreases the flux density which allows a greater slip of the rotor.

To operate at 1,600 r.p.m. on 60 cycles, an induction motor field should have four poles.   On this and lower frequencies solid poles cast in the main frame have been used, although this produced an excessive loss. To decrease the input and improve the characteristics a laminated field built up from punchings was developed.   The same method as with the

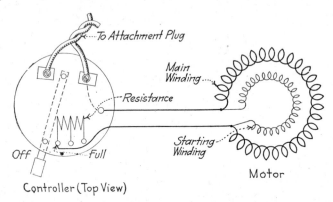

Fig. 137.—Split-phase fan winding with a high resistance starting winding.

133-cycle motors was used for starting in the earlier types of motors and is still used on some of the smaller and lower priced motors.   Speed change on these motors was obtained by inserting in series with the motor field coils either resistance or a choke coil to lower the voltage on the main field.   A diagram of a winding of this type is shown in Fig. 136.

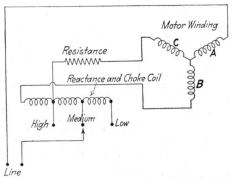

Fig. 138.—Split-phase fan winding with auxiliary resistance and reactance coils for starting.

Distributed Pole Fan Windings.—With the development of the laminated field built up from sheet steel punchings with several slots per pole, it was found that the winding could be distributed across the face of the pole and with the proper distribution the flux density was the greatest in the center teeth of the pole, decreasing in the outside teeth to make a quieter running motor.   This called for a distributed pole punching for an induction motor. An advantage of this punching, which has say 24 slots, is that it can be wound for either two poles for 25 cycles or four poles for 60 cycles, where a four blade fan with a speed of 1,400 to 1,600 r.p.m. is to be used; and wound four pole on 40 cycles, and six pole on 60 cycles, where a six blade fan with a speed of 1,050 r.p.m. is used.

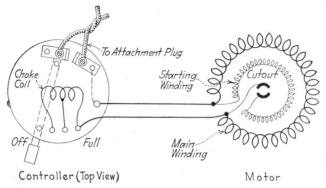

Fig. 139.—Split-phase fan winding with cut-out switch used in the starting winding.

This flexibility of winding on one punching is good from the manufacturing standpoint as it minimizes the number of dies and stock parts.

With the development of the distributed main field winding, it was found desirable to use a starting winding which was energized from the line. There are two types of this starting winding; one which remains

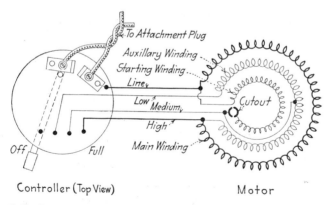

Fig. 140.—Split-phase fan winding with speed changed by taps on a winding auxiliary to the main winding.

in the circuit all the time in parallel with the main winding, as shown in Figs. 137 and 138; the other which has a cutout switch operated by the centrifugal force of weights on fingers attached to the rotor. As the rotor comes up to a predetermined speed this operation takes place. Diagrams of these windings are shown in Figs. 139 and 140.

With starting windings that remain in the circuit, the starting torque is that required to start the rotor from its static friction.   For this reason as small amount of power as possible is put into the starting winding as it is in the circuit all the time when the fan is running.   The total watts of the motor with this type of winding are higher than with a motor whose starting winding has a cutout switch.   The starting winding with the cutout switch is usually wound to take more watts on starting than the other type, but when the rotor is up to speed this winding is open circuited and a saving results.

Starting Windings.—In the first type of starting winding as shown in Fig. 137, there are two separate windings in the motor field.   The heavier or outside winding shown in the diagram is the main field, and is wound distributed in the slots of the poles, and produces the main field flux.   The lighter or inside winding is distributed, with the center of the pole of this winding placed approximately one-third the pole spacing from the center of the pole of the main winding overlapping the next pole of the main winding.   The total turns of the main field winding are greater than the total turns of the starting winding, therefore, the reactance is higher.   The resistance of the starting winding is very high in comparison to the resistance of the main winding.   The two windings are connected in parallel.   The current in the starting winding is very close to being in phase with the voltage, while the current in the main winding lags due to its reactance.   Since the flux of a pole is in phase with the current, the flux of the starting winding leads the flux of the main field winding and produces a rotating field and a rotation from the starting winding toward the main winding.   The power input to this winding is not an entire loss as there is some torque from it at running speeds.

Controlling the Speed of a Fan Motor.—For controlling the speed of a fan with this type of winding, either a choke coil or resistance can be used.   By placing either one of these in series with the motor winding the effective voltage on the motor is decreased and the current in the windings lowered.   With the drop in current the flux in the field decreases and the speed changes.   Resistance is usually used for manufacturing reasons and gives good performance.   Most fans use two steps of resistance, making three speeds for the fan.

The fan whose diagram is shown in Fig. 138 has three windings in the motor field.   These windings are connected at a common point in the motor.   They are usually placed one-third the pole spacing between centers of the poles of each winding.   As shown, A is connected to one line, B is connected to the other line through a choke coil or reactance, and C is connected to the same line as B except through a resistance.   This reactance and resistance is proportioned so that the current flowing through the winding A divides between B and C in such a manner that the field flux has the rotating characteristic of a polyphase motor, thus giving a starting torque. In some motors the added resistance in winding C is placed in the motor winding by using a smaller size wire or a high resistance coil. Since the current in the high resistance circuit leads the current in the reactance circuit and the combined current passes through A, the flux of the winding C leads the flux of winding A and the flux in winding A leads that in winding B, thus the direction of rotor travel is from C to A.

Speed regulation with a winding of this type is usually obtained by having more turns in the choke coil, which is in series with winding B, than are needed for the reactance necessary for the performance at high speed. Taps in these added turns are arranged so that they can be placed in series with the total winding of the motor including the resistance and reactance. This lowers the voltage on the motor and the effect is a decrease in speed of the fan.

The simplest winding with a cutout switch in the starting winding is shown in Fig. 139. The main winding is of heavy wire wound distributed

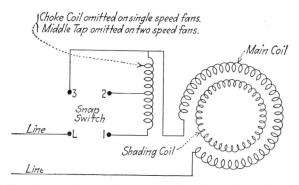

Fig. 141.—Ceiling type of fan winding with insulated shading coil used for starting.

and when the fan is running at its running speed this winding carries the load. The center of the starting winding pole is placed between the poles of the main winding and overlapping half of a pole on each side. The starting winding can be wound either distributed or concentrated as it makes but little difference in its performance, it being open circuited when the motor is running.

To decrease the speed of the fan with a motor wound with the above windings a choke coil is used. The starting current when the motor is connected to the line is several times higher than the running current, and if resistance were used for speed control the drop over this would be so great that the motor could not pull the fan up to the cutout speed of the starting switch. The choke coil is operated at a point where the iron is saturated and the increase of current at starting increases the voltage drop on the choke coils only a little above that at running conditions. This allows the motor to pull the fan up beyond the cutout speed of the starting switch. Here the torque of the main winding is less than when the full voltage is on the motor winding and the fan runs at the lower speed.

Speed Change by Taps on an Auxiliary Winding.—Figure 140 shows a desk fan winding diagram similar to that shown in Fig. 139 except that for speed change the motor winding has taps in the main coils. The high speed point is where there are the fewest turns in the field. Here the field flux is greatest and the torque and speed high. To lower the speed more turns are connected in the main winding. This decreases the flux and causes a decrease in speed, the change in connection being made by the contact lever in the base. The starting winding operates the same as that in Fig. 139. The advantage of this winding is in the reduction of the input to the motor on low speeds, there being no choke coil loss. Also a greater speed reduction can be obtained.

Windings for Ceiling Fans.—The development of the windings for ceiling fans has been along the same lines as for the desk fan. The speed of the ceiling fan is slow compared to that of the desk fan and for alternating-current motors they are wound with a greater number of poles. The principal winding used has the shading coil start, it being difficult to operate a centrifugal switch at such low speeds. Some motors have copper band shading coils over a portion of the pole, similar to the desk fan in Fig. 136. Others use a shading coil of heavy, flexible wire threaded through the slots on top of the primary or main winding with the ends soldered together forming a short-circuited winding, as shown in Fig. 141. The starting winding is insulated before being put in so that it does not ground the main winding. It produces the same shading in all the poles, making a quiet running motor. Speed regulation is obtained by using a choke coil in series with the main winding.

Construction of Fan Motor for Use on Direct or Alternating Current.—Along with the development of the induction motor for fans on alternating-current circuits, the series motor has had equal attention for both alternating and direct current, although the changes have not been so marked in the windings. The slotted armature punching for the drum-type armature makes a much better rotor than the ring type. Cast-iron field frames with solid cast poles were used for direct-current motors. To make a series type motor with a frame that could be used for either alternating or direct current, a laminated field was developed in combination with the armature punching. With this field and armature built up from punchings, the motor can be used on low frequencies to a better advantage than an induction motor, due to the speeds necessitated by a two-pole induction motor. The development of windings for series motors, since the use of the punched field and armature, has been in determining the proper field and armature turns to use on the different frequencies to give the best performance and highest efficiencies.

Induction Fan Motor Winding with High Starting Torque.—The latest development in induction fan motor windings has been a winding

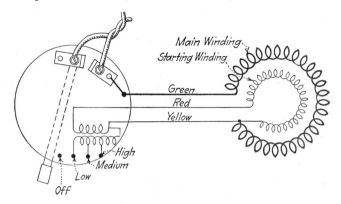

Fig. 142.—Split-phase fan winding with a series transformer used to shift the phase of the starting winding and improve the speed control.

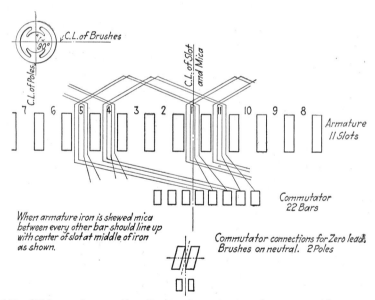

Fig. 143.—Wiring and connecting diagram for series type fan motor with commutator connections for zero lead.

with a high starting torque, high efficiency at running speeds without a cutout switch and with a large speed reduction. A diagram of this winding is shown in Fig. 142. The motor winding is the same as shown in Fig. 139 except that the cutout switch is omitted and the lead from the starting winding to the cutout switch is brought out of the motor to the

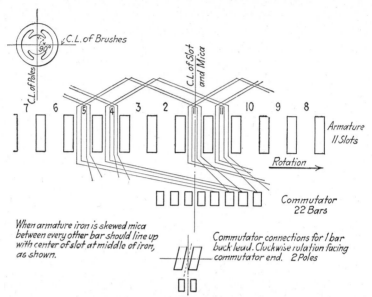

FIG. 144.—Wiring and connecting diagram for series type fan motor with commutator connections for one bar back lead.

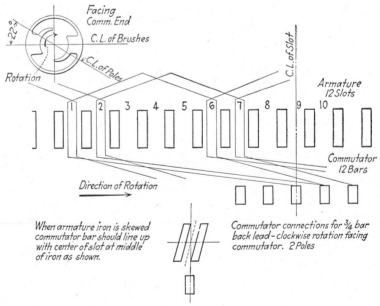

FIG. 145.—Wiring and connecting diagram for series type fan motor with commutator connections for ¾ bar back lead.

base, making two leads from the motor body to the base. In the base of the motor is a transformer, the primary winding of which is in series with the main winding of the motor, the secondary being connected across the starting winding. The characteristics of the transformer are similar to those of a series transformer with reactance in its secondary circuit. When the motor with this complete winding is thrown on the line, the current through the main winding passes through the primary of the transformer and the secondary voltage induced is impressed on the starting winding of the motor. The lag of the voltage of the secondary behind the main current in the primary, plus the lag caused due to the reactance of the starting winding causes a large phase angle between the currents in the main and starting winding in the motor fields. It has been found by

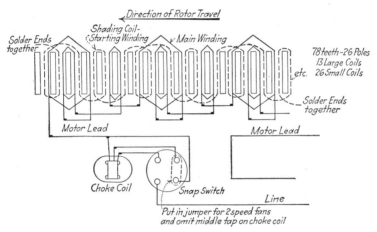

Fig. 146.—Winding diagram for 56-in. ceiling fan using shading coils and a choke coil.

test that the angle between these two currents on starting, with the proper design of the transformer, approaches 90 electrical degrees. This gives the effect of a two-phase motor on starting. In running, the angle changes slightly but always remains of a value to assist the main winding.

To lower the speed of the fan more turns are placed in the primary of the transformer. This has the effect of adding reactance in series with the motor main winding to reduce the flux density in the motor field. Also since the iron in the transformer is worked at a high density, the added turns in its primary with the decrease of primary current have the effect of keeping the secondary voltage of the transformer approximately constant. This makes possible a high starting torque at low speed and consequently a much greater speed change than could otherwise be obtained.

The advantages of this winding are as follows: A large amount of speed reduction, reduction of the watts input with the reduction of speed, high starting torque and a quiet running motor on single phase. The amount of speed reduction is from 25 to 100 per cent more than with any other type of fan motor winding. The reduction of watts input with the reduction of speed is nearly proportional. The high starting torque on all speeds eliminates trouble from burnouts on low voltage. This motor with its approximate polyphase winding is also quieter than a straight single-phase motor.

Effect of Changing Number of Blades on Fan Motor.—The following report from a repair shop explains the reasons for some fans burning out from no fault of the fan winding design:

When a number of six-blade induction-type fans were received for repairs during one season, an investigation and inspection revealed that

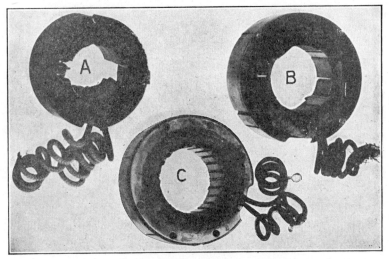

Fig. 147.—Some old types of single-phase fan motor stators.

A is a two-coil, two-pole series type; *B* is a series universal type winding with shading coils embedded in the pole faces for starting. This stator is of the consequent pole type, with two coils for four poles. *C* is an induction motor type.

in a number of cases the field winding and the series transformer in the base of the fan had been heated to such an extent that the insulation on the wires and around the coils was charred, and both windings were short-circuited. As the heating was generally distributed, the trouble was blamed on overload. This had been caused by substituting six-blade fans for the four-blade fans with which they were originally equipped.

When these fans were received in the damaged condition the style and serial number were checked and these proved that in each case the fans were originally of four-blade construction. By consulting the owners of the fans it was found that the following were the reasons for making such changes: (1) The owner wanted a greater volume of air, so he substituted

Fig. 148.—Six different types and sizes of fan motor stators. *A, D, E* and *F,* are split-phase induction types while *B* and *C* are series universal types. Note the clips on *C* into which the brush holders fit. One line lead connects to one lead of each field coil with the armature connected in series between the other two field coil leads.

six for four blades; (2) the original four blades were out of balance and could not be straightened. This was during a hot period and the owner could not get a set of four blades; so he took what he could get, which was six blades. The last example was from a dealer, who stated that when a call was received for a six-blade fan, the set of four blades was removed from a four-blade motor and the six-blade set substituted. This dealer had been substituting six blades for four in direct-current fans without any ill effects. These were all series motors and the substitution of six blades for four blades increases the load and slows down the fan, but the windings usually do not get warm enough to burn out.

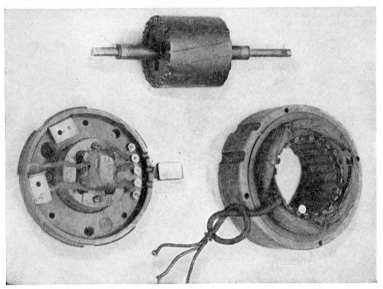

Fig. 149.—Rotor, stator and switch base of split-phase fan motor that uses a speed regulating series transformer.

With the induction type of fan the case is different. It is general practice to wind the stator of six-blade fans for six poles and the stator of four-blade fans for four poles. Hence the speed of each type is fixed. Furthermore the motor windings are of the single split-phase type and the load must be kept well within the pull-out torque of the motor. The synchronous speed of the four-pole motor is 1,800 r.p.m. The six-blade fan is made to run at 1,200 r.p.m. Therefore, if it is put on the four-pole motor its speed will be increased 50 per cent. The power required to turn the fan varies as the cube of the speed and, therefore, the four-pole motor would be working at a very great overload with a six-blade fan.

CHAPTER XXI

REWINDING SMALL TWO- AND THREE-PHASE MOTORS

For small two- and three-phase induction motors having partially closed slots, four different kinds of windings are commonly used:

    1. The basket winding.

    2. Two-layer diamond coils with one coil side per slot.

Fig. 150.—The armature winder is shown inserting turns of a two layer mush coil into partially closed slots of a small induction motor stator. Note the tools that are used.

    3. Two-layer flat diamond mush coils.

    4. Two-layer diamond mush pulled coils.

    5. A winding using strap-copper conductors.

    In this chapter the winding procedure for each of these windings is given.

The Basket Winding.—A good idea of the way to put in a basket winding is shown in Fig. 151. This winding derives its name from its

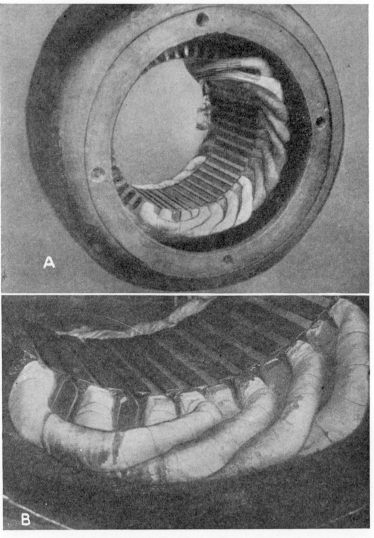

FIG. 151.—The coils lie like this in a basket winding. There is only one coil side per slot. The bottom sides of the coils are put in every other slot leaving the empty slots to accommodate the top sides of the coils.

appearance. As can be seen, the coil ends interlace in somewhat the same fashion as the parts of a woven basket.

In the first place, a basket winding can be used only where the number of slots is even. And in the second place, the number of slots spanned by a coil must be odd. In other words, the coil pitch must be 1 and 4, 1 and 6, 1 and 8, 1 and 10, etc. (the last figure being always even)

Checking Pitch of a Basket Winding.—To check the pitch of a basket winding to see whether or not the coils may be put in with this pitch, the following scheme may be used: Put down a line of figures like the middle line shown below to represent the numbers of the slots in the motor. Below these put the numbers of the bottom sides of the coils. The coil numbers should be directly under the numbers of the slots in which the coils lie. As shown, coil 1 is below slot 1, coil 2 is below slot 3 (skipping one slot because it is a basket winding), coil 3 is below slot 5, etc. After putting down the numbers representing the bottom of the coils, place in a line above the slot numbers the numbers corresponding

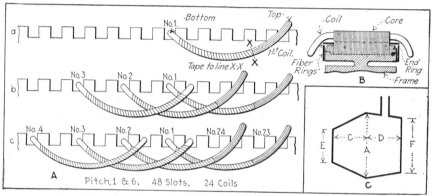

Fig. 152.—How the coils are inserted in winding a basket winding.

The drawings at *A* show three steps in the winding. At *B* is a side view of a coil showing how the ends are bent down. Notice also the fiber insulating rings which are used on some makes of motors to keep the coils off the iron. At *C* is the shape of the coils used in this winding, *F* being the bottom coil side and *E* the top coil side.

to the top side of the coils. Thus, in the example where the pitch is 1 and 6, the top of coil 1 is in slot 6, coil 2 is in slot 8, etc.

Example for pitch 1 and 6:

Top of coil No...............	..	..	..	..	..	1	..	2	..	3		
Slot No....................	1	2	3	4	5	6	7	8	9	10	11	etc.
Bottom, coil No............	1	..	2	..	3	..	4	..	5	..	6	

By completing the lines of figures it will be seen that with a pitch of 1 and 6 each bottom and each top coil will have its separate slot. Taking a pitch of 1 and 7, however, we find it is impossible to wind the motor.

Example for pitch 1 and 7:

Top of coil No...............	..	..	..	..	..	1*	..	2*	..	3*		
Slot No....................	1	2	3	4	5	6	7	8	9	10	11	etc.
Bottom, coil No............	1	..	2	..	3	..	4	..	5	..	6	

* One coil side is already in these slots, and therefore the winding is impossible with this pitch.

The top of coil 1 will fall in slot 7, which is already occupied by the bottom of coil 4. Likewise, the tops of the succeeding coils will fall into slots already occupied.

Drawing *C* in Fig. 152 shows the shape of a basket-winding coil. The coil is wound mush on a shuttle. The cell side, *F*, is at the bottom half of the coil and is made longer than *E*, the top, as the bottom has to be bent down. The leads are brought out on the long or bottom side. This makes the coil connections come on the outside.

Insulating the Slots and Core.—In *B* of Fig. 152 is shown how the core should be insulated with fiber rings to protect the coils from the iron when they are shaped down. The insulation used consist of 0.023-in. fish paper or combination paper (see Chap. III, page 27). This combination paper has a fish paper base with treated cloth shellacked to it, making a good mechanical and electrical slot insulation. The cell should be cut about $\frac{3}{8}$ to $\frac{1}{2}$ in. longer than the slot and should be bent to conform to the shape of the slot, as shown in the close-up view, *B* of Fig. 151.

Inserting Coils in a Basket Winding.—Figure 151 shows a 48-slot, 24-coil, six-pole motor, with a pitch of 1 and 6. Note in *A* of Fig. 151 that there are only two throw coils up. The way in which the throw coils are kept up is illustrated in *A* of Fig. 152, which represents the same winding as that in Fig. 151. As will be noticed, there is only one coil side per slot. Drawing *a* in *A* of Fig. 152 shows the first coil with only the bottom half put in slot No. 1. The top half is left up. The bottom half of the coil is then bent down as shown in *B* of Fig. 151 and *B* of Fig. 152. It is bent down in this way so that the slot adjacent to the right is left clear for the top half of another coil to cross and enter the slot. Then the wedge is put in. After the coil has been shaped it is taped with one layer of 0.008-in. treated-cloth tape and one layer of 0.007-in. cotton tape, both layers being half-lapped. In putting on the tape the slot cell and the wedge are sealed with the tape as shown in *B* of Fig. 151. In other words, the tape is wrapped around the ends of the cell and the wedge which stick out of the slot. The throw coils, when they are made, are taped only to the line *X-X* in *A* of Fig. 152. These ends are taped later, after they are put in place in the slots. All other coils are taped complete as they are first placed in the slots.

After the first coil is in place, coil No. 2 is put in the second slot to the left, as shown in *A* of Fig. 152. An empty slot is left between coils 1 and 2. Another slot is skipped and coil 3 is placed as shown. The top half of this coil can be put into a slot. This is allowable because the top of coil 3 will fall in a slot next to the bottom of coil 1. Until this condition is reached, only the bottom half of a coil can be put into a slot. Continuing in this manner, it will be seen that the top of coil 4 falls in the slot between the bottom of coils 1 and 2. This is correct and the winding should be completed in this way.

Two-layer Winding with One Coil Side per Slot.—An example of the two-layer winding having only one-coil-side-per-slot is shown in Fig.

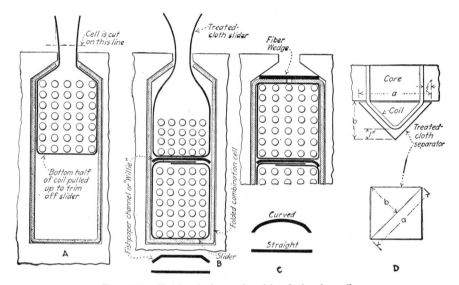

Fig. 153.—Slot insulation and end insulation for coils.

A, *B* and *C* illustrate the slot-insulating cell, the treated-cloth sliders, the fish paper spacer "willie" and the fiber wedge. At *D* is shown how to cut the treated-cloth triangles which are placed between the ends of coils in the stator.

155. This is a picture of the wound stator of a 72-slot, 36-coil, six-pole, three-phase stator having a two-layer, diamond-shape, one-coil-per-slot winding.

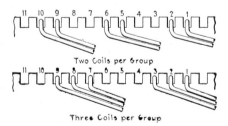

Fig. 154.—Starting a two-layer winding with one coil side per slot.

The winding shown in the upper drawing has two coils per group. It is like that shown in Fig. 155. In putting in the coils two slots are filled and then two slots are skipped. In the lower drawing where the winding has three coils per group, three slots are filled and three slots are skipped. The empty slots will be filled later by the top sides of coils.

This type of winding differs from a basket winding in that the coil is usually a pulled coil (mush) and diamond shaped, and that, in winding, as many slots are skipped as there are coils per group. In the basket winding, it will be remembered, only one slot is skipped before putting in each succeeding coil. Figure 154 illustrates the principle of the two-layer one-coil-per-slot winding. The top drawing shows how the coils are inserted if there are two coils per group. The bottom half of the first two coils are put in slots 1 and 2, then two slots are skipped and two more coils are put in, etc. This is the grouping used in the winding in Fig. 155. The bottom drawing in Fig. 154 shows a winding in which there are three coils per group. The general rule is: Put in adjacent slots as many coils as there are in one group; then skip the same number of slots and repeat.

Fig. 155.—Two-layer winding with one coil side per slot. This winding has two coils per group. It is put in the slots as shown in the upper drawing of Fig. 154.

Checking Pitch of a Two-layer Winding.—The possibility of using a certain pitch may be checked in the same way as explained for a basket winding. For instance, with the stator in Fig. 155 there are 72 slots and 36 coils. This is a three-phase, six-pole machine and therefore there will be (3 × 6) equals 18 groups. As there are 36 coils, there will be two coils per group.

If the pitch is 1 and 11, the check is as follows:

Top of coil No............	..	..	..	..	..	..	..	..	..	..	..	1	2	..	..	3	4
Slot No...................	1	2	3	4	5	6	7	8	9	10	11	12	13	14	15	16
Bottom, coil No...........	1	2	..	..	3	4	..	..	5	6	..	..	7	8		

The tops of the coils fall in slots not occupied by the bottoms of coils, and therefore this pitch is practicable. However, a pitch of 1 and 12 would not be possible, as shown in the following:

Top of coil No............	..	..	..	..	..	..	..	..	..	..	..	1	2*	..	..	3
Slot No...................	1	2	3	4	5	6	7	8	9	10	11	12	13	14	15	16
Bottom, coil No...........	1	2	..	..	3	4	..	..	5	6	..	..	7	8		

* Falls in a slot already occupied.

Before putting on this kind of a winding the slots are insulated as for a basket winding. Also, as each coil is put in place it is taped in the manner described for a basket winding.

Two-layer Windings with Flat Diamond Mush Coils.—Windings using a flat diamond mush coil are the commonest in small stators. There are a number of different ways of insulating and inserting such coils. Figure 153 (*A*, *B* and *C*) shows how the slots are insulated. A slot cell of combination insulation is used. This has a fish paper base with tan treated cloth shellacked to it. The best thickness is a total of 0.023 in. This cell is folded to fit the slot as shown, then a treated-cloth slider (cell) is used to protect the wires as they are fed into the slot. After the bottom half of the coil is in place, the slider is pulled up to the top of the slot and cut off as shown in *A* of Fig. 153. The coil is then forced down to the bottom of the slot and the ends of the slider are turned over on the coil. A spacer or "willie" is then put on top of the coil as shown in *B*. This spacer can be flat or channel-shaped. For springy coils and tight jobs, the flat spacer wide enough to make a tight fit is the best. When it is hammered down, the edges bind on the sides of the slot and hold the wires securely. The spacer, however, must not be made tight enough to tear the slot insulation.

Another slider is put in for the top coil. When the coil is in place this slider is cut off and bent over the coil and a wedge inserted. The wedge can be flat or curved. For narrow slots the curved wedge is the better, as the flat wedge has a tendency to slip up. The curved wedge is made from 0.056-in. fish paper.

Three Steps in Inserting Diamond Mush Coils.—In Fig. 156 are shown three steps in winding with diamond mush coils. In *A* may be seen the condition in which the coil comes to the winder. The coil is taped in the coil department, starting 1 in. on the bottom slot section and ending up on the end 1½ in. outside of the top cell. The leads are brought out on the bottom of the coil 1 in. from the diamond point or nose. They are reinforced with three turns of tape, thus sealing up this point and keeping out dust and dirt.

In putting this coil into the slot, the winder spreads the bottom untaped section of the coil out flat with his fingers, then starts the coil into the slot, putting the center of the bottom slot section into the corner of the slot as shown. Then the coil is pushed across the core until the part in the slot reaches the other end of core, when the coil drops down. It is now entirely down in the slot, but it sticks out too far at one end. It is brought back to its proper position by a sort of see-saw motion. After one gets the knack, he can put in a coil very quickly.

The top half has to be threaded in a few wires at a time. For this reason, when the coil is being made the tape is not brought around the top cell bend. However, this bare portion must be insulated. This is

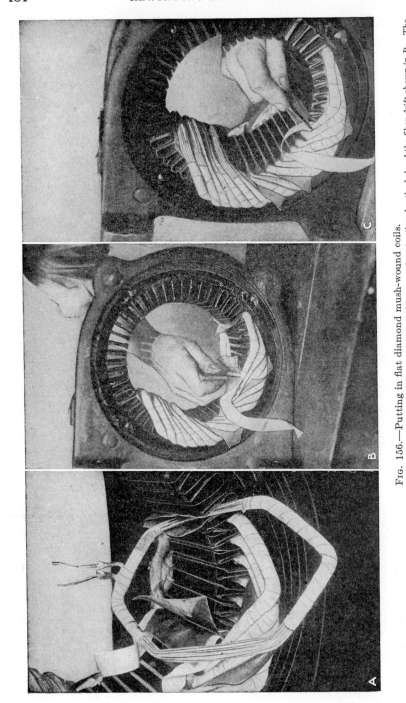

FIG. 156.—Putting in flat diamond mush-wound coils.

The bottom side is started in the slot as shown at A. The top side of the coil is forced in, one wire at a time by the help of the fiber drift shown in B. The part of the top side next to the slot is insulated with cotton tape, which is inserted under the slider before the coil is started in. The picture at C shows how the short end of this tape is tucked down in the slot after it is passed over the coil.

accomplished by placing one end of a length of 1-in. cotton tape ⅞ in. inside the slot under the treated-cloth slider for the top side of the coil. This slider projects well out of the slot.   After the coil is in place this slider and the tape form a lapped joint on the coil.   This is well illustrated in *C* of Fig. 158.

The quickest way to get the wires of the top coil side into the slot is to use a ¹⁄₁₆-in. fiber drift as shown in *B* of Fig. 156.   Start with the wire nearest the core.   Push one end of this wire into the slot with the drift. Pressing down with the drift, slide it along the wire until it is forced into the slot.   The principle to learn is to get the wire nearest the slot free

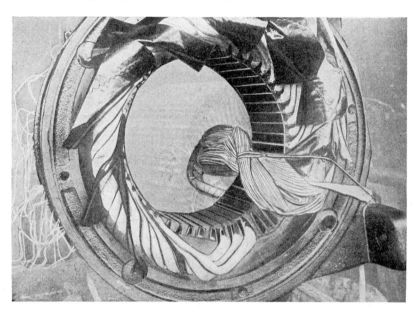

FIG. 157.—Throw coils tied back to allow bottom side of last coils to be inserted.   This is a two-layer winding with diamond mush pulled coils.

from crossings with other wires.   After it is once mastered, this method is a time saver.

The tape is then wound around the coil and slider, forming a sealed junction.   It is see-sawed up and down until the short end projects about 1½ in. above the iron.   This end is then tucked down into the slot by means of a blunt and dull knife as shown in *C* of Fig. 156.   Then the long end is wound around the bare part of the coil until it is covered. The weakest spot in the winding is at the end of a coil.   Dust, etc., will accumulate at this point, and if the coils are not well taped a failure will result.

Extra Insulation between Phase Coils.—Extra insulation is required at the point between two coils of different phases.   One good way to

furnish such insulation is to insert triangles of tan treated cloth between
the phase coils.   Such pieces are shown in *A* of Fig. 156 and *C* of Fig. 158.
These pieces of cloth are cut as shown in *D* of Fig. 153.   The distance *a*

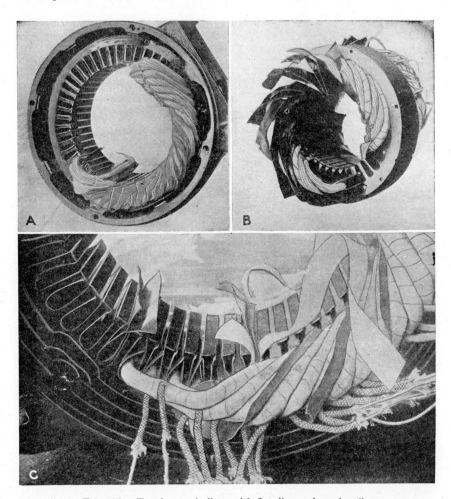

Fig. 158.—Two-layer windings with flat diamond mush coils.

At *A* none of the coils are taped.   They are insulated from each other at both ends by treated-cloth triangles under every coil.   At *B* the treated-cloth triangles are used and in addition one coil out of every three is taped to afford extra protection between phases.   At *C* all of the coils are taped and treated-cloth triangles are inserted at every point where two phases come together.   At the left of the last coil a slider is shown ready to receive the bottom side of the next coil to be inserted.   Near the center is shown a slider ready to receive the top side of the coil.   A strip of 1-in. cotton tape is inserted under the end of this slider, projecting about ⅛ in. out of the slot.   After the coil and wedge are put in, this tape is used to make a sealed insulating joint for slider, wedge and coil.

equals the distance between outside edges of the coil plus 1 in.   The
length *b* equals the distance from the iron to the nose of the coil plus 1 in.
A trial piece should be cut to the proper size.   Then, using this as a guide,
cut the cloth into squares as shown and cut these into two pieces along

the diagonal.   Insert one of these triangles at each end of the coil before putting the top side in the slot.   The edges of the triangle are allowed to project until the winding is completed.   Then they are trimmed close to the coils.   When properly done, this makes a thorough job for motors which must operate in dirty, dusty or damp places or in locations with metallic particles in the air.

There are other methods of insulating the coil ends.   One of these is used with coils which are not taped.   The end insulation is then furnished entirely by the treated-cloth triangles inserted beneath each coil.   This type of insulation is shown in *A* of Fig. 158.   This method of insulating the coils is very quick and is satisfactory for most applications when the complete winding is thoroughly impregnated.   For 110, 220 and 440 volts, one thickness of 0.009-in. insulation is sufficient.   It is not necessary to put an additional thickness between phases.

Another method of insulating coil ends where extra phase insulation is required, due to dust, etc., is shown in *B* of Fig. 158.   This consists in taping only the last coil of each group with one half-lapped layer of 0.007-in. cotton tape in addition to the treated cloth between coil ends.

Two-layer Winding with Diamond Mush Pulled Coils.—The mush pulled coil is another type that is used on partly closed slots of stators.

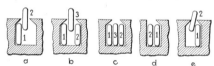

FIG. 159.—How strap-copper coils are put into the slots. The figures on the straps indicate the order of placing them in the slot.

Such a coil is not wound in layers and is not taped.   It is tied together at each of the diamond points.   These coils are fed into the slots in the same way as the flat diamond mush coils just described and also shown in Fig. 150.   At the left are some of the coils and a stator partly wound. The coil ends are not taped but are insulated with triangular pieces of treated cloth, as already described.   Figure 157 shows how the throw coils on this or any other type of winding may be tied back out of the way to allow the last coils to be put in the bottom of the slots.

When winding any type of stator the less pounding that is done to shape the coil, the better.   It is the duty of the coil department to furnish coils of the right size.   They should not be smaller than the old sample coil, a little larger, if anything.   With a proper size and shape of coil very little pounding is required, only a light tap at the nose of the coil and on the sides of the ends.

Threaded-in Strap-copper Coils.—There are some stators having partially closed slots which are wound with coils made of strap copper.   Figure 159 illustrates the methods of putting such coils in the slots.   At *c* is shown a three-turn coil with the slot opening in the center and just wide enough to pass one strap at a time. The numbers on each strap in the drawing indicate the order in which they are put in. At *a*, strap No. 1 is put in and pushed over to the left as far as it will go. Then No. 2 is put in and pushed to the right, after which No. 3 is forced between 1 and 2 as at *b*.

At *d* is shown a two-turn coil in an overhanging slot. Bar No. 1 is put in and forced under the overhang of the tooth and then No. 2 is forced down straight. At *c* is a two-turn coil with the opening in the middle of the slot. The last strap has to be inclined a bit to get it in.

CHAPTER XXII

CHANGING SINGLE-PHASE WINDINGS FOR TWO- AND THREE-PHASE OPERATION

Requests frequently come to a repair shop to change a single-phase, induction-type motor for operation on a two- or three-phase circuit in order to eliminate the centrifugal switch used in starting a single-phase motor. In such a case the core, frame and rotor is available and the first puestion that comes up is the rating that can be expected for two- or three-phase operation.

Estimating the Two- and Three-phase Rating of a Single-phase Motor Frame.—A single-phase motor frame is about 1.5 times the size of a corresponding two- or three-phase motor of the same horsepower and speed, which means that when changing from single-phase to three- or two-phase with the speed remaining the same, the single-phase horsepower rating can be increased 1.5 times.

There is another and better method for determining what horsepower a given frame is capable of developing, that can be used when an old core on which the winding has been removed is available. This method makes use of the number of cylindrical inches in the core, using the inside diameter, which is the bore B squared, times the length of the core. Thus $(B \times B \times L)$ determines the maximum horsepower rating of any frame.

In Table II are given the minimum cylindrical inches allowance for each horsepower rating from $\frac{1}{4}$ to $7\frac{1}{2}$. The values given are for cores of four-pole, 60-cycle, 1,800-r.p.m. motors. In a footnote under Table II the formula for determining the cylindrical inches required for six- and eight- and ten-pole, 60-cycle motors is given.

Table III gives some values taken from rewound motors. These values can be used for comparisons or checks.

In Table IV are given the cylindrical inches of stators having a bore of $2\frac{1}{2}$ in. to $9\frac{1}{2}$ in., in steps of $\frac{1}{8}$ in., and the length of core from 1 in. to 4 in. The first column gives the bore in inches, the second column the value of bore B squared $(B \times B)$; then each succeeding column gives the value of $(B \times B \times L)$ or cylindrical inches, corresponding to the bore at the left of the line and the length of core at the head of the column.

How to Use Tables for Finding Hp. Rating of Single-phase Frame for 2- or 3-phase Change.—The following example will show how to use the accompanying tables. Assume a stator that has a bore of 6 in. and a core length of 2½ in.: What are the cylindrical inches?   First locate the figure 6 in the bore column in Table IV.   Then look along this line until under the heading of 2½ in. we find 90, which is the cylindrical inches of this core.   According to Table II this core is good for 3 hp. at 1,800 r.p.m., 60 cycles; or 3 ÷ 1.5 equals 2 hp. at 1,200 r.p.m.; or 3 ÷ 2 equals 1.5 hp. at 900 r.p.m.; or 3 × .365 equals 1.095 hp. at 720 r.p.m.   The above procedure can be followed for determining the horsepower rating of any core within the limits given.

How to Determine Turns, Size of Wire and Coil Pitch When Changing Single-phase Winding.—The next step is to determine the number of turns, size of wire, and coil pitch.   To get the turns, the flux per pole per phase must be figured.   This is done by the use of the formula (0.636 $\times S_1 \times L \times Bm$), where S_1 is the pole pitch which is equal to (bore $\times$ 3.14) divided by number of poles.   Values for S_1 are given in Table V; L equals length of core.   When length of core is stated, it means actual length of iron, not including ventilating ducts or endplates.   *Bm* is the magnetic density in the air gap in lines per sq. in. and runs from 20,000 to 30,000 for motors up to 7½ hp. with closed slots.   A good average value for four and six poles is 25,000 lines per sq. in.   For an eight-pole motor it would be 20,000.   Then the flux per pole for a 6- by 2½-in. stator would be figured as follows: S_1 according to Table V for four poles is, 4.712.   Then the flux equals (0.636 × 4.712 × 2.5 × 25,000) equals 187,250 lines.

Size of Wire Required and Number of Turns.—To help in estimating the size of wire required the table on page 192 is given.   This table gives the ampere rating, efficiency and power factors for 220 volts.   For 110 volts multiply these values by 2; for 440 volts divide by 2; for 550 volts multiply by 0.4.

In the following examples we will use 80 per cent coil pitch, or coil pitch equals (1 and 1 plus number of slots divided by number of poles . times .80).   For forty-eight slots and four poles, the coil pitch is (1 and 1 + 48 ÷ 4 × .80) equals [1 and 1 + (12 × .80)] or (1 and 1 + 9.6 which is 1-and-10.

For a two-phase motor, the turns per phase with a series connection will be:

$$T = (E \times 100,000,000) \div (4 \times \Phi \times F),$$ where E equals the line voltage, Φ the flux per pole, and F the frequency.   Then the turns per coil equal T divided by the coils per phase.

For three-phase, the turns per phase for a series-delta connection will be:

$$T = (E \times 100,000,000) \div (4.25 \times \Phi \times F).$$ For a series-star connection, the turns per phase become $(E \times 100,000,000) \div (7.35 \times \Phi \times F)$.

A series-star connection requires less turns of a larger wire, and a series-delta connection a greater number of turns of a smaller wire.   The majority of motors are star-connected.   So the safe procedure is to figure out the turns for a series-star connection and then if the wire is too large try a series-delta connection.

We will next work out one or two examples: First, take the stator having a 6-in. bore and 2½-in. length of iron. This motor is good for 3 hp. at 1,800 r.p.m. When it is to be operated three-phase, 220 volts, 60 cycles, the flux per pole equals (0.636 × 4.712 × 2.5 × 25,000) or 187,250 lines. Then for a series-star connection, T per phase equals (220 × 100,-000,000) ÷ (7.35 × 187,250 × 60) equals 266 turns. As this stator has forty-eight slots, we will use a two layer, diamond-shape mush coil. There will be forty-eight coils, or 48 ÷ 3 equals 16 coils per phase. Then the turns per coil equal 266 ÷ 16, equals 16.6 or sixteen turns will be close enough.

By the table on page 192, a 3-hp. 220-volt, four-pole motor will take 8.1 amp. From Table II we find that a 3-hp. motor requires 600 circ. mils per ampere. This size of wire in circ. mils equals 8.1 × 600 equals 4,860 circ. mils. Then from wire Table VI we find the nearest size is No. 14 with 4,107 circ. mils or No. 13 with 5,178. No. 14 will do, but if there is enough room in the slot for No. 13 it would make a more efficient motor.

The best method of determining whether an estimated size of wire can be wound is to insulate one slot; then cut up small lengths of wire of the gage size figured and fill the slot with the required number of turns. In this case we would try 2 × 16 equals 32, No. 14 double-cotton-covered wires.

When the size of wire required is above No. 15 and it is desired to make a mush coil, the better procedure would be to double the turns, halve the size of wire and use a parallel connection. This makes a coil that is easier to handle and shape. In this case we could use thirty-two turns of one No. 17 wire per coil and connect for two-parallel star.

When a delta connection is used the amperes per terminal, as given in Table I, must be divided by 1.73 to get the amperes per phase. Or in the case just figured, 8.1 ÷ 1.73 equals 4.624 amp. Then the circ. mils required equals 4.624 × 600 equals 2,774.4, or a No. 16 wire will do.

Another and better method of figuring the size of wire in circ. mils for a delta connection is to take the value given in the table on page 192 for the proper voltage and multiply it by 0.57. Then multiply this answer by the circ. mil allowance given in Table II for the required horsepower rating. In the case just figured (8.1 × .57 × 600) equals 4.617 × 600 or 2.770.2, which is close enough.

Determining the Coil Pitch.—The next step is to find the coil pitch. This equals [1 and 1 + (48 ÷ 4) × .8] equals (1 and 1 + 12 × .8) equals 1 and 10.6, or 1-and-10.

The method outlined above can be used in the same manner for two-phase machines. All unnecessary calculations have been eliminated, the purpose being to enable the average electrician to develop a motor that will run and carry its rated load satisfactorily and with reasonable efficiency.

The rotor can be used as it is, but see that all joints between end-rings and bars make good contact. The cutout switch used on the single-phase winding should be removed.

TABLE I.—AMPERE RATINGS, EFFICIENCY AND POWER FACTOR FOR TWO- AND THREE-PHASE, 60-CYCLE, 220-VOLT, 40-DEG. MOTORS

Three-phase					Two-phase				
		Amp. per terminal	Per cent				Amp. per terminal	Per cent	
Hp.	Poles		Efficiency	Power factor	Hp.	Poles		Efficiency	Power factor
¼	4	.90	71.0	76.0	¼	4	.82	69.0	75.0
½	4	1.61	76.0	80.0	½	4	1.45	74.0	79.0
½	6	1.90	72.0	73.0	½	6	1.71	69.0	72.0
½	8	1.92	71.0	72.0	½	8	1.80	68.0	70.0
¾	4	2.33	77.0	82.0	¾	4	2.09	75.0	81.0
¾	6	2.48	75.0	80.0	¾	6	2.17	73.0	80.0
¾	8	2.65	73.0	71.0	¾	8	2.32	72.0	78.0
1	4	2.95	80.0	83.0	1	4	2.65	79.0	82.0
1	6	3.02	79.0	81.0	1	6	2.81	78.0	81.0
1	8	3.60	75.0	71.0	1	8	2.97	76.0	80.0
1½	4	4.42	82.0	82.0	1½	4	3.82	82.0	82.0
1½	6	4.48	81.0	80.0	1½	6	3.88	81.0	80.0
1½	8	5.15	77.0	74.0	1½	8	4.01	80.0	79.0
2	4	5.7	82.0	87.0	2	4	5.0	81.0	86.0
2	6	6.0	79.0	81.0	2	6	5.3	78.0	79.0
2	8	7.9	78.0	63.0	2	8	7.4	77.0	59.0
3	4	8.1	86.0	87.0	3	4	7.2	82.5	86.0
3	6	8.7	83.0	79.0	3	6	7.5	82.0	83.0
3	8	9.7	81.0	73.0	3	8	8.5	81.0	73.0
5	4	13.1	87.5	87.0	5	4	11.5	85.6	87.0
5	6	13.6	85.0	86.0	5	6	12.1	85.0	82.0
5	8	14.1	84.0	82.0	5	8	12.6	83.0	81.0
7½	4	19.1	87.0	88.3	7½	4	17.1	87.0	87.0
7½	6	19.5	86.0	87.0	7½	6	16.8	87.0	85.0
7½	8	20.6	85.0	82.0	7½	8	20.0	86.0	82.0

TABLE II.—MINIMUM CYLINDRICAL INCHES

These values are per horsepower for 4-pole, 60-cycle, 1,800 r.p.m. motors

Hp.	Min. $B \times B \times L$	Circ. mils per amp.
$\frac{1}{4}$	12.00	320
$\frac{3}{8}$	20.00	375
$\frac{1}{2}$	25.00	450
$\frac{3}{4}$	30.00	475
1	40.00	500
$1\frac{1}{2}$	55.00	525
2	75.00	550
3	90.00	600
5	120.00	650
$7\frac{1}{2}$	200.00	675

$\Phi = 0.636 \times S_1 \times L \times Bm.$
$Bm = 20{,}000$ to $35{,}000$ lines per sq. in.
$S_1 =$ Pole pitch $= (B$ by $3.14) \div$ (Number of poles)

B^2L required equals:
for 6 poles $= 1.5 \times (B^2L$ for 4 poles)
for 8 poles $= 1.85 \times (B^2L$ for 4 poles)
for 10 poles $= 2.70 \times (B^2L$ for 4 poles)

TABLE III.—VALUES TAKEN FROM REWOUND MOTORS FOR CHECKING PURPOSES

Hp.	Poles	Bore	Length	$B \times B \times L$
$\frac{1}{4}$	4	$3\frac{1}{4}$	$2\frac{1}{8}$	22.49
$\frac{3}{8}$	6	5	$2\frac{1}{4}$	56.25
$\frac{1}{2}$	4	$3\frac{5}{8}$	$2\frac{3}{8}$	31.21
$\frac{3}{4}$	4	$4\frac{3}{8}$	$1\frac{5}{8}$	31.10
1	4	$4\frac{1}{4}$	$2\frac{1}{2}$	45.15
1	4	$5\frac{1}{4}$	2	55.12
1	6	5	3	75.00
1	6	$5\frac{7}{8}$	$2\frac{1}{8}$	73.35
1	10	7	$2\frac{1}{4}$	110.25
$1\frac{1}{2}$	6	$5\frac{1}{8}$	$3\frac{1}{8}$	82.08
2	4	6	$2\frac{1}{2}$	90.00
2	4	5	3	75.00
2	4	$5\frac{1}{4}$	$3\frac{1}{4}$	89.57
2	6	6	3	108.00
3	4	$5\frac{5}{8}$	$3\frac{1}{8}$	98.88
3	6	7	$3\frac{1}{8}$	153.13
5	4	$6\frac{5}{8}$	$2\frac{7}{8}$	126.18
5	4	$7\frac{1}{8}$	3	152.31
5	6	8	$3\frac{3}{8}$	216.00
5	8	$9\frac{1}{2}$	$3\frac{3}{4}$	338.44
$7\frac{1}{2}$	6	$8\frac{1}{2}$	$4\frac{3}{8}$	316.09
$7\frac{1}{2}$	4	. . .	. . .	270.85

TABLE IV.—CYLINDRICAL INCHES OBTAINED FROM BORE AND LENGTH OF IRON OF STATOR

Bore in inches	(B × B) bore squared	Cylindrical inches or (B × B × L)												
		*1.0	1.25	1.50	1.75	2.00	2.25	2.50	2.75	3.00	3.25	3.50	3.75	4.00
2½	6.25	6.25	7.81	9.37	10.93	12.50	14.06	15.62	17.18	18.75	20.31	21.87	23.44	25.00
2⅝	6.89	6.89	8.62	10.32	12.05	13.78	15.50	17.21	18.94	20.67	22.40	24.12	25.82	27.56
2¾	7.66	7.66	9.58	11.33	13.41	15.32	17.24	18.99	20.91	22.98	24.90	26.82	28.57	30.65
2⅞	8.26	8.26	10.33	12.40	14.46	16.53	18.60	20.66	22.73	24.79	26.86	28.93	31.00	33.06
3	9.00	9.00	11.25	13.50	15.75	18.00	20.25	22.50	24.75	27.00	29.25	31.50	33.75	36.00
3⅛	9.76	9.76	12.20	14.65	17.09	19.53	21.96	24.41	26.85	29.29	31.73	34.16	36.61	39.06
3¼	10.56	10.56	13.20	15.85	18.49	21.12	23.76	26.41	29.05	31.70	34.32	36.96	39.61	42.25
3⅜	11.39	11.39	14.23	17.08	19.93	22.78	25.62	28.47	31.31	34.17	37.01	39.85	42.70	45.56
3½	12.25	12.25	15.32	18.38	21.43	24.50	27.57	30.63	33.70	36.75	39.82	42.89	45.95	49.00
3⅝	13.14	13.14	16.43	19.72	23.23	26.28	29.57	32.86	36.15	39.42	42.71	46.00	49.29	52.56
3¾	14.06	14.06	17.58	21.09	24.61	28.12	31.64	35.15	38.67	42.18	45.70	49.22	52.73	56.25
3⅞	15.01	15.01	18.77	22.52	26.27	30.03	33.79	37.53	41.29	45.05	48.80	52.56	56.32	60.06
4	16.00	16.00	20.00	24.00	28.00	32.00	36.00	40.00	44.00	48.00	52.00	56.00	60.00	64.00
4⅛	17.01	17.01	21.27	25.52	29.77	34.03	38.28	42.53	46.79	51.04	55.30	59.55	63.80	68.06
4¼	18.06	18.06	22.58	27.09	31.61	36.13	40.64	45.15	49.67	54.18	58.71	63.22	67.73	72.26
4⅜	19.14	19.14	23.93	28.71	33.49	38.28	43.17	47.85	52.64	57.42	62.21	67.10	71.88	76.56
4½	20.25	20.25	25.31	30.37	34.43	40.50	45.56	50.62	55.68	60.75	65.81	70.87	75.93	81.00
4⅝	21.39	21.39	26.74	32.08	37.42	42.78	48.13	53.47	58.82	64.17	69.52	74.87	80.21	85.56
4¾	22.56	22.56	28.20	33.84	39.48	45.12	50.76	56.40	62.04	67.68	73.32	78.96	84.50	90.24
4⅞	23.76	23.76	29.70	35.64	41.60	47.53	53.46	59.40	65.34	71.29	77.23	83.16	89.00	95.06
5	25.00	25.00	31.25	37.50	43.75	50.00	56.25	62.50	68.75	75.00	81.25	87.50	93.75	100.00
5⅛	26.26	26.26	32.83	39.40	45.96	52.53	59.10	65.66	72.23	78.79	85.38	91.93	98.50	105.06
5¼	27.56	27.56	34.45	41.35	48.23	55.12	61.90	68.91	75.80	82.69	89.57	96.35	103.25	110.25
5⅜	28.89	28.89	36.11	43.38	50.55	57.78	65.00	72.27	79.49	86.67	93.89	101.11	108.38	115.56
5½	30.25	30.25	37.81	45.38	52.93	60.50	68.06	75.63	83.19	90.75	98.31	105.87	113.46	121.00
5⅝	31.64	31.64	39.55	47.46	55.37	63.28	71.20	79.10	87.00	94.92	102.83	110.75	118.66	126.56
5¾	33.06	33.05	41.32	49.59	57.86	66.12	74.38	82.65	90.91	99.18	107.44	115.70	124.97	132.25
5⅞	34.51	34.51	43.14	51.77	60.40	69.03	77.65	86.28	94.91	103.54	112.17	120.79	129.42	138.06
6	36.00	36.00	45.00	54.00	63.00	72.00	81.00	90.00	99.00	108.00	117.00	126.00	135.00	144.00
6⅛	37.51	37.51	46.90	56.27	65.65	75.03	84.41	93.78	103.16	112.54	121.93	131.30	140.68	150.06
6¼	39.06	39.06	48.82	58.59	68.36	78.12	87.92	97.65	107.42	117.18	126.94	136.71	146.48	156.24
6⅜	40.64	40.64	50.80	60.95	71.12	81.28	91.44	101.59	111.76	121.92	132.03	142.23	152.40	162.56
6½	42.25	42.25	52.80	63.37	73.83	84.50	95.05	105.62	116.08	126.75	137.30	147.87	158.33	169.00
6⅝	43.89	43.89	54.86	65.83	76.80	87.78	98.75	109.72	120.69	131.67	142.64	153.61	164.58	175.56
6¾	45.55	45.55	56.94	68.32	79.71	91.10	102.49	113.87	125.26	136.65	148.04	159.42	170.83	182.20
6⅞	47.27	47.27	59.08	70.90	82.72	95.54	106.35	118.17	130.00	141.81	154.62	165.44	178.26	191.08
7	49.00	49.00	61.25	73.50	85.75	98.00	110.25	122.50	134.75	147.00	159.25	171.50	183.75	196.00
7⅛	50.77	50.77	63.46	76.15	88.85	101.54	114.23	126.92	139.62	152.31	165.00	177.69	190.39	203.08
7¼	52.56	52.56	65.70	78.84	92.00	105.12	118.26	131.40	144.56	157.68	170.82	183.96	197.12	210.24
7⅜	54.39	54.39	67.98	81.58	95.18	108.78	122.37	135.97	149.57	163.17	176.76	190.36	203.96	217.56
7½	56.25	56.25	70.31	84.37	98.44	112.50	126.56	140.62	154.69	168.75	182.81	197.87	210.94	225.00
7⅝	58.14	58.14	72.67	87.20	101.75	116.28	130.81	145.34	159.88	174.42	188.95	203.48	218.03	232.56
7¾	60.06	60.06	75.07	90.09	105.10	120.12	135.13	150.15	165.16	180.18	195.19	210.21	225.22	240.24
7⅞	62.02	62.02	77.52	93.03	108.53	124.04	139.54	155.05	170.55	186.06	201.56	217.07	232.57	248.08
8	64.00	64.00	80.00	96.00	112.00	128.00	144.00	160.00	176.00	192.00	208.00	224.00	240.00	256.00
8⅛	66.02	66.02	82.52	99.03	115.53	132.04	148.54	165.05	182.55	198.06	214.56	231.07	247.57	264.08
8¼	68.06	68.06	85.07	102.09	119.11	136.12	153.13	170.15	187.17	204.18	221.19	238.21	255.23	272.24
8⅜	70.14	70.14	87.67	105.21	123.77	140.28	158.81	176.35	193.91	210.42	227.95	247.49	263.05	280.56
8½	72.25	72.25	90.31	108.37	126.44	144.50	162.56	181.62	198.69	216.75	234.81	253.87	270.94	289.00
8⅝	74.39	74.39	92.98	111.58	130.18	148.78	167.37	185.97	204.57	223.17	241.76	260.36	278.96	297.56
8¾	76.56	76.56	95.70	114.84	134.00	153.12	172.26	191.40	210.56	229.68	248.82	267.96	287.12	306.24
8⅞	78.77	78.77	98.46	118.15	137.85	157.54	177.23	196.92	216.62	236.31	256.00	275.69	295.39	315.08
9	81.00	81.00	101.25	121.50	141.75	162.00	182.25	202.50	222.75	243.00	263.25	283.50	303.75	324.00
9⅛	83.12	83.12	103.90	124.68	145.46	166.24	187.02	207.80	228.58	249.36	270.14	290.92	312.70	332.48
9¼	85.85	85.56	106.95	128.34	149.73	171.12	192.51	213.90	235.29	256.68	278.07	299.46	320.85	342.24
9⅜	87.89	87.89	109.86	131.83	153.81	175.78	197.75	219.72	241.70	263.67	285.64	307.61	339.59	351.56
9½	90.25	90.25	112.81	135.37	157.94	180.50	203.06	225.62	248.20	270.75	293.31	315.87	338.44	361.00

* Values given in this line are lengths of core in inches.

TABLE V.—VALUES OF POLE PITCH FOR DIFFERENT BORES AND POLES

Bore in inches	Bore times 3.14	S_1 = pole pitch in inches			Bore in inches	Bore times 3.14	S_1 = pole pitch in inches		
		2-pole	4-pole	6-pole			2-pole	4-pole	6-pole
2½	7.85	3.975	1.987	1.325	6	18.85	9.425	4.712	3.141
2⅝	8.25	4.125	2.062	1.375	6⅛	19.24	9.620	4.810	3.206
2¾	8.64	4.320	2.160	1.440	6¼	19.64	9.820	4.910	3.273
2⅞	9.03	4.515	2.257	1.505	6⅜	20.03	10.015	5.007	3.338
					6½	20.42	10.210	5.105	3.403
3	9.42	4.710	2.355	1.570	6⅝	20.81	10.405	5.202	3.468
3⅛	9.82	4.910	2.455	1.636	6¾	21.21	10.605	5.302	3.535
3¼	10.21	5.105	2.552	1.701	6⅞	21.60	10.800	5.400	3.600
3⅜	10.60	5.300	2.650	1.767					
3½	10.99	5.495	2.747	1.831	7	21.99	10.995	5.497	3.665
3⅝	11.39	5.695	2.847	1.898	7⅛	22.38	11.190	5.595	3.730
3¾	11.78	5.890	2.945	1.963	7¼	22.78	11.390	5.695	3.796
3⅞	12.17	6.085	3.042	2.028	7⅜	23.17	11.585	5.792	3.861
					7½	23.56	11.780	5.890	3.926
4	12.57	6.285	3.142	2.095	7⅝	23.95	11.975	5.987	3.992
4⅛	12.96	6.480	3.240	2.160	7¾	24.35	12.175	6.087	4.058
4¼	13.35	6.675	3.337	2.225	7⅞	24.74	12.370	6.185	4.123
4⅜	13.74	6.870	3.435	2.290					
4½	14.14	7.070	3.535	2.356	8	25.13	12.565	6.282	4.188
4⅝	14.53	7.265	3.632	2.421	8⅛	25.53	12.765	6.382	4.255
4¾	14.92	7.460	3.730	2.486	8¼	25.92	12.960	6.480	4.320
4⅞	15.32	7.660	3.830	2.553	8⅜	26.31	13.155	6.657	4.385
					8½	26.70	13.350	6.675	4.450
5	15.71	7.855	3.927	2.618	8⅝	27.10	13.550	6.775	4.516
5⅛	16.10	8.050	4.025	2.683	8¾	27.49	13.745	6.872	4.581
5¼	16.49	8.245	4.122	2.748	8⅞	27.88	13.940	6.970	4.646
5⅜	16.89	8.495	4.247	2.835					
5½	17.28	8.640	4.320	2.880	9	28.27	14.135	7.067	4.711
5⅝	17.67	8.835	4.417	2.945	9⅛	28.67	14.385	7.192	4.795
5¾	18.06	9.030	4.515	3.010	9¼	29.06	14.530	7.265	4.843
5⅞	18.46	9.230	4.615	3.076	9⅜	29.45	14.725	7.362	4.908
					9½	29.85	14.925	7.462	4.975

TABLE VI.—DIMENSIONS OF BARE, DOUBLE-COTTON-COVERED AND SINGLE-COTTON-COVERED AND ENAMELED WIRE

Size B. & S. gage	Diameter in inches			Area	
	Bare	D. C. C.	S. C. and En.	Sq. in.	Circ. mils
1	.2893	.3073	......	.06753	83,690
2	.2576	.2756	......	.05213	66,370
3	.2294	.2474	......	.04134	52,630
4	.2043	.2223	......	.03278	41,740
5	.1819	.1999	......	.02600	33,100
6	.1620	.1780	......	.02062	26,250
7	.1443	.1603	......	.01635	20,820
8	.1285	.1425	......	.01297	16,510
9	.1144	.1264	......	.01028	13,090
10	.1019	.1119	......	.00815	10,380
11	.0907	.1007	.....	.00647	8,234
12	.0808	.0908	.0875	.00513	6,530
13	.0720	.0820	.0787	.00407	5,178
14	.0641	.0731	.0707	.00323	4,107
15	.0571	.0661	.0637	.00256	3,257
16	.0508	.0598	.0573	.00203	2,583
17	.0452	.0542	.0516	.00161	2,048
18	.0403	.0493	.0467	.00128	1,624
19	.0359	.0449	.0423	.00101	1,288
20	.0320	.0410	.0382	.00080	1,022
21	.0285	.0375	.0346	.00064	810.1
22	.0253	.0343	.0315	.00050	642.4
23	.0226	.0316	.0286	.00040	509.5
24	.0201	.0291	.0262	.00032	404.0
25	.0179	.0269	.0239	.00025	320.4
26	.0159	.0249	.0219	.000199	254.1
27	.0142	.0232	.0201	.000158	201.5
28	.0126	.0216	.0185	.000125	159.8
29	.0113	.0203	.0170	.0000995	126.7
30	.0100	.0190	.0158	.0000789	100.5

CHAPTER XXIII

TESTING SINGLE-PHASE MOTORS WHILE AND AFTER WINDING

While rewinding single-phase motor stators of the split-phase, universal or repulsion type, there are number of faults that may occur. How to locate these faults is dealt with in this chapter.

Locating Grounds.—The commonest fault or defect is the grounding of the running or starting windings in some way. To locate a ground, test the winding with the type of transformer shown on page 224 of Chap. XXIV and apply 900 volts between each winding and ground. By watching for smoke or a flash, the point of contact can usually be found. It is best to test the winding for grounds after the coils (running and starting) are in place and all the slot wedges driven in before connecting.

Testing for Short Circuits.—The next step is to test for short-circuited turns. This can be done by means of the screw driver test as explained in Chap. XIII (page 107) or by the use of the small growler described on page xii. Place the growler in the field and over one slot. Then place a piece of thin steel strip over the slot on the opposite side of the pole that contains the other half of the coil. If there is a shorted turn in either of these two slots, the steel strip will be attracted to and will vibrate over the slot on which it is held. Now, move the growler and steel strip one slot at a time, being sure to keep the steel strip (sometimes called a feeler) one coil pitch away from the growler. With concentric windings start on the outside coil of each group and work both growler and steel strip or keeper one slot at a time towards the center coils. The same method should be followed for either running or starting windings of the split-phase type and also for the series and compensated universal motor types and the stators of repulsion motors.

Checking Polarity of Windings.—After connecting the coils, the polarity of each winding and coil should be tested. To do this pass direct current through a lamp bank connected in series with the stator. Then with a compass or a magnetized steel needle suspended on the end of a string, test the polarity of each coil. For salient poles they should alternate north, south, etc. For consequent poles *each coil* should have the same polarity but a pole of opposite polarity should be formed between the coils, this pole being formed by the flux set up in each coil.

The polarity of the starting coil in reference to the running coils determines the direction of rotation as explained in Chap. XVIII.

Balancing the Rotor.—The rotor should be balanced to lessen vibration. This operation is illustrated in Fig. 160 which shows the balancing

Fig. 160.—Balancing knife edges for truing up single-phase rotors. Metal is drilled out of the side on which the high spot is found.

Fig. 161.—Method of making a torque test. When this test is made one man should take the scale readings in pounds and the other the meter readings so as to get simultaneous readings.

ways for truing up small rotors. Metal is drilled out on the heavy side of the rotor.

Testing Rotor for Poor Bar Contact.—After the motor is assembled, the rotor can be tested for poor bar contact as follows: Apply a low alternating current voltage to the stator with a suitable ammeter in circuit. Then turn the rotor slowly and note the meter needle. If it remains steady the rotor is O.K. but if it fluctuates, the amount of fluctuation depends upon the degree of contact in the rotor. If much deflection is noticed, it is advisable to resolder the rotor.

Another method of testing rotor contact is by the torque the motor has when put on full line voltage. In cases of very poor contact the difference in torque can be felt with the thumb and finger, but for more elaborate torque tests the outfit shown in Fig. 161 can be used. This is the well-known prony-brake test.

Testing Centrifugal Switch.—The centrifugal switch should be tested by starting and stopping the motor a number of times. This will show up sticking or defective operation.

Testing for Brush Position.—The straight series-type motor can be tested for brush position as explained in Chap. XVIII, page 156. Also a study of the diagrams in Chap. XX on fan motors will help trace out the brush position in reference to coil and field. After a winder becomes familiar with the compensated winding and can tell the main winding, the poles can be located and the brush position determined as explained.

Checking for Wrong Connections.—In some cases a wrong connection of coils is used; that is, a series where it should have been parallel, or vice versa, or a 220-volt winding is put in a 110-volt stator, etc. These defects can be determined by the motor torque, heating, etc.

If a motor is connected in series instead of parallel and put on its rated voltage it will develop less torque than expected since the torque decreases as the square of the voltage. If connected in parallel instead of series, the torque will be increased, but the motor will get hot and make quite a noise since it is operating on twice normal voltage.

Locating Troubles in Single-phase Repulsion Motors.—The following instructions for inspecting and testing single-phase repulsion induction motors for operating troubles are taken from a bulletin published by the Wagner Electric Corporation, St. Louis, Mo., and in general apply to other similar designs.

Failure to Start.—This may be due to the following causes:

1. Fuse blown. Replace fuse.

2. No voltage or low voltage. Measure voltage with a reliable voltmeter.

3. Excessive load. Reduce the load on the motor.

4. Motor connected for the higher voltage rating and lower voltage rating applied. Change motor connection to correspond to the line voltage on which motor is to operate. See Fig. 165.

Failure to Release Brushes on Full Load.—The following are possible causes of this trouble:

1. The commutator may be dirty. Clean with a piece of fine sand paper wrapped over a block of wood.

Fig. 162.—Rotor of single-phase motor showing weights that flyout and short circuit the commutator when the brushes are released from it.

2. Brushes worn too short to make good contact. Replace brushes with new ones.

3. Frequency of supply circuit too high. If the generator is near by, the frequency may be determined by multiplying the revolutions per

Fig. 163.—Rotor of single-phase motor showing spring against which the short circuiting weights act.

minute of the generator by number of poles, and dividing by 120. It may also be determined by means of standardized frequency meter. It is not sufficient to take the frequency or the speed from the nameplate of the generator, as the governor of the engine may have changed, thus changing the speed. If the motor will start and release its brushes with belt off, its speed will be very close to synchronous speed. Approximate normal no-load speed of motor is the full-load speed stamped on the nameplate, divided by 0.95.

High frequency decreases the starting torque so that the motor may not be able to reach the speed at which the brushes are normally released. Rarely, however, is the frequency high enough to cause this trouble. The remedy is to decrease the frequency, if possible, and if not, decrease pulley size to give the driven machine or the line shaft the same speed as

Fig. 164.—Field, rotor and brush assembly for Wagner single-phase repulsion motor.

with normal frequency. (See paragraph on adjustment of spring tension.) In any event, the motor will not develop full capacity.

4. Low voltage. Starting torque, or turning power of motor, decreases as the square of the voltage. Therefore, a decrease in voltage will cause a much greater decrease in torque. Voltage should be raised to normal operating value. If the motor is at the end of a long line, measure the voltage at both ends of the line, when motor is starting, and when motor is running. If the drop is considerable, a larger wire should be used. If the voltage at the service entrance is low, the generator voltage should be raised. If this is impossible the voltage may be raised by installing a transformer with variable voltage taps.

5. Brush setting incorrect. Even if rocker arm mark is opposite index, try moving slightly each way from index. The brush setting as

determined by the factory is for average conditions of service, and special conditions may require a slightly different setting.

6. High-voltage motor connection on lower voltage line. Change motor connection to correspond to line voltage upon which motor is to operate. See Fig. 166.

7. Excessive load. A Wagner single-phase motor may be able to start an excessive load and still not be able to carry this load up to the normal speed at which the brushes will be released.

8. Governor weight studs loose. Remove end plate and tighten if there is any more side play of governor on stud than is necessary for free operation.

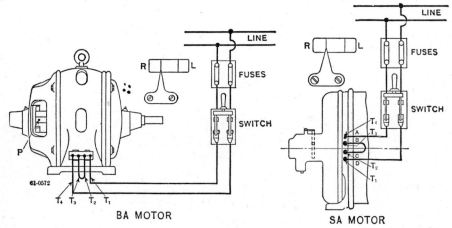

Fig. 165.—Terminal connections for highest voltage stamped on name-plate.

Failure to Release Brushes on No Load.—Look for these causes:

1. Armature rubbing on the field. This may be due to:

   (*a*) Extraneous material in the air gap.

   (*b*) A sprung shaft, though not likely in a Wagner motor, unless it has had extremely rough handling in transit.

   (*c*) Worn bearings.

2. Broken parts of the governor mechanism can be determined only by dismantling. (See following paragraph on motor assembly.)

3. Governor weights stick. Remove spring of governor mechanism. Governor weights should move on their pivots freely.

4. Short circuit in armature. This will decrease the starting torque of the motor and increase the starting current. Short-circuited coils are indicated by excessive heating of these coils during starting period. Short circuit may be determined by removing the brushes and closing the line switch. A failure to revolve the armature easily by hand indicates a short circuit. The motor armature may rotate part of a revoluton, and then stop suddenly.

Brushes Return to Commutator after Being Released.—One of the following conditions will usually be found:

1. The governor device operates at a speed greater than the speed under load. Such a condition may be caused by low frequency or too great tension on the governor spring. The latter need not be expected unless motor has recently been dismantled or adjusted.

2. The governor device operates at a speed so low that the induction motor torque is insufficient to pull the load up to speed. In this case the motor will usually behave more or less normally without load. Such a condition may be due to a frequency several per cent higher than normal, or to insufficient tension of the governor spring. (Refer to the paragraph on adjustment of the spring for models shown in Fig. 158.)

Hot Bearings.—This may be due to the following:

1. Poor grade of oil. Always use a good grade of red engine oil such as recommended by leading oil refiners.

2. Dirty oil. If the motor is in a dusty place, the oil will soon become gritty, and the bearings will become hot and wear rapidly. Oil wells should be drained at least once at month, and clean oil substituted. A practically dust-proof bearing can be supplied at a small extra cost.

3. Insufficient oil. Be sure that the oil level is always up to the oil well limit overflow. The overflow in most of the smaller sized motors, is a drilled hole in the end of the bearing housing, while in the larger size motors, the overflow holes are arranged in the sides of the oil well, with hinged brass covers.

4. Oil rings not rotating. Open oil well cover and note whether oil rings are carrying oil up to the bearings. If the ring is rotating but not carrying oil, there is insufficient oil in the well. Very little trouble need be looked for from this source, if the oil is kept at the proper level as determined by the oil overflow hole. On this account some of the bearings are arranged so that an inspection of the oil rings is impossible.

5. Bearings out of alignment, caused by dirt or foreign matter in the joint between motor frame and end plate. This will cause a binding in the bearing, which will tend to make it run hot.

6. Motor throws oil. If it is found that oil is drawn into the motor, from the bearings, thus tending to flood the windings, it probably will be found that oil has been poured into the oil well, above the level of the overflow hole, or that the duct leading back to the oil well from the ends of the bearings, has become stopped with foreign matter.

Motor Heats on Light Loads.—Such trouble may be due to:

1. Low frequency. (Only if very low.)

2. High voltage. (Considerably above normal.)

3. Local heating in stator winding, due to short circuit in winding.

4. Lower voltage motor connection, on higher voltage line. Change motor connection to correspond to line voltage. See Fig. 165.

Motor Heats When Loaded.—This may be due to:

1. Incorrect frequency.
2. Low voltage.
3. Excessive overloads.

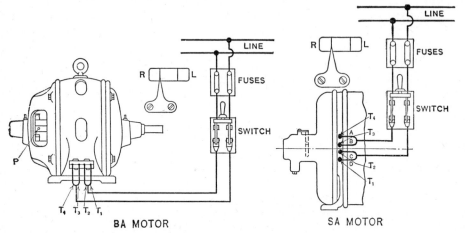

FIG. 166.—Terminal connections for lowest voltage stamped on name-plate.

4. Incorrect line connection to motor leads.

5. Note that a motor should not be considered in danger because it feels hot to the hand. A thermometer should be used to determine the temperature rise if excessive heating is suspected.

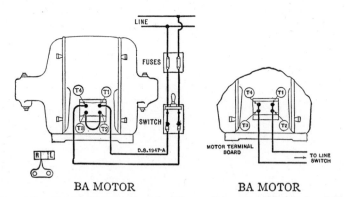

FIG. 167.—Terminal connections for Wagner BA motor (Models 8 and 9).

Spring Barrel Assembly Shown in Fig. 171.—Place brush holder ring (*P*-2) on spring barrel (*Q*-2). Screw in spring barrel nut (*F*-2) until brush holder ring (*P*-2) can be moved back and forth on spring barrel about $\frac{1}{16}$-in., and screw hole is opposite slot in spring barrel. Insert spring barrel nut screw (*G*-2).

Spring Barrel Assembly Illustrated in Fig. 172.—Place brush holder ring (*P*-3) flange side first on spring barrel (*Q*-3). Screw in spring barrel nut (*F*-3) until it holds brush holder ring (*F*-3) flush with end of spring barrel (*Q*-3). Turn spring barrel nut (*F*-3) until screw hole is opposite slot in spring barrel. Insert spring barrel nut screw (*G*-3). Screw brush holder ring nut (*N*-3) into brush holder ring (*P*-3) until flush with brush holder ring, and screw hole is opposite hole in brush holder ring. Insert brush holder ring screw (*O*-3).

Spring Barrel Assembly Illustrated in Fig. 173.—Place brush holder ring (*P*-4) flange side first, on spring barrel (*Q*-4). Insert spring barrel

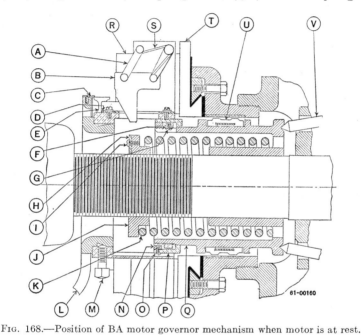

Fig. 168.—Position of BA motor governor mechanism when motor is at rest.

(A) Knock-off link; (B) Brush holder knock-off; (C) Brush holder index pointer; (D) Brush holder clamp; (E) Brush holder rocker arm; (F) Spring barrel nut; (G) Spring barrel nut screw; (H) Spring nut key; (I) Spring nut key screw; (J) Spring nut; (K) Governor spring; (L) Rocker arm bracket; (M) Rocker arm set screw; (N) Brush holder ring nut; (O) Brush holder ring screw; (P) Brush holder ring; (V) Spring barrel; (R) Brush; (S) Brush holder spring; (T) Commutator; (U) Short-circuiting weight; (V) Connecting rod; (W) Spring barrel snap ring.

snap ring (*W*-4) until spring barrel snap ring (*W*-4) until it snaps in place.

Spring Barrel Assembly Illustrated in Fig. 174.—Place brush holder ring (*P*-6) flange side first on spring barrel (*Q*-6) with spring barrel washers (*Z*-6) next. Insert spring barrel snap ring (*W*-6) until it snaps in place.

Motor Assembly.—Refer to Fig. 168, which shows the assembly of motors of the larger models. Place short-circuiting weights (*U*) in groove in spring barrel, straight edge to spring barrel, and supporting wire end toward brush holder ring. Place whole assembly on shaft and push back into armature until stopped by connecting rods (*V*).

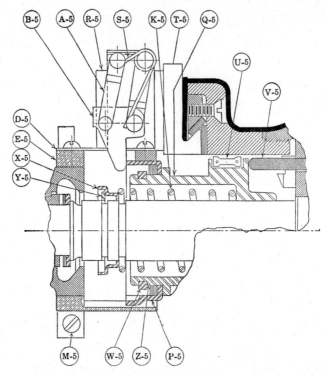

FIG. 169.—Position of governor mechanism at rest, Models 8 and 9-BA.

(A-5) Knock-off link; (B-5) Brush holder knock-off; (D-5) Brush holder clamp; (E-5) Brush holder rocker arm; (K-5) Governor spring; (M-5) Rocker arm set screw; (P-5) Brush holder ring; (V-5) Spring barrel; (R-5) Brush; (S-5) Brush holder spring; (T-5) Commutator; (U-5) Short-circuiting weight; (V-5) Connecting rod; (W-5) Spring barrel snap ring; (X-5) Governor spring retainer washer; (Z-5) Spring barrel fibre washers.

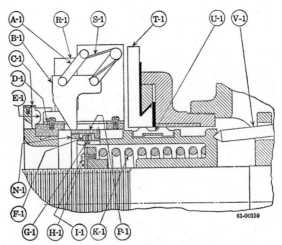

61-00159

FIG. 170.—Position of BA governor mechanism when motor has attained full speed. Note brush holder knock-off (B-1) rides on brush holder ring (P-1).

Place spring (*K*) in spring barrel (*Q*). Screw on spring nut (*J*) until it clears the end plate, when armature floats freely between bearings. In models 8-*SA* and 9-*BA* lock spring nut (*J*) by turning spring nut until lock screw hole is opposite half round slot in shaft, and insert fillister head screw so that it registers in shaft slot.

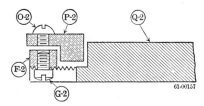

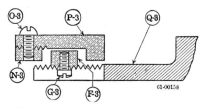

Fig. 171.—Detail of spring barrel assembly, Models 8-SA, 9-BA, 11-BA and 14-LBA.

Fig. 172.—Detail of spring barrel assembly, Models 14-BA, 17-BA, 17-LBA, 19-BA, and 22-BA.

In models 11-*BA* and 14-*LBA* insert spring nut key (*H*) in spring nut slot and turn spring nut (*J*) until key (*H*) will engage slot in shaft. Insert spring nut key screw (*I*).

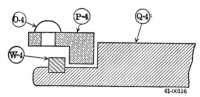

Fig. 173.—Detail of spring barrel assembly, late construction, for Models 8-SA, 9-BA 11-BA, 14-LBA, 14-BA, 17-LBA, 17-BA and 19-LBA.

Figure 169 refers to models 8 and 9 in which the brush-lifting device differs from models to which Fig. 165 refers. An enlarged view of spring barrel mechanism detail is shown in Fig. 174. In assembling motor,

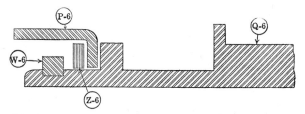

Fig. 174.—Detail of spring barrel assembly for Models 8 and 9-BA.

proceed as follows: Place spring (*K*-5) in spring barrel (*Q*-5). Push retainer (*X*-5) against spring (*K*-5) until retainer washer (*Y*-5) will fit in first or outer groove of shaft. If speed at which governor mechanism operates is too low, put retainer washer (*Y*-5) in second groove.

Replace end plate, lifting oil ring until shaft slides through bearing, *making sure* that brush holder ring screw (*O*), Fig. 172, fits into groove in brush holder rocker arm.

Be sure that end plate and frame joints are perfectly clean, or the bearing may be out of alignment when the bolts are tightened up, causing the bearing to run too hot.

Be sure that there is no more side play of brushes than is necessary for them to slide freely in the holders.

Adjustment of Models Referred to in Fig. 168.—Remove load. Connect motor to line. Close switch. If motor knocks off brushes at speed slightly lower than full load, spring adjustment is correct. If the motor does not knock off brushes at all, see first that the voltage and frequency are correct for the motor. If it is, the spring is too strong, and if the spring nut cannot be unscrewed, thus lessening spring tension, without having it rub on end plate, small pieces should be cut off the spring until the motor throws off the brushes before full load speed is reached.

Grind end of spring so that it will be similar to the uncut end, and give a full bearing on the spring nut.

If the motor throws off brushes too soon it may not pick up its load, and the spring nut should be tightened until the brushes are released at speed indicated above. When brushes have been released, see that brush holder knock-off (*B*) rides upon the knock-off ring as shown in Fig. 170.

Adjustment of Models Referred to in Fig. 169.—Proceed as above by removing load, connecting motor to line and closing the switch. If spring adjustment is found to be too strong and tension cannot be decreased by inserting retainer washer in first or outer groove of shaft, small pieces of spring should be cut off until the proper tension is obtained. The end of spring should be ground and shaped after cutting to give a full bearing on spring retainer.

CHAPTER XXIV

REPAIR SHOP TOOLS

Just how much can be profitably invested in shop tools and what tools are required, depends entirely on the volume and kind of repair work being handled. It is, however, essential to provide those tools that are frequently needed but proprietors of repair shops have varying ideas of what equipment is necessary for everyday use and usually buy as little as possible.

The following list includes the shop equipment which can be effectively used in a well-organized shop doing a fairly good volume and wide range of work:

Suitable special benches
Small speed lathe
Sensitive drill
Air compressor of about 35 cubic foot capacity for blowing out stators, for gas-air torches, paint sprayers, etc.
Insulating cutting shear
Insulation cell former
Insulating varnish tank
Drying oven
Electric soldering irons
Electrically heated solder pot
Air pressure paint sprayer
Commutator undercutting tool
Test board and instruments including, 110 to 220 a.c. voltmeter, direct-current millivoltmeter, and direct-current ammeter with shunt.
Head phones
Growler
Arbor press
Small balancing ways
Scales for torque test
Gang winding moulds
Bench holders for small alternating-current stators
Winding stand and crank for small direct-current armatures

Hand and Bench Tools

Rawhide mallett—Nos. 1 and 2.	T-shaped cell drift
Side cutting pliers—6- and 8-in.	Wedge driver
Files	Riveting hammer
Screw driver—four sizes	Machinists hammer
Center punch.	Scissors
Flat steel drift	Lead scraper
Assorted fiber slot drifts	Large knife.

A shop can be overequipped with special tools just as it can be under-equipped and in each case the result is the same. In the former case the saving on a few jobs is more than eaten up by the interest and insurance on the special equipment when infrequently used while in the latter case with too few tools, labor costs are high on hand work that can be done by machines, when a large volume of the same kind of rewinding is handled. The repair shop is the birthplace for numerous home-made devices, some of which are great time savers and others, makeshifts that cost practically as much as standard tools and have a narrower range of application. This is particularly true of coil winders and spreaders—two pieces of equipment most essential when large numbers of form-wound coils are used. For small motor work skein moulds, adjustable winding forms and gang moulds provide in many cases the difference between profit and no profit on this work when price cutting competition is faced. Suitable work benches, reliable testing apparatus, varnish and oven equipment falls into this class also.

A Convenient Work Bench.—A shop bench that keeps a winder from running about the shop for small tools, miscellaneous small materials and facilities for testing, is worth every penny it costs. In Fig. 175 a bench is shown that was developed by a shop handling a large volume of small direct-current armature rewinding mostly for automobile starting motors and generators.

The top of the bench is large enough to hold all tools and materials ordinarily needed, while the drawer provides storage space for those which are not often required. If the drawer is provided with a lock, tools may be safely stored when the bench is out of service for a time. The bench is built of wood with the exception of the turntable, the winding centers and their supporting base, which are made of iron.

The armature-supporting centers are carried on a turntable so that the work may be turned to any position with ease. Where armatures of only one size are handled the center supports may be made of wood and may be non-adjustable, but where shafts of various lengths must be handled it is best to secure a regular cast-iron center support with one adjustable end. A ball-bearing turntable support is used under the turn-

Fig. 175.—This bench is built for convenience in winding small armatures.

A, adjustable center support for holding armature. *B*, lever for locking revolving center support base in any position. *C*, lamp in series with test leads. *D*, test leads on lighting circuit. *E*, trimming strip around bench. This projects a short distance above the top of the bench.

Fig. 177.—Foot controlled power operated winding stand for small direct current armatures. Note the tools that are used by the winder. The construction of this winding form is shown in Fig. 178.

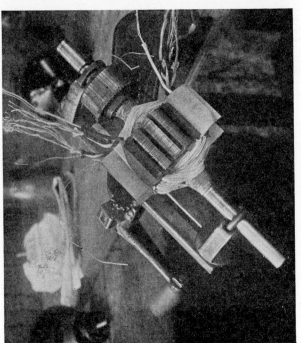

Fig. 176.—Hand operated holder for winding small direct-current armatures, that is provided with a turn counter.

table shown, but a spindle of any convenient type mounted on the top of the bench will serve satisfactorily in most cases.

The pipe carried at the top of the two standards at the back of the bench is provided to support the reel or reels from which the winding wire is taken. Reels of about 10-lb. capacity are most convenient, being light enough to be handled easily and still holding wire enough for several jobs. The lamp on the right-hand standard is connected in series with

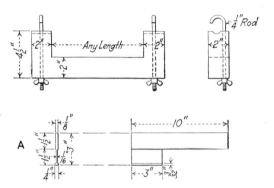

Fig. 178.—Construction of holder for winding stand shown in Fig. 177.

the lighting circuit and the coil of test leads shown on the top of the bench. The test leads serve as a convenient source of current for testing out the work as it progresses.

Armature Centers and Stator Holders.—A convenient form of winder for small armatures provided with a suitable turn counter is shown in Fig. 176. Another type that can be power driven is shown in Figs. 177

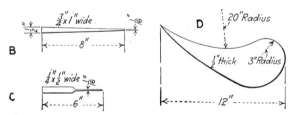

Fig. 179.—Special winding tools used by winder shown in Fig. 177.

and 178 with construction details. A convenient type of holder for winding an armature in a horizontal position is shown in Fig. 180.

Stator holders in a variety of forms are used from a V-block such as shown in Fig. 180 to special stands such as illustrated in Fig. 112, Chap. XVI, page 137. For the small shop, however, a flexible strap-iron holder like that shown in Fig. 181 will be satisfactory. The strap-iron is about 28 in. long, bent into the shape of a U-clamp, with the upper ends held in

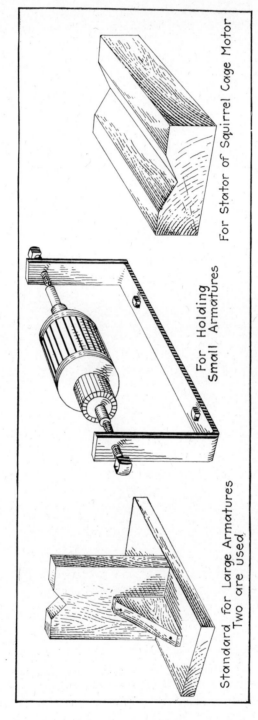

Fig. 180.—Two armature stands and a V-block for small stators that are easy to make.

place by an adjustable bolt and nut. The lower end is bolted to the bench and the whole outfit forms a springy receptacle which can be

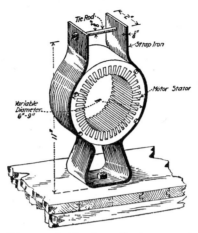

Fig. 181.—Details of flexible stator holder that will take stators from 6 to 9 in. in diameter.

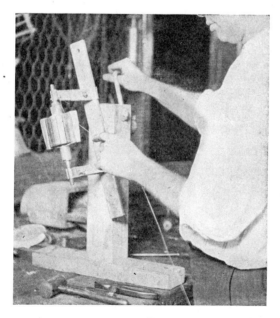

Fig. 182.—The base of this winding device is a piece of 2- by 4-in. wood, while the upright is a piece of 4- by 4-in. The shaft and crank of the rotating part are made of iron. The bar which supports the armature is a piece of ½- by 2-in. iron, about 18 in. long. The holding clamps are of light strap iron, 4 in. to 6 in. long.

adjusted to a wide variety of motor frames ranging in diameter from 6 to 9 in. The strap-iron of which the holder is made is 2 in. wide and ⅛ in.

thick; the tie rod at the top is ⅜ in. in diameter, and a ⅜-in. bolt fastens it to the bench. It stands about 11 in. high.

Special Chuck for Winding Small Coils.—For winding a variety of sizes and shapes of small formed coils as exact duplicates of the ones used in an old winding, the chuck shown in Fig. 183 can be used on a small speed lathe.

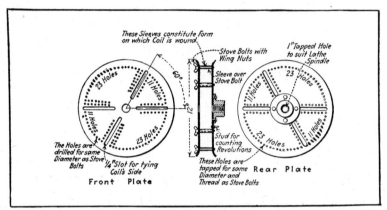

Fɪɢ. 183 —Convenient chuck arrangement by which old armature coils can be duplicated in a variety of sizes on a small speed lathe.

This winding chuck is made up of two iron plates ³⁄₁₆ in. thick and 12 in. in diameter. To the center of the back plate is bolted a hub with a 1-in. hole threaded for mounting on the spindle of a small speed lathe. The front plate is a duplicate of the back plate and is held to the latter by the bolts that are used to provide a frame on which the new coil is to

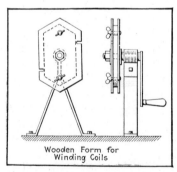

Fɪɢ. 184.—Simple coil form for mounting on a bench.

be wound. In drilling the holes in these plates they were securely clamped together and the front plate was drilled with a ⁷⁄₃₂-in. drill. After passing through the front plate the location of the hole was only spotted on the back plate. The front plate was then removed and the back plate drilled as an exact duplicate according to the spots, with a

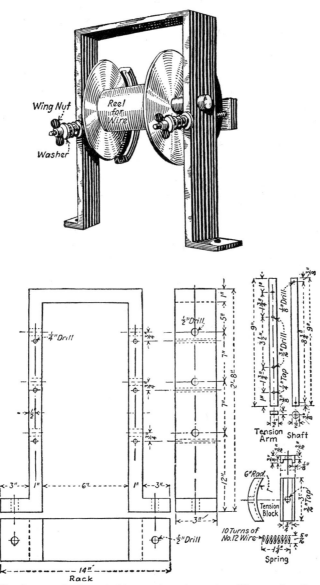

Fig. 185.—Tension on wire is varied by turning wing nuts. The construction details of this rack for wire reels are shown in the drawings.

$\frac{5}{32}$-in. drill. These holes were then tapped with a No. 10 tap with twenty-four threads per inch. This made it possible to screw ordinary stove bolts in the back plate to make up the form for winding a new coil. Since many coils are usually wound on the same form, it was found advisable to use threaded bolts in the back plate, as these bolts support the front plate, which must be removed on the completion of each coil, and also to make a rigid form for winding the coil. Six stove bolts $1\frac{1}{2}$ in. long, with sleeves made from $\frac{1}{8}$-in. pipe, are used at the points of an old coil in making up the form for winding new ones. Thumb nuts on these bolts make it easy to clamp on the front plate. As shown in the accompanying illustration, the edges of the plates are curved outward to prevent cutting the insulation of the wire when winding the coil.

For counting the numbers of turns of an old coil used in laying out the form for a new one, the back disk is provided with a stud that operates a small revolution counter mounted on the head of the lathe. This device has been found convenient for winding field coils as well as armature coils of direct-current and alternating-current motors.

Another common type of wood form for winding coils is shown in Fig. 184.

Holders for Wire and Tape Reels.—Since the tension under which wire is drawn from reels in winding operations affects the ease and speed of the winding job, a rack such as shown in Fig. 185 is a convenient device. This rack will take reels of wire ranging in size from No. 20 to No. 40. The tension is adjusted by springs which control the pressure of blocks against the ends of the reels.

The blocks are attached to a cross arm with machine screws, the ends of the screws being filed flush with the concave surface of the blocks. The tension bolts are threaded and firmly screwed into the two outside holes tapped in the arm, so the bolts will not turn when adjusting the wing nuts. To load the rack the reel is held so that the ends fit into the grooves of both tension blocks. The shaft is slipped through the reel and the cotter pins replaced so the shaft will be held in place. The reel may be rotated in either direction.

A handy tape reel is shown in Fig. 186. It provides an easy means of keeping tape out of the way when working around the bench. The brass circular sides are 3 in. in diameter and are provided with a U-shaped clamp with rods at the upper end through which the tape is fed. A wing screw enables the movement of the reel to be adjusted for the friction required to pull out the tape. With this reel enough tape to handle the immediate requirements of the job is fed forward.

Tension Block for Magnet Wire.—When winding enamel-covered magnet wire it is often difficult to apply tension to the wire without injuring the insulating covering. The same difficulty is encountered in only a lesser degree in winding either single or double-cotton-covered wire.

A device that can be used with both of these varieties of wire is easily and cheaply made from an ordinary carpenters' wooden screw clamp, is shown in Fig. 187. The friction blocks are made of felt.

The clamp selected should have jaws about 1½ in. wide. Cut off the beveled ends of the jaws where the bevel starts, and fasten the remaining portions of the jaws together with four pieces of ¾-in. wood. The inside space between the two jaws should be about 4¾-in. for ordinary work. Use flathead wood screws for fastening the various parts together. Guide plates, of ⅜-in. wood, with holes of a number, size and arrangement to suit the work in hand, should be made for the front and rear of the device. The edges of the holes should be carefully smoothed and rounded with sandpaper.

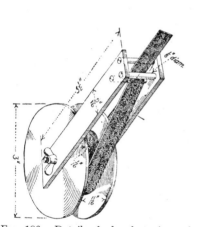

FIG. 186.—Details of a handy taping reel.

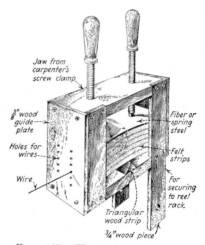

FIG. 187.—The felt strips permit desired tension on the wire without injury to the insulation.

A small strip of hard wood, triangular in cross section, is then fastened crosswise to the middle of the lower jaw. The sides of the triangle are all ½ in. wide. Cut strips of solid, heavy felt, ½ in. thick, to fit snugly between the side and end pieces as shown. As many strips are used as there are horizontal rows of holes in the guide plates. They should be topped with a piece of light spring steel or ⅛-in. thick fiber. The screws bear on this top plate, and it will be found necessary to cut them off a bit in order that they will not project so far that they are clumsy for the operator to handle.

The wire is threaded through both guide plates and between the pieces of felt. Tension is applied and adjusted by means of the two screws and may be very closely regulated without injuring the insulation cf the wire. The projection of the side piece on the back end affords a flexible means for attaching the device to the reel rack which holds the spools of wire.

Slot Insulation Cutter and Former.—The trimming and cutting of fish-paper, pressboard, mica or flexible micanite is one of the jobs always on hand where motors are made or repaired. To do this with reasonable accuracy where the only tools are a straight-edge and a knife or a pair of shears, is a tedious task as anyone will agree who has had to mark out and cut up slot insulation with such tools. And yet the work may be done very easily even though the shop cannot provide one of the large, standard insulation shears, for practically any establishment can

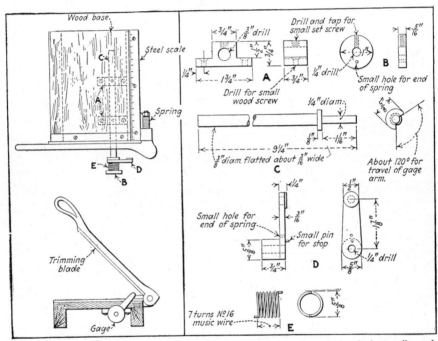

Fig. 188.—A photograph trimmer provided with a gage will cut strip insulation easily and accurately. Construction details are shown.

afford to make up the trimmer shown in Fig. 188 (described by J. M. Welsh, May 1922, *Industrial Engineer*).

The basis of this trimmer is an ordinary wood-base photograph trimming board of a size suitable to the work to be handled. A board should be selected of the type having the blade-wear taken up by spring pressure as shown in the sketch. The wooden scale which is ordinarily part of the trimmer as purchased should be removed and an old steel scale fastened in its place, or one leg of a cheap metal square may be used. With these changes the trimmer is ready for work and it will cut cleanly and neatly all of the materials above mentioned.

Where many strips of uniform width are required, the use of a gage is advantageous. With the help of the machine shop the stop gage shown in the drawing can be easily produced. This gage has the special advantage that it can be used for very narrow strips as it is automatically depressed out of the way of the blade when the latter cuts, reappearing in proper position when the blade is lifted.

The various parts are all made of wrought iron or cold-rolled steel, and the dimensions given are for a gage used on an 8-in. trimmer. This gage might also be used on a larger trimmer without much change. The stop *D* is set to give the proper width of cut by means of the two set screws

Fig. 189.—Handy gauge and knife for cutting insulation for armature slots.

in the pillow blocks, *A* and *A*, which support the gage rod, *C*. The spring *E* returns the stop arm to its proper position after the blade is lifted if the work is so narrow as to cause the blade to strike the gage.

For cutting fiber in very narrow widths the home-made gage (described by K. Knowles, February, 1922, *Industrial Engineer*) can be attached to a standard paper cutter as shown in Fig. 189. The gage consists of a straight bar, 21 in. long, 1¾ in. high and ³⁄₁₆ in. wide, attached to angle pieces which are seated against two sliding blocks arranged to move back and forth, as required, on the regular stop of the cutter. A ½-in. rod connects the sliding blocks and is fitted with a spring to hold the gage in a horizontal position parallel to the face of the cutter. The gage can be fixed in any position along the cutter by set-screw adjustment, and the fiber can be cut to hair-widths if desired.

For forming insulation for cells of partially closed slots, the devices shown in Fig. 190 can be used. It is shown attached to a 40-in. strawboard cutting machine of the kind used in many repair shops. This fixture folds the cells and puts on a lip $\frac{1}{32}$ in. wide as shown in the drawing. The bender is made of $\frac{1}{2}$- by $1\frac{1}{2}$-in. cold-rolled steel. Two vertical bars hold a long bending bar to the cutting arm. Figure 190

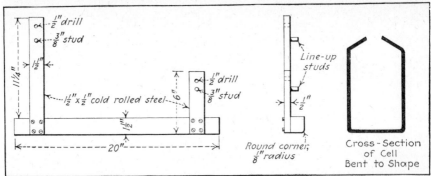

Fig. 190.—This device for bending slot insulating cells to shape can be attached to a cutting machine.

shows the vertical bars attached to the cutter with two thumb screws. The knife holder has to be faced to receive the two vertical bars. The holes are drilled to receive the line-up studs.

It will be noticed that one vertical bar is longer than the other, in order to give a long bending surface to press against the cell. The edge that goes against the stationary cutter is rounded off with $\frac{1}{8}$-in. radius to prevent the insulation being cut. One bend is made at a time and then the strip of insulation is moved over to the position for the next bend.

Testing Equipment.—For testing small motors for short circuits, grounds, open circuits and the like, a convenient form of "growler" is a handy device. In Fig. 191 such a growler is shown that can be used on a 110-volt, 60-cycle circuit. It was made from an old direct-current fan-motor armature by removing the shaft and cutting off the teeth as shown in the illustration.

A slot was then cut in one side to allow the wires of the winding to be inserted in the hole formerly occupied by the shaft. A thousand turns of No. 34 double-silk-covered wire were wound on. After the winding was put in, wedges were inserted to hold it in place. Lamp-cord leads were fastened to the growler and taped.

To test for shorts, this small growler is placed on the stator teeth and a tin feeler is used across the slots, one coil pitch in advance of the growler. If the tin vibrates there is a short in that slot. To test for grounds, place the growler on the core and then touch one lead of the stator winding to the iron core. If a spark is produced, the winding is

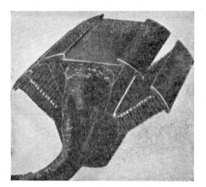

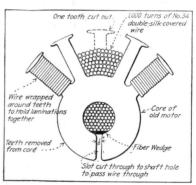

Fig. 191.—Growler used to locate grounds and shorts in small stators.

Fig. 192.—Details of the construction of the small growler shown in Fig. 191.

grounded. This test can be made after a stator is rewound and before connecting it up. Try each coil in the starting and running winding. The slot the ground is in can be located by making a good steady contact with one lead of the grounded coil to the stator core; then apply the growler and use the tin feeler to bridge the slots until it vibrates.

Transformer for High-voltage Tests.—A transformer that provides test voltages from 100 to 1,500 in ten intermediate steps is shown in Fig. 193. It can be constructed as follows:

For the core, use laminations of the shape shown in the drawing. One-half of these laminations are of the dimension shown at A and are $2\frac{1}{2}$ in. wide, while the others are of the dimensions shown at B, and are 3 in. wide. Build up the laminations to a height of 4 in. One-half of the core should be built at one time, the B laminations alternating with the A laminations. After the two halves are built up, bolt them together

FIG. 193.—This transformer can be used for testing for grounds and short circuits with voltages of from 100 to 1,500 volts.

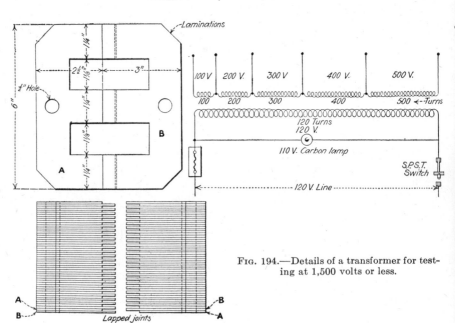

FIG. 194.—Details of a transformer for testing at 1,500 volts or less.

with $\frac{3}{8}$-in. bolts and put the coils in place. Then the halves of the core can be shoved together.

For the primary winding use a coil of 120 turns of No. 16 gage double-cotton-covered wire. For the secondary winding use No. 26 double-cotton-covered wire and about 1,800 turns. Bring out six taps, including the end terminals, as shown in the drawing. Between the first terminal and the second tap, provide 100 turns; between the second and third 200 turns, and so on, according to the figures in the drawing. By means of these taps the twelve different voltages shown in the accompanying table may be obtained.

TAPS FOR DIFFERENT VOLTAGES

Voltage desired	Connect high-voltage leads to taps shown below
100	1 and 2
200	2 and 3
300	3 and 4
400	4 and 5
500	5 and 6
600	1 and 4
700	3 and 5
900	4 and 6
1,000	1 and 5
1,200	3 and 6
1,400	2 and 6
1,500	1 and 6

In bringing out any tap, the wire should be insulated with a varnished cambric sleeve, if this tap is to be covered by further layers of wire. The core itself should be insulated from the winding by fiber or fish paper, and the primary coil should be insulated from the secondary by the same material.

After this transformer is built it can be mounted upon a baseboard and another board with terminal posts for the secondary can be mounted above the coils. In series with the primary side connect a fuse block for using an open fuse wire. Across the primary terminals connect a 110-volt carbon lamp. This lamp is a safety feature, as it is lighted whenever there is voltage on the primary side.

Connect the primary leads to a flexible cord having on its other end a detachable plug to fit in an ordinary 110-volt outlet. The secondary leads should be flexible, heavily insulated wires. For the high-voltage terminals use wires which are wrapped with varnished cambric and outside of this place rubber tubing.

In operation, if a ground or short circuit is detected by the secondary leads, the fuse blows.   On touching the secondary terminals to the conductor and frame and removing them, a light blue snapping spark indi-

FIG. 195.—Low voltage testing transformer with high current capacity.

The primary winding has 448 turns of No. 15 single cotton covered enameled wire with a tap brought out at each 112 turns.   The secondary winding consists of four strips of 20-mil copper each of which is wound around the primary a different number of turns.   Short pieces of busbar copper were sweated to the strips to serve as terminals.   By connecting the test leads to the different terminals, a comparatively wide range of voltage can be obtained, as shown in the table on page 227.

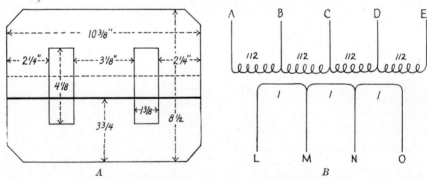

FIG. 196.—Dimensions of laminated core of the transformer shown in Fig. 195 and ratio of turns in primary and secondary windings.

cates only charging current and does not show a fault.   A red or yellow flaming spark, however, shows that power current is passing and that a short circuit or ground exists, depending upon what is being inspected. Usually when there is such a short circuit or ground the fuse will blow.

Low-voltage High-current Capacity Transformer.—A source of high amperage is very useful around a repair shop for testing series coils, blowing out grounds and for other purposes. The design and construction of a small transformer for this purpose that will deliver 500 to 1,000 amps. at low voltage from a 220-volt circuit is shown in Fig. 195 (described by H. B. Willmott, September, 1924, *Industrial Engineer*).

As shown in Fig. 196*A* the laminations are $10\frac{3}{8}$ in. long and $8\frac{1}{2}$ in. wide with slots for the winding. The laminations are stacked 5 in. high.

The primary winding consists of 448 turns of No. 15 s.c.e. wire with a tap brought out at each 112 turns. This winding can be wound on a simple wooden form, then taped, dipped in insulating varnish and baked.

SECONDARY VOLTAGES OBTAINED ON 220-VOLT PRIMARY

Connections		Secondary voltage*
Primary	Secondary	
A to B A to C A to D A to E	L to M	2 1 $\frac{2}{3}$ $\frac{1}{2}$
A to B A to C A to D A to E	L to N	4 2 $1\frac{1}{3}$ 1
A to B A to C A to D A to E	L to O	6 3 2 $1\frac{1}{2}$

* If 110 volts are used on the primary divide the secondary voltage by 2.

The secondary winding consists of three turns of laminated copper wound around the primary coil by hand and tapped at every turn. A short piece of $\frac{1}{4}$- by 2-in. bus copper can be used as a terminal. To the end of this, four strips of 20-mil copper $3\frac{7}{8}$ in. wide are securely sweated and one complete turn made around the primary coil. Then another piece of $\frac{1}{4}$- by 2-in. bus copper should be soldered on and one of the 20-mil sheets cut off. The three sheets remaining are carried around for the second time using $\frac{1}{32}$-in. fibre as insulation and sweated to a third piece of bus copper. Then another sheet is cut off leaving two sheets to go around for the third time.   The ends should then be soldered to a fourth piece of copper for the end of the winding.

The ratio of the turns in the winding is shown in Fig. 196*B*.   Inasmuch as both primary and secondary windings of the transformer are tapped, a number of voltages are available as shown in the table.   If still lower voltages are desired, 110 volts may be used on the primary and the table voltages halved.

The whole winding should then be stacked into the iron, suitable insulation being provided and arrangements made for tapping off flexible leads.   Hold the laminations firmly together by clamping them between short pieces of light angle iron placed at the end.   The complete transformer, shown in Fig. 195 is rather heavy and may be mounted on a small truck or dolly in order that it may be moved easily about the shop.

When using leads (*L*) and (*O*) on the secondary, the copper will carry 500 amp.   If (*L*) and (*M*) are used, 750 amp. can be obtained, and with (*L*) and (*N*) 1,000 amp.   These are, of course, intermittent ratings.

Telephone Head Set Testing Outfit.—The outfit shown in Fig. 197 can be used for locating short circuits, grounds and open circuits (described by D. F. O'Donnell, October, 1922, *Industrial Engineer*).

The parts needed are two or three dry cells, a small buzzer, a single-pole snap switch, one telephone induction coil and a 70-ohm head receiver.

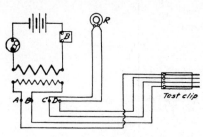

The battery, switch, buzzer and primary of the coil are all connected in series.   A neat outfit can be made by procuring an old wall-type telephone box or any small container that will hold the cells, buzzer and coil.   The switch can be mounted on one end and the four terminals for the secondary on the other end.   The

Fig. 197.—Testing outfit for small motor windings.

leads (*a*) and (*b*) go to two of the binding posts and receiver wires (*c*) and (*d*) to the other two

When testing for grounds, connect (*b*) and (*c*) together.   Leads are then taken from (*a*) and (*d*).   Energize the primary circuit and apply leads (*a*) and (*d*) to the windings to be tested.   If a dead ground is present a loud hum will be heard in the receiver.   Partial grounds will give a sound somewhat less in intensity than that produced by shorting the test leads together.   A slight clicking noise caused by the condenser action of the winding under test will always be heard, but you can easily recognize it.

When testing for shorts, opens, etc., a good contact clip can be made from a piece of ⅜-in. fiber and a few thin brass strips, as shown in the sketch of Fig. 197 and connect as illustrated.   The two center contacts should be adjusted to bridge two adjacent segments on the commutator and the outer clips to rest about six segments apart. A normal coil will give a definite buzz in the receiver. Opens are indicated by a loud buzz and shorts by an absolute silence. Partial shorts will be indicated by a noise in proportion to the resistance of the defect.

After a few trials a winder can test field coils and small alternating-current windings with results as accurate as those obtained with direct-current armatures.

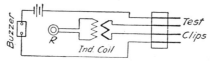

Fig. 198.—Connections for buzzer, telephone receiver and a telephone induction coil in testing out motor windings.

This set is extremely sensitive, the intensity of the sound varying with the slightest alteration in the resistance of the circuit being tested. It can be used for many purposes besides those mentioned here.

Another similar outfit is shown in Fig. 198 (described by G. R. Thatcher, December, 1922, *Industrial Engineer*). The telephone induction coil is used as an intensifier, with the high-tension winding connected directly across the receiver. With this connection a partial short-circuit in a large armature can be located with absolute certainty. The

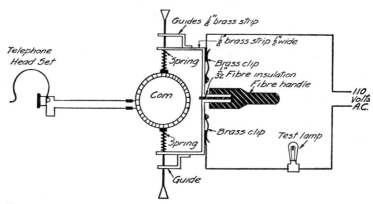

Fig. 199.—Details of a device for using a test lamp with a bar to bar test.

best results are obtained by using a wireless test buzzer. In this particular buzzer the vibrations are considerably greater than in the common buzzer, giving out a high-pitched, evenly maintained note.

For using a test lamp and 110-volt lighting circuit with a telephone head set for a bar to bar test of a winding, the device shown in Fig. 199 will be found handy. (Described by R. C. Standford, September, 1922, *Industrial Engineer*.) When using the telephone receiver, as shown in the diagram, a low buzzing in the receiver indicates a good coil, when the receiver is held to adjacent bars between connections of the test lamp which are placed on opposite sides of the commutator. A loud buzzing indicates an open circuit. No buzz at all indicates a shorted coil.

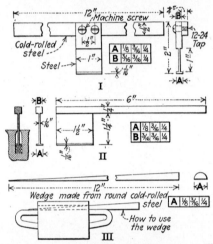

Fig. 200.—When the slot opening is narrow, tools like these will help to get the right number of wires in the slot.

Winder's Hand Tools.—Some handy drifts for use in winding motors that have partly closed slots and threaded-in types of windings are shown in Fig. 200. The tool shown at I was made to enable the winder to force down the wires in the slots on some small stators which had a bore

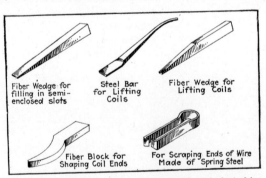

Fig. 201.—Five convenient tools for the winder's kit.

of 4 in. and a core length of 6 in. It is obvious when considering these dimensions that there was no room in which to use a mallet. Therefore a small drift was fastened to a long piece of cold-rolled steel as shown. The length of steel was drilled and tapped and clearance holes were drilled in the "T" drift for the machine screws. In using this tool the winder inserts the drift into the slot and presses down on each end of the bar.

The tool shown at II is a modification of that at I. The handle in this case is made integral with the drift. This tool is very handy, as the winder can hold it and pound along without fear of hitting his fingers.

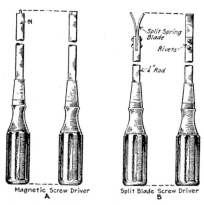

Magnetic Screw Driver
A

Split Blade Screw Driver
B

Fig. 202.—These magnetic and split-blade screw-drivers are useful when inserting small screws in close places where the workman cannot reach with his hands.

The widths given for *A* as the base of the tool will meet most cases. If a wider slot is encountered then a piece of $\frac{1}{16}$-in. or $\frac{1}{8}$-in. fiber can be cut to fit the slot and used under the "T" slot drift, or the drift can be held crosswise in the slot.

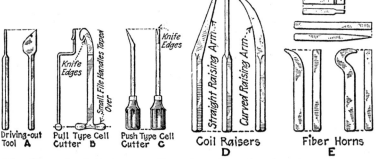

Driving-out Tool **A**   Pull Type Cell Cutter **B**   Push Type Cell Cutter **C**   Coil Raisers **D**   Fiber Horns **E**

Fig. 203.—These simple tools are easily made and can be adapted to armature repair work in any shop.

The drawing at III shows a steel wedge which is a great time saver when winding small single-phase stators. This tool is made from round cold-rolled steel of the proper sizes. The three sizes given in the drawing will cover the majority of slot sizes. One side of the tool is ground flat. Grind as shown by the dotted line, making a wedge starting with a thickness of $\frac{1}{32}$ in. up to the full diameter of stock used. After grinding, round

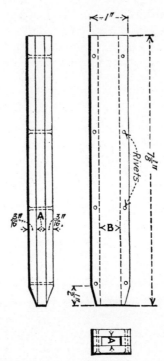

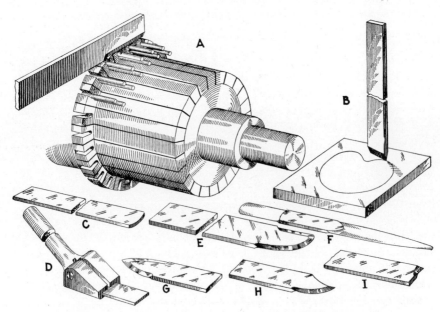

Fig. 204.—A loosely fitting plunger 7¾ in. long fits into this wedge driver.

Fig. 205.—Some handy tools which were made from old hacksaw blades.

off the sharp corners to prevent the tool from cutting the insulation on the wires. In use this tool is forced through the slot as far as it will go without damaging the core or wires. Then the end of the tool projecting beyond the core is worked up and down to force down the wires. Care must be taken not to use force enough to bend the laminations.

These tools will be found great time savers in winding almost any stator or rotor with partly closed slots.

Slot Wedge Driver.—The wedge driver shown in Fig. 204 is made of five pieces of cold-rolled steel with the front end tapered to permit the tool to be used in restricted spaces. The sizes most used have A and B dimensions of $\frac{1}{16}$-in. and $\frac{7}{16}$-in.; $\frac{5}{64}$-in. and $\frac{7}{16}$-in.; $\frac{1}{8}$-in. and $\frac{9}{16}$-in.

Tools Made from Old Hacksaw Blades.—Broken or worn-out hacksaw blades make handy winding tools that require sharp edges. Several described by Nelson Hale in *Industrial Engineer*, May, 1923, are shown in Fig. 205. They need only to be ground to shape and, if they are too hard, their temper can be drawn. For use in the electrical repair shop, blades ground sharp make good tools for cutting the ends of conductors at the commutator as shown in drawing A. The thinness of the edge makes it cut with light blows of a hammer, so that the commutator bars are not knocked down. Some of the other shapes shown may be used to clean surfaces, to skin wire, and to do general service in the kit.

Large blades ground like C make good single- and double-end scrapers. These blades are fine for light work and especially for removing accumulations from machines which have been idle for a time. Sometimes short blades can be put into a holder like D to good advantage.

To make a tool useful to a pattern maker, take a power hack-saw blade, grind the teeth off and shape the end like E, sharpening it all the way around. This makes a good knife for reaching inaccessible places around the pattern. At B is a blade ground like a skew chisel and used for tracing lines for inlay work. By holding the upper end of the chisel with one hand and tapping it with a hammer one can work out any shape. At F is a double-ended palette knife good for mixing or spreading color, glue, putty or plaster of paris.

Arbor Press and Tool for Removing Fields from Single-phase Motor Housings.—The tool shown in Fig. 206 (described by V. H. Todd, *Electrical Record*, November, 1924) can be used for removing the fields from Westinghouse fan motors. This tool is in the form of an iron cylinder A fitting snugly into the field and has recessed at one end a steel ring B, just like the piston ring on an automobile engine piston. This ring also slides through the field and when in position is spread by forcing down four taper-end pins C. The field is now set on the anvil D of an arbor press, which has a hole to pass the field but which catches the edge of the shell. A steel rod E is now inserted in the shaft hole and the arbor press handle pushed down to force the field and cylinder out through the anvil D.

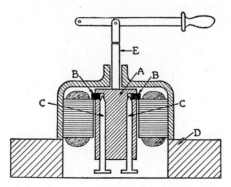

Fɪɢ. 206.—Special tool and arbor press used for removing fields from Westinghouse fans.

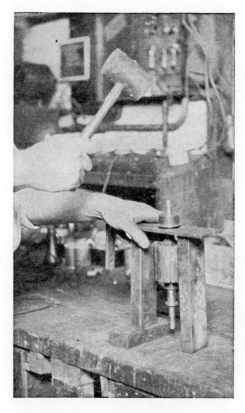

Fɪɢ. 207.—Removing commutator by pounding with rawhide hammer on end of shaft, while the armature is suspended on two flat iron bars supported on wooden uprights.

This same method is employed in the direct-current field except that a short piece of steel is laid across the inside ends of the field and then forced out with the arbor press.

In many cases the fields may be removed by one person holding the field with the fingers gripped through the armature hole while another hammers on the edge of the case with a hammer and copper chisel. This method relies on the inertia of the field to shift when hammered. It unfortunately often damages the finish on the fan.

In extreme cases where even the arbor press will not remove the field, the case is slit with a hack-saw, split, removed and replaced with a new one.

Fig. 208.—This varnish tank and **rack** provide for dipping thirty-six armatures at one time.
All armatures should be dried at a temperature of about 220°F., for approximately two hours in an oven before being dipped. The varnish should be maintained at about 100°F. Allow armatures to soak until all bubbling stops and tenh drain for 30 to 45 minutes.

Dipping Armatures Wound with Single Cotton and Enamel Insulation. A few hints on dipping armatures wound with single cotton and enamel-covered wires will be appropriate at this point. Heat the armatures to about 170 to 200°F., then give them a quick dip 1 to 5 min. depending upon the size of the armature in a thick varnish (never shellac). Allow the armature to drain and then put it in an oven. If a thin varnish is used it will have more of a tendency to soften the enamel than a thick varnish. The alcohol in shellac will soften the enamel quicker than will benzine or gasoline. A thin varnish contains a greater percentage of solvent than a thick varnish and it is the solvent of the varnish that attacks the enamel. Figure 208 shows a dip tank and rack for dipping 36 armatures at one time. Note that the armatures are dipped with the commutator end up, so that the drain is away from the commutator.

Varnishes for Coil Insulation.—Because the desirable characteristics for a perfect varnish cannot be combined into one compound, a number of varnishes have been developed, each having its own characteristic. The purposes of some insulating varnishes are indicated in the following table. Where more than one varnish can be successfully used the different types are indicated as first, second and third choices.

CORRECT VARNISH TO USE FOR INSULATING COILS

Characteristics of clear and black baking insulating varnishes and uses for which they are recommended*	Clear varnishes			Black varnishes			
	Clear quick baking	Clear quick elastic baking	Clear elastic baking	Black quick baking	High-heat-resisting baking	Black plastic baking	Black elastic baking
Dielectric strength	3	1	1	3	2	2	1
Mechanical strength	3	1	2	3	4	5	2
Flexibility	3	2	1	3	3	2	1
Plasticity	..	..	..	..	..	1	
Oil resistance	2	1	1	2	3	4	1
Water resistance	2	2	1	2	2	1	1
Life under heat	4	3	2	4	2	1	2
Treating cloth, paper and thin fibrous materials	3	2	1	3	3	2	1
Treating fullerboard and heavy fibrous materials	2	1	2	2	3	3	2
Small high-speed armatures	3	1	2	3	..	..	2
Intermediate-speed armatures	3	1	2	3	3	3	2
Large low-speed armatures	3	2	1	3	2	2	1
Field and stator coils	3	2	1	3	2	1	1
Automobile-starting motors	..	1					
Vacuum-cleaner motors	1	1	..	1			
Washing-machine motors	..	1	1	..	1	1	1
Street railway and electric locomotive							2
motors	..	..	2	..	..	1	2
Fan motors	3	1	2	3	2	..	2
Magnetos and induction coils	..	1	2	..	..	..	2
High-potential apparatus	..	1	2	..	..	..	2
Transformers	..	1	2	..	..	..	2
Average repair shop conditions	..	2	..	..	2	1	

* Numbers indicate order of suitability (Sherwin-Williams Company).

All of the varnishes mentioned in the table are of the baking type. However, insulating varnishes in general may be divided into several general classes, such as clear varnishes, black varnishes, baking varnishes and air-drying varnishes. The most marked difference between the clear and the black varnishes of course is the color, but owing to fundamental differences in the characteristics of the ingredients entering into their composition, there are also some differences in the physical properties of the varnishes themselves. As a general rule clear varnishes possess greater mechanical strength and resist oil better than black varnishes. An exception to this is the black elastic baking varnish shown in the table. Where extreme mechanical strength is required, as on small high-speed armatures, clear varnishes are best.

Black varnishes are not quite so strong mechancially as clear varnishes but are sufficiently strong for most purposes. On stationary windings, as on alternating current stator windings, the varnish is not subjected to centrifugal stresses and there is no advantage in using a clear varnish. Certain black varnishes are made from plastic materials and have the ability to withstand long-continued heating without hardening. Black varnishes, as a rule, are cheaper than clear varnishes, and are more commonly used.

Fig. 209.—Small oven suitable for baking small armatures. (Made by *Despatch Manufacturing Company.*)

The chief difference between baking varnishes and air-drying varnishes is in the proportion of oxidizing ingredients contained. The baking varnishes are tougher, more elastic, more resistant to oil and water, and have longer life under heat. Speed in drying is always accomplished at the expense of these characteristics, and the air-drying varnishes are less durable and elastic than the baking varnishes.

Baking Armatures and Stators.—Before small armatures and stators are dipped in varnish they should be baked in an oven for at least two hours at a temperature of about 220°F. After being dipped in varnish they should be again baked after each dip. For armatures up to 10 in. in diameter these directions can be followed.

First, bake for two hours at 220°F. Then dip while hot in black plastic varnish and allow the armature or stator to soak until all bubbling stops. Drain for ½ hour. Dip armatures with commutator end up but do not

immerse commutator unless a Bakelite dip is used when the whole armature can be immersed.   After draining bake again at 200 to 220°F. for
6 to 8 hours.

An electric oven suitable for baking small armatures is shown in Fig.
209.   It has a temperature range of 100 to 400°F. and a maximum current consumption of 900 watts on high heat, 400 watts on medium heat
and 200 watts on low heat.   These ovens operate on all standard voltages,
either direct or alternating current.   The heating elements are so con-

Fig. 210.—Small bench lathe suitable for turning commutators of small armatures.

structed that they do not become red, eliminating any chance of fire or
explosions.   Such an oven measures about 18 in. wide, 14 in. high, and
14 in. deep.

Points on Soldering.—Soldering may be regarded as a chemical
operation carried out by heat.   The following practical pointers in order
to do a good job were given by James Dixon in *Industrial Engineer* for
November, 1922.

The parts must be clean and covered with some substance, known
as a flux, which will dissolve the oxides that form on the metal by the

action of the air, so that the solder can get into chemical contact with the clean metal.

Soldering can be done by using an "iron" to transmit heat to the joint, or by heating the joint by dipping it in melted solder, or by blowing a flame on it. Soldering irons are made in a variety of sizes and shapes, depending on the character of the work.

Common solder is known as "half and half," as it is composed of equal parts of tin and lead. This grade is used for most work and has the characteristic of softening at a fairly low temperature and remaining mushy until considerably hotter, when it becomes very thin. The other kind of solder used in electrical work is called hard or AC solder. It has more tin in it, takes more heat to soften it and gets very thin almost as soon as it softens. It is used for soldering squirrel-cage rotors and stators, also for soldering wires into commutator necks of small motors that operate in hot places such as on head-light motor generator sets, etc.

Burnley's soldering paste is a good flux for soldering copper. When it is used on joints which are to be taped, they should be washed off with gasoline after soldering, to remove any excess of flux. Another flux is made of rosin dissolved in benzine or rosin alone, or even good rosin varnish can be used. This is best for general use in soldering small armatures and stators. Acid soldering solution or salts should never be used for electrical connections as the residue will absorb moisture and cause corrosion, which will ruin the insulation. The following formula for a non-corrosive soldering fluid is taken from the National Electrical Code: Saturated solution of zinc chloride, 5 parts; alcohol, 4 parts; glycerine part.

In soldering joints in windings, an iron is used except in the case of alternating-current stators where the end connections can sometimes be sweated by pouring. In this case the connections to be soldered are allowed to stand out and two ladles are used. One ladle should have a long snoot and the other can be of any type. When soldering, hold the ladle with the long snoot under the joint and pour the hot solder from the other ladle on the joint so as to catch the solder in the long snoot ladle. A number of joints can be made in this way with a ladle full of solder.

Soldering commutator tails is an important job, inasmuch as a poor joint is sure to cause trouble in the shape of black spots and overheating. As it is impossible to get at the side, all of the heat must be transmitted from the iron to the joint through a small area at the top. The joints must be perfectly clean and wedges driven in to bring the copper of the tails as close as possible to the leads. The irons must be well tinned by rubbing, while hot, on sal ammoniac crystals and solder. Time must be given for the joint to heat up thoroughly, so that the solder will run in all the way and not merely around the edges. To avoid delay in waiting for hot irons, a torch flame may be held on the iron as long as it works satisfactorily. This is practically as good as a gas iron. It requires two men; one to hold the iron and feed solder, and another to hold the torch. For small tails a soldering iron tip for the torch works well. Electric irons are not so good for this work, as they do not stay hot enough. It is safe to say that success in soldering depends 90 per cent on getting joints ready and clean and on having good tools, properly heated.

APPENDIX

SPECIAL ALTERNATING CURRENT MOTORS

THE SINGLE-PHASE CAPACITOR MOTOR

The capacitor or condenser type of motor is a recent development in single-phase designs with improved operating characteristics over split-phase and repulsion-induction types as to efficiency and power factor. In the *Electrical World* (March 31, 1928) Prof. Benjamin F. Bailey of the University of Michigan gave the following details of performance and operation of this type of motor:

The connections of a condenser motor are shown in Fig. 1 at (a). As in the split-phase motor, there are two windings, 90 electrical degrees from each other. Winding 2, however, would usually have approximately as much copper in it as winding 1, although the number of turns in the two windings need not be the same.

In most cases it would be advantageous to use more turns in winding 2 than in winding 1 and a correspondingly smaller size of wire, making the weight of the two windings approximately equal. Instead of a resistor, a condenser C is connected in winding 2. This condenser remains permanently in circuit, although, as will be shown, it is usually advisable to use more capacitance when starting than when running.

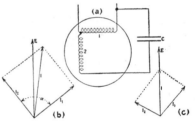

Fig. 1.—Circuits of a condenser motor. Vector diagram (b) when starting and (c) when running at full load and 100 per cent power factor.

Starting and Running Conditions.—The vector diagram of the motor when starting is shown at (b) in Fig. 1. The current in the winding I_1 lags, but by using a proper value of the capacitance the current in winding 2 may be made to lead. The total current is of course the vector sum of the two and may be made to be very nearly in phase with the voltage. The motor has therefore nearly 100 per cent power factor when starting. The angle α between I_1 and I_2 may be made nearly 90 deg. The starting torque for the same phase currents is therefore much greater and the sum of the currents is less, since they are added together at approximately 90-deg. phase difference.

The starting torque of the motor, in fact, can be made as great as or greater than that of a polyphase motor, and since the currents add at nearly 90 deg. the line current will be less. The motor will therefore develop about the same torque as a polyphase motor with about 70 per cent as much current, giving a decidedly higher starting efficiency.

As in the case of the ordinary single-phase motor, the starting torque can, if necessary, be very much increased by reducing the number of turns in winding 2. In general, however, winding 2 may have more turns than winding 1 and the motor will still develop ample starting torque. This makes possible the use of a smaller and cheaper condenser.

The vector diagram of this motor under full load and 100 per cent power factor is shown at (c) in Fig. 1. The current I_1 lags less than when the motor is starting, and the current I_2 with the proper value of capacitance is nearly at right angles to I_1. The motor is therefore operating practically as a two-phase motor. It has the advantage over the latter, however, in that the currents I_1 and I_2 combine at such an angle that their resultant I, which is of course the line current, may be in phase with the line voltage E. The line current may of course be made to lead the line voltage if this is desirable.

If the capacitance of the condenser is so adjusted that the motor gives its best all-around performance under normal load it will be found that the starting torque with the same condenser will be quite low, usually in the neighborhood of

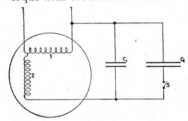

FIG. 2.—Method of varying capacitance after starting with high value.

50 per cent. By using a condenser several times as large as this the starting torque can be increased to from 200 to 400 per cent. If the static torque of the load to be started is very low, but increases rapidly with the speed, a motor with a fixed condenser may be satisfactory. For example, a fan requires very little torque at the instant of starting and the necessary torque increases approximately as the square of the speed. A motor using a condenser adapted to give the best running conditions will be found to have a similar speed-torque curve (see Fig. 11) and, hence, may be used with advantage for such an application. Centrifugal pumps and grinders also have such speed-torque characteristics that they can probably be satisfactorily handled with a fixed condenser.

If, however, the motor must start a load such as a refrigerator compressor having large static friction it will be necessary to use a much greater value of the condenser at start and then reduce this to a suitable value for normal running. One method of doing this is shown in Fig. 2. Switch S, which may be operated either by a relay or by centrifugal force, is used to disconnect the condenser C_2 as soon as the motor has reached about two-thirds of normal running speed.

Since the condenser C_2 may have several times the capacitance of the condenser C_1 its cost would be excessive if it were of the usual

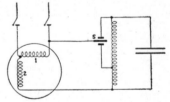

FIG. 3.—Method of varying capacitance by use of a transformer.

construction. This would be particularly true in the case of low-voltage motors. One method of reducing this cost is to use an electrolytic condenser in the place of C_2.

Another connection designed to effect the same object is shown in Fig. 3. A condenser is connected to the motor through a variable-ratio transformer.

Preferably an autotransformer is used, since this is somewhat cheaper and more efficient than the ordinary type of transformer.

At the instant of start the switch S is closed on the lower contact of the transformer. The voltage applied to the condenser is increased and the current taken by the condenser is increased in the same ratio. The current flowing through the motor circuit is again increased by this same ratio owing to transformer action. For normal running the switch closes on the upper contact and the effect of the condenser is correspondingly reduced. The upper tap on the autotransformer, at least for higher voltage motors, might preferably be made at the extreme upper end. In normal running the transformer would therefore be inactive. Providing the necessary switches were not too complicated it might be entirely disconnected.

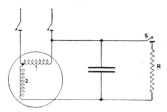

Fig. 4.—Connection of motor for moderate starting-torque requirements.

It is obvious that with this scheme a condenser of smaller capacitance may be used. On the other hand, it must not be forgotten that the thickness of the dielectric must be sufficient to stand the higher voltage. If we compare the condensers on the basis of their volt-ampere capacity this scheme effects no saving. It is, however, true that a condenser of a given volt-ampere capacity is less costly at say 440 volts than at 220. This saving is at least partially offset by the cost of the autotransformer and the cost of the more complicated switch. There is, of course, a constant loss in the transformer, and this reduces the running efficiency of the motor by about 2 to 4 per cent.

If only a moderate starting torque is necessary and if a comparatively large starting current is not objectionable the scheme shown in Fig. 4 may be used. Here a resistor is substituted for the condenser C_2. A motor operated in this manner will have better starting characteristics than a plain split-phase motor

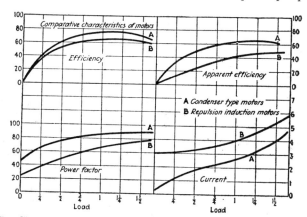

Fig. 5.—Characteristic curves of condenser and repulsion-induction motors.

but will, of course, not be so good in this respect as the condenser motor. The scheme is obviously cheap and might perhaps be satisfactory in connection with such applications as motors for oil burners or washing machines.

Comparison with Other Single-phase Motors.—In Fig. 5 the characteristic curves of a condenser motor and those of the best motor of the ordinary repulsion-induction type are shown. Both motors are of the same rating, namely, ¼ hp., 1,800 r.p.m., 60 cycles, and 110 volts. The full-load efficiency of the condenser

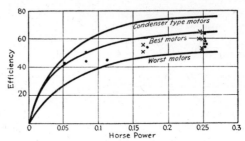

Fig. 6-a.—Efficiencies of small motors, 110 volt, 60 cycles, 1,800 r.p.m. Split-phase motors are indicated by dots and repulsion-induction motors by crosses.

motor is 75 per cent; that of the repulsion-induction motor 64 per cent. In other words, the customer's bill for the condenser motor would be 85 per cent of that with the best available repulsion-induction motor. The power factor of the

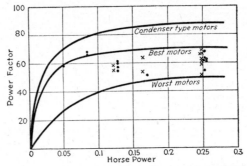

Fig. 6-b.—Power factors of small motors, 110 volt, 60 cycle, 1,800 r.p.m. Split-phase motors indicated by dots and repulsion-induction motors by crosses.

condenser motor at full load was 86 per cent; that of the other 66 per cent. By using a larger condenser the power factor of the condenser motor could be raised to 100 per cent. The apparent efficiency of the condenser motor at full load is 64 per cent and that of the repulsion-induction motor 42 per cent. The corresponding full-load currents are respectively 2.6 and 4 amp.

In building the condenser motor a standard split-phase ¼-hp. motor was used. The stator winding was removed and replaced by a winding suitable for the condenser motor. Otherwise the motor was unchanged. The total weight of the motor exclusive of condensers was 28 lb., whereas the repulsion-induction motor with which it was compared weighed 43 lb. The improvement in characteristics was not obtained by using a large and expensive motor. It should also be emphasized that the repulsion-induction motor with which it is compared is one of the best, if not the best, on the market. For example, the full-load current of this motor was 4 amp. Other motors of the same rating which have been tested have taken full-load currents as large as 6.5 amp., giving an apparent efficiency of only 25.5 per cent. In Fig. 7 these same data are shown graphically. In addition it will be noted that these two motors develop approximately the

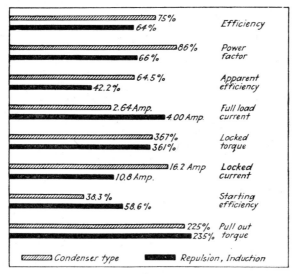

Fig. 7.—Graphic comparison of condenser and repulsion-induction motors.

same locked torque. The locked current of the condenser motor is, however, 41 per cent greater than that of the repulsion-induction motor and its starting

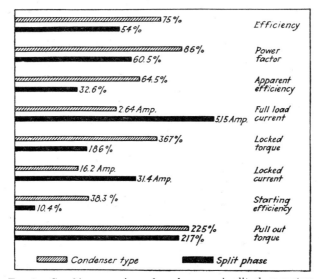

Fig. 8.—Graphic comparison of condenser and split-phase motors.

efficiency is correspondingly lower. The pull-out torques of the two motors are approximately the same.

In Fig. 8 a similar comparison is shown between the same condenser motor and the best of a number of split-phase motors tested. The difference in efficiency, power factor, apparent efficiency, and current is even more marked than before. In fact, it will be seen that the full-load current of the split-phase motor is nearly double that of the condenser motor. The locked torque of the split-phase motor is much less than that of the condenser motor and its locked current is much greater. The torque per ampere of the condenser motor is nearly four times as great as that of the split-phase motor, as indicated by the comparative starting efficiency. In pull-out torque the two are about the same.

Comparison of Two-phase and Condenser Motors.—In order to get an accurate comparison between a polyphase motor and a condenser motor a standard ½-hp., 1,800-r.p.m., two-phase, 60-cycle, 220-volt motor was obtained. This motor was first carefully tested as a two-phase motor, with the results shown in Fig. 9. Without any change whatever the motor was then connected as a con-

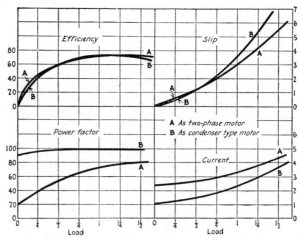

Fig. 9.—Standard two-phase motor characteristics compared with operation as a condenser motor.

denser motor, with the results shown in the same figure. It should be noted that the efficiency of the single-phase compares well with that of the two-phase. It is, however, slightly lower at light loads and at overloads owing to the fact that the currents do not divide evenly between the two windings. This naturally results in greater I^2R loss. At full load the efficiencies are practically the same. The power factor of the single-phase motor is much the better, being nearly 100 per cent throughout the usual working range. The slip in the two types of motor is practically the same. Since the efficiencies at full load are nearly the same, there is but little difference in heating at full load. The rating as a single-phase motor would be nearly as great as that of the two-phase motor.

The pull-out torque of the single-phase motor is, however, decidedly less. With the particular value of capacitance used it was 207 per cent, in comparison with 316 per cent in the case of the motor operated two phase. It was, however, amply high for all practical purposes and could have been made still higher by using somewhat greater capacitance.

The starting characteristics are shown in the following table:

	Starting characteristics				Ratio winding 1 to 1, power factor, per cent
	Torque, per cent	Starting current	Starting watts	Starting efficiency, per cent	
Two-phase..................	307	19.7	2,980	26.3	68.8
Single-phase condenser motor...	362	17.72	3,880	34.5	99.5

It will be seen that the condenser motor has considerably more starting torque than the two-phase motor. If necessary, this could have been greatly increased by reducing the number of turns in the auxiliary winding. The starting current of the two-phase motor was 9.85 amp. per phase, or 19.7 amp. in all, whereas the single-phase motor required only 17.72 amp., or approximately 90 per cent as much. The single-phase motor necessarily took more power in starting, but its

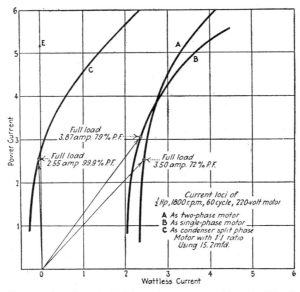

Fig. 10.—Curves taken from test of two-phase motor with and without condenser.

starting efficiency was much better. The power factor at start of the single-phase motor was 99.5 per cent and that of the two-phase motor 68.8 per cent. It is apparent that the starting characteristics of this type of motor are better even than those of a polyphase motor. Moreover, they can be varied to suit different conditions by changing the ratio of turns in the two windings and by changing the capacitance.

Figure 10 will help to make clear the relative action of the two-phase, single-phase, and condenser motors. These curves were all taken with a small two-phase motor. Curve *A* shows the locus of the current when the motor is operated two phase. The angle between the vector marked E and any line drawn from the origin to the curve A indicates the lag of the current behind the voltage. The cosine of this angle is of course the power factor. In order to make the curves comparable the current plotted is that taken by both phases of the two-phase motor. It will be evident that the power factor will rise to a maximum at somewhat above full load and will then decrease for greater loads than this.

Similarly, curve B shows the locus of the current when operating on one of the two phases. It will be seen that in general the power factor of the single-phase motor is worse than that of the two-phase motor, particularly for heavy loads. By adding a condenser and connecting as shown in Fig. 1(a) we obtained the curve marked C. At light loads the current leads the voltage by a small

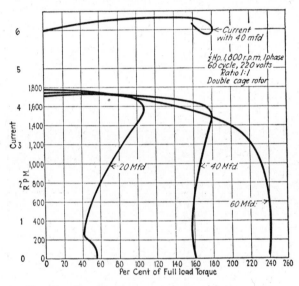

Fig. 11.—Speed-torque curves for a condenser motor.

angle. At full load it is nearly in phase with it, giving practically 100 per cent power factor, and for overloads the current lags, giving a power factor slightly lower than unity. The decided improvement in power factor will be evident from the diagram.

A frequent complaint in connection with the repulsion-induction motor is that while it will start the load it will not pull it up to speed. In Fig. 11 the complete speed-torque curves for a condenser motor are plotted. It will be seen that the torque remains nearly constant from standstill until the motor has attained normal running speed. However, with a small value of capacitance there is a decided increase of torque as the motor speeds up. This, as was previously pointed out, makes it possible to start certain kinds of loads even though the initial torque is rather small.

Figure 12 will serve to show the possibilities of the condenser motor. The motor in question was rated at only ⅙ hp. In spite of the small size a full-load efficiency of 73 per cent and maximum efficiency of 75 per cent were attained with a full-load power factor of 86 per cent. The motor developed a starting torque of 320 per cent. This large torque was not obtained by the use of a high-resistance rotor, as will be evident from the fact that the slip at full load is only 2.5 per cent. Such performance is entirely beyond the possibility of the split-phase or repulsion-induction motor, or, to put the matter a little differently, no matter how good the performance of a split-phase motor might be, it could be very much improved by rewinding and operating it as a condenser motor.

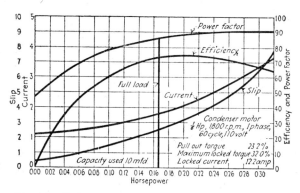

Fig. 12.—Performance possibilities of a condenser motor.

The above facts serve to show that it is now possible to build single-phase motors nearly equal in efficiency to two-phase motors and far superior in power factor. Compared with split-phase motors, the characteristics of the condenser motor are superior in every respect. They are better than those of the repulsion-induction in every respect except in locked torque per ampere. The pull-in torque, however, is much better than that of the repulsion-induction motor. The condenser motor is particularly quiet in operation due to the fact that it operates practically as a two-phase motor.

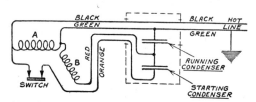

Fig. 13.—Connections for a single-phase condenser motor.

Radio Interference from Motors.—Much of the interference in radio reception due to the operation of small single-phase motors can be eliminated by use of the non-interfering types. Motors which have commutators or starting switches are the most common sources of radio interference. This does not mean that all commutator motors cause interference. For instance, the repulsion-induction motor has a commutator, but when the construction is such that the brushes are automatically lifted from the commutator after starting and the commutator bars short-circuited when the motor is up to speed, there can be no trouble from this motor.

The so-called universal motor, that is, the design intended for operation on either direct- or alternating-current service, is probably the most frequent cause of radio interference. Even with these motors the trouble can be largely eliminated when the armatures are dynamically balanced to eliminate vibration and thus to reduce all possible sparking between carbon brushes and the commutator due to this cause. The commutator should also be very carefully machined so that it will be concentric with the armature shaft with tolerances that are even closer than used in the machining of shafts.

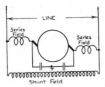

Fig. 14.—Condenser connections for correcting radio interference of a direct-current motor.

In the case of direct-current motors used on household refrigerating machines, sump pumps, etc., some manufacturers are building in small condensers connected across the commutator and grounded. One side of the condenser used is grounded to the motor frame and the other side is attached to the brush bracket with leads as short as possible. These condensers have 0.07-mf. capacity and should stand 500 volts on continuous and 1,000 volts on momentary test.

Single-phase, fractional horsepower motors of the split-phase type have no commutator and cause very little radio interference. The use of this type, however, is limited, owing to the low starting torque and the trouble from excessive starting current when the load connected is hard to start.

The single-phase condenser motor which is provided with a starting and running condenser can generally be used in those cases where the split-phase motor cannot be used and in such cases will cause no radio interference.

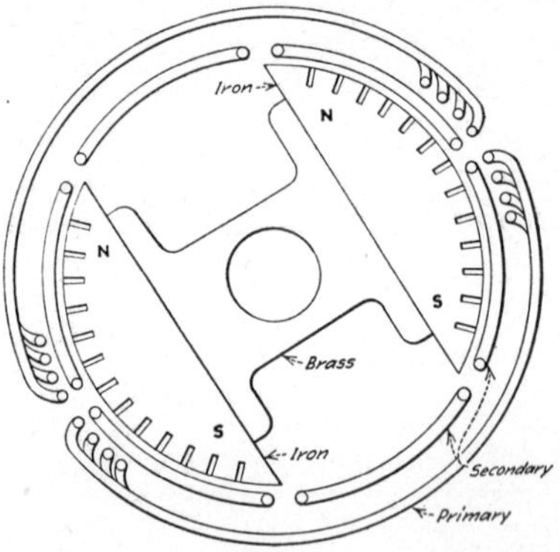

SQUIRREL-CAGE INDUCTION MOTOR USED AS FREQUENCY CHANGER

Fig. 15.—Frequency changer designed for 1 to 3 ratio using two-pole primary and six-pole secondary in stator, 60 to 180 cycles.

The slip-ring induction motor with the rotor separately driven has been used as a frequency changer but a more recent development is a modified squirrel-cage induction motor in which the brushes and driving motor are eliminated. In this motor two windings are placed on the stator in the same slots, one for the frequency of the supply circuit and the other for the desired different frequency. The rotor differs from that of the standard induction motor only in the shape of the core. In the *Electrical World* (January 23, 1932), A. W. Forbes gave the following details of construction and operation of such a frequency changer:

Construction and Operation.—The basic principle of design is indicated in Fig. 15. Only one phase of each winding is shown, but both windings (the two-pole primary for 60 cycles and the six-pole secondary for 180 cycles) are usually polyphase windings identical with the windings of ordinary induction motors. In this design the rotor consists of two pieces of iron supported on the shaft by brass or other non-magnetic material. The two iron pieces are made of the right length to span two poles of the six-pole winding. When the magnetization by the primary phase shown is at a maximum, the rotor will take the positions shown and it is magnetized by the two-pole primary as indicated at N and S. If the rotor is made to turn at exactly synchronous speed of the two-pole winding, each phase in turn will keep the rotor properly magnetized, with the result that the six-pole winding delivers 180 cycles.

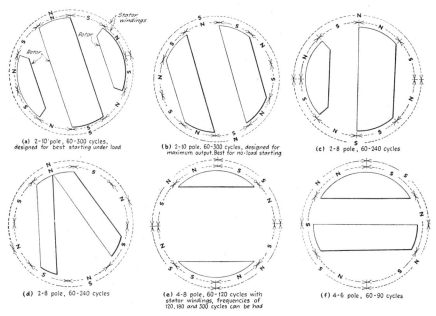

(a) 2-10 pole, 60-300 cycles, designed for best starting under load

(b) 2-10 pole, 60-300 cycles, designed for maximum output. Best for no-load starting

(c) 2-8 pole, 60-240 cycles

(d) 2-8 pole, 60-240 cycles

(e) 4-8 pole, 60-120 cycles with stator windings, frequencies of 120,180 and 300 cycles can be had

(f) 4-6 pole, 60-90 cycles

FIG. 16.—Arrangement of poles of primary and secondary windings for various frequency transformations. The arrowheads indicate extent of poles of one phase for each winding.

Once the rotor is at synchronous speed the revolving field produced by the primary or 60-cycle winding will keep it in step. In practice the rotor maintains synchronism on heavy overloads and in most designs will not fall out of step even under short-circuit conditions. A low-resistance squirrel-cage winding is used to bring the rotor up to synchronism. This resistance can be as low as desired, since the rotor turns freely without any starting load. The weakest point is on pulling into synchronism, and the final bringing into step is by magnetic attraction alone. In practice it is found that some designs of frequency changers will pull into synchronism with 50 per cent load on the secondary winding and in others with but 20 or 30 per cent. In all cases it is recommended that the frequency changer be started first, applying the load to the secondary after the rotor is up to speed.

Methods of Obtaining Other Frequencies.—A wide range of frequency transformations can be secured by proper designing of rotor-pole and stator-winding relationships and considering whether starting under most favorable conditions or delivery of maximum output is the controlling element. The 1 to 3 transformation ratio is the simplest and cheapest to build. A 1 to 2 ratio, with two and four poles, seems simpler, but it is impossible to build such a unit with the iron even approximately balanced. Badly unbalanced magnetic pull results in noise and vibration. For the 1 to 2 ratio it is necessary to build with four and eight poles. Ratios of 1 to 3, 1 to 5, and 1 to 7 are all cheaper than 1 to 2. Even ratios of transformation are more difficult than the odd ratios, since the latter permit a symmetrical design of the rotor iron.

Intermediate ratios like 2 to 3, 3 to 4, 2 to 5, etc., require more complex structures in theory if not in mechanical arrangement. Unbalancing has to be compensated for even in small sizes, and this is done by either modifying the theoretical shape or by increasing the air gap. Both courses reduce the efficiency of transformation, but in many applications this is not a serious objection.

Fig. 17.—Complete frequency changer rated 1 kva., 60 to 180 cycles. Assembled unit is shown at *A*; and disassembled stator, rotor and end shields at *B*.

In certain cases it is possible to design a single unit to deliver several frequencies. With modifications of the iron structure, as by making pieces a little large for one service and a little small for another, and by the use of several windings on the stator, various frequencies can be obtained. Thus, in one case, by modifying the iron structure of the rotor and putting five windings on the stator, we obtain 120, 180, and 300 cycles from a single frequency changer. A two-speed motor, two and four pole, when operated by such a frequency changer, will give speeds of 1,800, 3,600, 5,400, 7,200, 9,000, 10,800, and 18,000 r.p.m. Other combinations can be had, each being a separate design.

Up to this point each piece of rotor iron has been considered as a solid piece. It is undesirable to laminate the rotors as in ordinary induction motors, but there are certain subdivisions which improve performance. In general, the iron should be so divided and the parts so separated as to produce the greatest possible magnetic reluctance when the rotor is turned to any position except that in which it is intended to be. However, the flux must be free to move across the squirrel-cage bars when starting. Simplicity of construction must also be sought, and there is room for study in the disposition of material.

Field of Application.—A further development of the frequency changer which is specially applicable to internal grinders, woodworking machines, etc., utilizes the frequency changer as a source of excess mechanical power for special driving. The frequency-changer shaft can be directly connected to the feed of a machine, for example, while the high-frequency current operates the spindle or cutting head. In such service, the unit is really a frequency-changing motor. It is an induction motor, as simple mechanically as the ordinary induction motor but supplying the high-frequency current without further complications.

The advantages of the design described are chiefly in the line of simplicity, freedom from care, and absence of required skilled attendance. The field of usefulness runs up to about 10 kva.; from 10 to 50 kva. there is competition with the synchronous motor generator set. As for the slip-ring induction motor type of changer, which is intermediate between the multiple-winding unit and the synchronous set in simplicity, performance, and price, its power factor and voltage regulation are inferior to the synchronous outfit, and it is the only type that does not maintain its frequency exactly.

The multiple-winding unit in small sizes is often less than half the price of the synchronous set. Lack of injury under short-circuit is a valuable point; and under short-circuit this unit drops its voltage and remains running without overload. The power factor is low as compared with the synchronous set, but there are many applications where this is not vital. Despite the fact that an alternator will give closer voltage regulation, the unit will serve the requirements of ordinary motor applications. The larger sizes also require more active material—a factor which is unimportant in numerous smaller applications.

FLAT-FRONT INDUCTION MOTORS

For grinders and for circular saws, induction motors have been built with the shaft close to one side of the frame. This construction calls

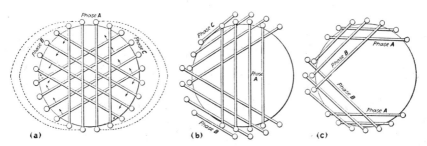

Fig. 18.—(*a*) Standard three-phase induction-motor stator winding. (*b*) Three-phase winding with coils shifted. (*c*) Diagram of two-phase, four-pole, flat-front motor winding.

for unsymmetrical windings and special arrangements of the coils. In the *Electrical World* (Vol. 88, No. 6, p. 278), A. W. Forbes gave the following details for such windings:

The induction type of motor must have a uniformly rotating field for satisfactory operation. The flat front makes impossible a uniform distribution of coils around the stator. The problem, therefore, is to secure a uniformly rotating field with irregularly distributed windings. This has been solved in a number of ways for different applications and two are described in what follows.

Distribution of Windings.—Figure 18(*a*) shows a theoretical distribution of the windings of the standard two-pole induction motor, with but few coils in a group so that the phases do not overlap. In practice the coils would follow the dotted lines, but to make the theory simpler they are drawn straight across. It is readily seen that there is no place where the coils can be omitted for 90 deg. of the periphery without disturbing two phases, and it is necessary to omit the coils for 90 deg. in order to make it possible to cut a substantial amount from the motor frame. To omit the coils from these 90 deg. would unbalance the phases completely. Each phase of a two-pole winding is really a single magnet with its axis at right angles to the coil. The fact that the coils actually take the shape of the dotted lines does not affect the electrical result. If we move the coils of phases *B* and *C* in the direction indicated by the arrows, the axis of the coils remains the same, straight across the center of the motor. The result of such motion is shown in Fig. 18(*b*).

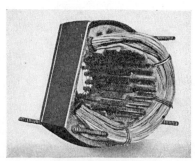

Fig. 19.—Stator winding of the motor shown in Fig. 20.

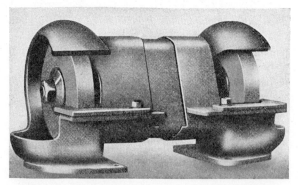

Fig. 20.—Application of flat-front motor to a grinder.

Arrangement of Coils.—The axis of each coil has remained in the same position, the three phases being spaced at 60 deg. around the motor. Now, if the proper number of turns is found for each of the three phases, the result is a uniformly rotating field exactly like the field of the standard induction motor. In Fig. 18(*b*) is shown a clear space of 90 deg. with no windings. As far as the theoretical conditions for normal operation are concerned, the problem is solved, but there are mechanical features in arranging the coils that have to be considered, as well as electrical phenomena during the starting period that are hard to analyze.

In practice the windings of phases *B* and *C* are bunched so that a larger proportion of their turns is in the end slots next to the flat front. The coils of phase *A* are also shifted along its axis away from the flat front. The actual winding data used in the grinder illustrated in Fig. 20 are as shown in the following table. There are 18 slots, numbered from one end next to the flat.

This winding arrangement is entirely satisfactory for an application like the grinder in Fig. 20, where high starting torque is not essential. It has one fault,

WINDING DATA USED IN THE GRINDER
MOTOR (FIG. 20)
Phase *B*

Coil	Turns	Placed in slots
1	10	1 and 7
2	95	1 and 8
3	40	1 and 9
4	30	2 and 9
5	75	2 and 10
6	10	2 and 11
7	35	3 and 11
8	15	3 and 12

Phase *A*

Coil	Turns	Placed in slots
1	30	2 and 13
2	75	3 and 14
3	100	4 and 15
4	75	5 and 16
5	30	6 and 17

Phase *C*

Coil	Turns	Placed in slots
1	15	7 and 16
2	35	8 and 16
3	10	8 and 17
4	75	9 and 17
5	30	10 and 17
6	40	10 and 18
7	95	11 and 18
8	10	12 and 18

however, for general application, and that is a sharply defined point at just half speed where the torque is very low. Research is now being conducted to eliminate this point of low torque without introducing worse troubles. It is easy to eliminate this point by the sacrifice of running conditions, but it is undesirable to accomplish the result in this fashion.

These winding data can be copied for other motors only where the requirements are identical except for size and voltage. Each problem requires a different treatment. In the case of a two-phase four-pole motor the problem of a uniformly rotating field was solved in an entirely different manner. Figure 18(c) illustrates the principle. Phase A has the usual standard windings for two opposite poles, but as these have the same polarity, it produces two poles of the opposite polarity between them. So phase A is magnetically complete. On the other hand, phase B has only two adjacent poles. These two poles are placed in the proper phase relation to phase A, so that the result of the omission of the other two poles is but slight.

It is unlikely that these flat-front motors will ever be built as a standard line. Their field is distinctly one for built-in motors, to be built in the same quantities as the machines on which they are used. But although their applications are not numerous, there are places where they make a direct motor drive practical and where otherwise belts or gearing would be needed.

INDEX

A

Advantages and disadvantages of:
    chorded split-loop winding, 47
    diametrically split winding, 62
    loop winding, 35
    progressive-split-hand winding, 66
    special chorded split-pitch loop winding, 41
    split V-loop winding, 59
Alternating-current small motors, information to record before stripping them, 112
Arbor press and tool for removing fields from single-phase motor housings, 233
Armature centers and stators holders, 213
Armature coils:
    connecting in d.c. armatures, 80
    connecting in single-phase motors, 144
    connecting skein wound, 140
    finding turns per coil, 21
    finding turns, size of wire and pitch when changing a.c. windings, 190
    locating troubles in, 98
    recording data for d.c. armature, 21
    testing while and after winding, 90
    winding compensating coils, 160
Armature core, insulation of, 24
Armatures, d.c. testing while and after winding, 90
Automobile starter and generator armatures:
    card form for recording information on, 20
    cleaning, 69
    connecting coil leads to commutator, 75
    data required for, 70
    details of windings for, 69
    insulation required, 69
    layer windings for, 72

Automobile starter and generator armatures:
    size of wire for coils, 72
    split V-loop winding for, 60
    varnishing and baking, 72
    winding data for, 20
    winding 32-volt armatures, 72

B

Bakelite used for armature insulation, 69
Baking armatures and stators, 237
Baking and varnishing winding, 119
Balancing single-phase rotors, 198
Bar-to-bar test, reasons for variations in readings of, 102
Basket winding for a.c. motor, 178
    checking pitch of, 179
    inserting coils in, 180
Bearings and shaft, wear of, 9
Billing information, 4
Blades on far motor, effect of changing, 174
Bringing out stator leads, 128
Brush position in universal motor, location of, 156
Brushes, location for full and chorded pitch windings, 81
Building up new cores, 25

C

Capacitor motor (*see also* Condenser type), 241
    starting and running conditions, 241, 242
Causes for repulsion motor failing to start, 108
Ceiling fans, windings for, 170
Centrifugal switch for single-phase motor, 199
Charts for winding chorded split-loop windings, 53, 56, 57
    for progressive-split winding, 65, 66

Checking up field coils, 5
Checks to make after connecting up com-
    mutator, 88
Chorded-pitch winding, commutator po-
    sition for, 76
Chorded split-loop winding:
    advantages of, 47
    steps when winding, 47
    use of winding machine for, 54
    when number lots is not divisible
        by four, 51
    winding charts for, 50, 53, 56, 57
Chorded split-pitch loop winding, 41
Chuck for winding small coils, 216
Circuit switch, troubles when starting, 108
Cleaning slots, 24
Closed-slot armatures, insulation for
        slots of, 58
    shove through coils for, 57
Coil connections, checking for reversed
        or crossed leads, 94
Coil ends, locating shorts between, 102
    tied with cord, 120
Coil insulation, varnish for, 236
Coil leads, locating shorts between, 101
Coils for closed-slot armatures, 57
    for flat-front motors, 254
    winding without cutting wire be-
        tween, 133
Color of sleeves, reversed coil leads due
        to wrong use of, 95
Colored sleeves:
    for loop winding, 39
    for special chorded split-pitch
        winding, 43
    for split V-loop winding, 60
    marking coil leads, 81
    precautious when inserting, 61
    progressive-split winding, 68
Combination cell for insulating slots, 118
Commutator:
    checking position with armature
        in motor, 78
    checks to make after connecting,
        88
    connecting first coil leads for split
        V-loop winding, 85
    determining position on shaft, 76
    distance to be pressed on shaft, 78
    filling out between coil ends, 82
    leads of first coil, 82

Commutator:
    lining up slots with commutator
        mica or bars, 78
    location of brushes on, 81
    position for chorded-pitch wind-
        ing, 76
    position for full-pitch winding, 76
    soldering leads to, 89
    test to locate top leads, 85
    testing for shorts, 91
    tests to locate grounds in, 91
    when there are several leads in one
        sleeve, 83
    when there are two or more coils
        per slot, 84
Commutator bars, marking of, 12
    examples for, marking, 16
Commutator motors series type, 111
Commutator necks, milling of, 33
Commutator type series fan motors,
        164
Comparison condenser motor with other
        single-phase motors, 244
Compensated series type universal motor,
        149
Compensating winding for universal
        motors, 153
    winding coils in, 155, 160
    winding compensating coils, 160
    winding main coils, 160
Condenser type single-phase motor, 241
    comparison with other single-
        phase motors, 244
    comparison with two-phase motor,
        246
Connecting loops to commutator of
        special chorded-pitch loop wind-
        ing, 45
Connecting single-phase motors, 144
Connections for main and compensating
        fields in universal motor, 155
Connections of coils, checking for re-
        versed or crossed leads, 94
Construction of transformer for locating
        troubles in d.-c. armatures, 6
Continuous strip insulation for slots, 28
Controlling speed of fan motors, 168
Core, how to keep wires of coils from
        climbing above when winding,
        132
Core and winding insulation, 117

Cores, building up new, 25
    insulating ends of, 26
Cost information forms, 4
Customers' requirements ways to record, 2

D

Defects in armature winding, how to locate by tests, 90
Diametrically split winding, 62
    steps when winding, 62
Diamond mush coils, three steps in inserting, 183
Dipping armatures wound with single cotton and enamel insulation, 235
Direct-current armatures:
    commutator position for, 76
    connecting up, 81
    recording data for coils of, 21
    special windings for, 35, 41, 47, 49, 62
    stripping of, 21
    testing while and after winding, 90
    turns per coil, quick way to determine, 21
Distributed pole fan windings, 166
Drill and grinder windings, 148
Drink mixer windings, 148

E

Easy method for winding a skein, 125
Easy method for winding split winding, 54
Enameled wire for small motors, 31
End rings to protect overhanging coils, 120
Estimating new work, forms for, 4
Estimating rating of single-phase motor frame, 189

F

Fan motor blades, effect of changing, 174
Fan windings single-phase:
    commutator type series, 164
    controlling speed, 168
    distributed pole, 166
    effect of changing number of blades on, 174

Fan windings single-phase:
    induction type, 165
    induction winding with high starting torque, 171
    speed change by taps on auxiliary winding, 170
    starting windings, 168
    universal fan motor, 170
    windings for ceiling fans, 170
Fiber head and end washers, for d. c. armatures, 30
Field coils, testing of, 5
Finishing operations, record form for, 4
Fish-paper only for insulating slots, 117
Fish-paper and treated cloth for insulating slots, 117
Flat-front induction motor, 253
    arrangement of coils, 254
    distribution of windings, 254
Former and cutter for slot insulation, 220
Forms for repair record system, 1
Frequency-changers, small size, 250
    construction and operation of, 251
    field of application, 253
    methods of obtaining frequency, 252
Full-pitch winding, commutator position for, 76

G

Grounds, location of in single-phase windings, 197
Grounds, tests to locate in commutator, 91
    testing winding for, 92
Growler for locating troubles in d.c. armatures, 7
    for locating shorted coils, 97

H

Hand and bench tools, 210
Hand and skein windings, information needed, 115
Hand and skein wound stators, connecting coils of, 140
Hand tools for winders, 230
Hand winding, how it is put on a stator, 131
Hand wound coils, starting of, 131
High-voltage test transformer, 223

Holders for armatures and stators, 213
Holders for wire and tape reels, 218

I

Induction type fan motor, 165, 171
Information for job tickets, 3
Information needed for hand and skein windings, 115
Information needed for rewinding jobs, 11
Information to record for small a.c. motors, 112
Inspecting slots for defects, 24
Inspection tests, 5
Insulating armature core, 24
    continuous strip method, 28
Insulating the core and the winding, 117
Insulating ends of old cores, 26
    shafts of d.c. armatures, 27
    slots of d.c. armatures, 27
Insulating slots with combination cell, 118
Insulating slots with fish-paper only, 117
Insulating slots with fish-paper and treated cloth, 117
Insulation between phase coils, 185
Insulation for different sizes of wire, 33
Insulation required for automobile armatures, 69
    strap coils insulated for Bakelite dip, 70
    use of liquid Bakelite, 69

J

Job records, 1
Job ticket form, 3

L

Laminations, correcting flare of, 24
    truing up, 24
Lap winding, recording data for, 17
Layer winding for automobile armatures, 72
    connecting to commutator, 75
    making ends of coils wind in layers, 74
Leads, how to bring out of stator, 128
Left-hand and right-hand loop windings, 36

Liquid Bakelite for automobile armature insulation, 69
Locating trouble in d.c. armatures, 6
Loop winding:
    advantages and disadvantages of, 35
    colored sleeving for, 39
    having more than one coil per slot, 39
    having more than one wire in hand, 39
    how coils are wound in place, 35
    left-hand and right-hand, 36
    starting of, 35
    starting first two coils, 38
    steps in winding, 37
    testing for grounds, 40
    winding last two coils, 40
Low-voltage (d.c.) armature windings, 69
Low-voltage high-current capacity transformer, 227

M

Marking slots and bars, 12
Material and time tickets, 4
Method of putting on chorded split winding, 51
Motor starts but will not pull load, how to locate troubles, 108
Motors that will not start, how to locate troubles in, 107
Mould and hand winding, 138

O

Old motors, how to get winding and connecting information, 112
Operations to check time on, 12
Overhanging coils protected by end rings, 120

P

Phase coils, insulation between, 185
Pitch of two-layer (a.c.) winding, 182
Points on soldering, 238
Polarity of single-phase windings, 197
Portable electric tool windings, 148
Precautions when inserting sleeves on coil leads, 61

Progressive-split-hand winding, 64
chart for winding, 65, 66
how it saves time in rewinding, 64
points to watch, 68
sequence for winding in coils for, 67
when slots are divisible by four, 65
when slots are not divisible by four, 66
winding in coils of, 66

R

Radio interference from motors, 249
Rating of single-phase motor frame, estimated, 189
tables for finding hp. rating, 189, 190
Reasons for variations in readings with bar-to-bar test, 102
Receiving tag, 1
Record system for wide variety of work, 1
Recording connections to commutator, 16
coil and commutator throws, 17
Recording data for lap winding, 17
for coils, 21
Recording data for wave winding, 19
Repair bench tests board, 7
Repair instructions, 2
Repair records, 1
Repair shop tools, 209
Repairs needed, tests to determine, 5
Repulsion motor assembly, 205
adjustments, 205, 207, 208
Repulsion motor fails to start, 108
Repulsion-starting motors, 110
Reversed or crossed leads, checking coil connections for, 94
due to use of wrong color of sleeves, 95
Rewinding information, 11
forms for recording, 14, 15, 18, 19
Rotation, direction of when connecting skein wound coils, 141

S

Scraping slots, tool for, 24
Series motors of the commutator type, 111
Series type universal motor, 148
Shading-coil motors, 111
Shaft, wear of, 9
insulation for d.c. armature, 27

Shorts, between coil turns, 98
between top and bottom halves of coils, 98
determining whether in winding or in commutator, 100
finding slot in which it is located, 99
locating by use of a growler, 97
location between coil ends, 102
location between coil leads, 101
testing commutator for, 91
testing winding for, 96
Shove through coils for closed-slot armatures, 57
Single-phase fan windings (*see* Fan windings single-phase).
Single-phase motors, changed for operation at two speeds, 146
connecting various types, 144
main features of, 138
special designs, 241
Single-phase rotors, balancing of, 199
testing centrifugal switch, 199
testing for brush position, 199
testing for poor bar contact, 199
Single-phase winding, checking polarity of, 197
how to determine turns, size of wire and coil pitch, 190
testing for shorts, 197
Six points to note before stripping a stator, 116
Skein or hand-wound stator, connecting of, 140
Skein, how to calculate length of, 128
easy method for winding, 125
for small a.c. stators, 121
how to make up and wind it in small a.c. stators, 121
starting in proper place on stator, 122
winding on stator, 121
Skein split, when it can be used, 126
Slot insulation cutter and former, 220
Slot wedge driver, 233
Slot wedges, 31
Slots, common shapes of, 26
continuous strip insulation, 28
examples for marking, 16
insulated with combination cell, 118
insulated with fish-paper only, 117

Slots, insulated with fish-paper and treated cloth, 117
  insulation for a.c. armatures, 27
  marking of, 12
Slots and teeth, lining up with commutator mica or bars, 78
Soldering, points on, 238
Special chorded split-pitch loop winding:
  advantages of, 41
  colored sleeves for, 43
  connecting loops to commutator, 45
  precautions when connecting up, 46
  single-phase motors, 241
  starting the winding, 42
  wound with one wire in hand, 42
Speed change by taps on auxiliary fan winding, 170
Split-phase motors, 110
Split V-loop d.c. winding, 59
  advantages and disadvantages of, 59
  connecting leads of first coil, 85
  used on automobile generator armatures, 60
Starting d.c. loop winding, 35
  chorded split-loop winding, 47
  special chorded split-pitch loop-winding, 42
  split V-loop winding, 60
Starting hand-wound coils, 131
Starting and running coils distributed in slots, 135
Starting and running conditions, for condenser motor, 241
Starting and running windings, how distributed in slots, 135
Starting winding, position of with reference to main winding, 137
Starting winding in proper place on a stator, 122
Starting windings for fan motors, 168
Stator leads, how to bring out, 128
Steps in winding a loop winding, 37
  chorded split-loop winding, 47
  split-loop winding, 60
  diametrically split winding, 62
  progressive-split winding, 66
  layer winding, 74
Strip and rewind when troubles cannot be located, 103

Stripping a stator, six points to note, 116
Stripping d.c. armatures, 21
Stripping universal motor, 151

T

Tags to indicate repair work to be done, 2
Tape reel holders, 218
Telephone head set testing outfit, 228
Tension block for magnet wire, 218
Test before removing connections to commutator necks, 17
Test board for repair bench, 7
Test to locate top leads of coils, 85
Testing armatures while and after winding, 90
Testing commutator for grounds, 91
  for shorts, 91
Testing equipment, 223
Testing inspection to determine repairs required, 5
  outfits for accurate tests, 6
Testing and locating faults in small a.c. motors, 107
Testing loop winding for grounds, 40
Testing single-phase winding for shorts, 197
Testing transformer, 6
Testing winding for grounds, 92
  for short circuits, 96
Tests to make when winding d.c. armatures, 90
Thirty-two volt armatures, 72
Threaded-in-strap copper coils, 187
Time-ticket form, 5
Tool for removing single-phase motor housing, 233
Tools for repair shop, 209
Tools made from old-hacksaw blades, 233
Transformer for high-voltage-tests, 223
Transformer for locating troubles in d.c. machines, 6
  construction of, 6
Transformer low-voltage high-current capacity, 227
Treated cloth and fish-paper for insulating slots, 117
Troubles, how to locate when motor will not start, 107
Troubles, locating in small d.c. armatures, 6

Troubles, location of when motors starts but will not pull load, 108

Troubles in single-phase repulsion motors:
brushes return to commutator after being released, 203
failure to release brushes on full load, 200
failure to release brushes on no load, 202
failure to start, 199
hot bearings, 203
motor heats on light-loads, 203
motor heats when loaded, 203

Troubles in universal motor, location of, 109

Troubles with starting circuit switch, 108

Truing up laminations, 24

Turns, size of wire and coil pitch for changed single-phase winding, 190

Two speeds, single-phase motors changed for, 146

Two-layer (a.c.) winding with one coil side per slot, 181
checking pitch of, 182
flat diamond mush coils for, 183

Two-layer flat diamond mush coils, 183
extra insulation between phase coils, 185
three steps in inserting, 183

Two-layer winding with diamond mush pulled coils, 187

Two-phase motor, comparison with condenser type, 246

Tying ends of coils with cord, 120

U

Universal fan motor construction, 170

Universal motor, compensated-series type with two windings, 149
compensating windings for, 153
connections for main and compensating fields, 155
with distributed field and shifted brushes, 149
insulating slots and coils, 157
kinds of windings used, 151
locating troubles in, 109
straight series type, 148

Universal motor, stripping of, points to remember, 151
unusual features of, 156
winding coils in, 155
winding troubles when main coil slots are not marked, 157

V

Vacuum cleaner windings, 148
Varnishes for coil insulation, 236
Varnishing and baking winding, 119
Vibrator windings, 148

W

Wave winding, recording data for, 19
Wear of bearings and shaft, 9
Wedge driver, 233
Winder's hand tools, 230
Winding and coil insulation, 117
Winding chart for chorded split-loop winding, 53
Winding chorded-split winding with machine, 54
Winding coils without cutting wire between coils, 133
Winding data, how to record, 10
for automobile armatures, 20
forms for recording, 11, 14, 15
card records for, 11
coil diagrams showing, 11, 18, 19
that prevent mistakes, 11
things to record, 10
Winding a loop winding, steps for, 37
Winding a skein, easy method for, 125
Winding a skein on the stator, 121
Winding stator, proper place to start, 122
Winding table for split-loop winding, 54
Windings for ceiling fans, 170
for flat-front motors, 254
for portable electric tools, 148
for vacuum cleaners, drink mixers, vibrators, etc., 148
Windings used on small a.c. motors, 177
on universal motors, 151
Wire insulation for small motors, 31
asbestos wire for high heat, 32
kinds for different wire sizes, 33
Wire reel holders, 218
Wires, how to keep from climbing above core, 132
Work bench, 210
Work order form, 3